Essential Physics for Ordinary Level

The cover shows part of a multiflash photograph of a golfer in action. The speed of the clubhead at various stages may be calculated from it. *Courtesy: A. G. Spalding & Bros. Inc.*

Essential Physics for Ordinary Level

T. B. Akrill, M.A.
Clifton College

C. J. Millar, M.A.
The King's School
Canterbury

P. M. Whelan, M.A.
Sherborne School

John Murray Albemarle Street London

Printed Offset Litho in Great Britain by
Cox & Wyman Ltd, London, Fakenham and Reading
0 7195 2046 0

Preface

This book is a completely revised version of the authors' book *Physics Revision Notes for Ordinary Level,* tailored to the needs of current syllabuses and using SI units (and following the recommendations of the ASE publication *Signs, Symbols and Abbreviations for Use in School Science*). The change of title is due to two considerations. The first is the need to avoid confusion with the original book, which was published in 1967 and will continue in use for some time to meet the needs of O Level candidates. The second and more important reason, however, is that further reflection, and numerous comments from users of the book, indicate that the term 'Revision Notes' may imply a much more summary treatment of O Level Physics than is in fact given here. What this book provides is a concise and complete account of the essentials of O Level Physics, and the experience of those who have used the original version of the book suggests that it may serve as the basic textbook around which the O Level course is built.

What we have tried to do in this book, therefore, is to produce a text which can be used throughout the last two years of an O Level course. Since some of the subject matter was introduced into O Level syllabuses only recently, we cannot claim that these notes are the fruit of many years' experience and development, but do claim that they implement accurately the spirit of the latest changes.

Each of us has written a part of the book; the others have read, criticized and discussed what they did not write, and very much more time has been spent in discussion than in actual writing. We hope that the result of this is a rigorous and clear text.

Content

The more familiar material appears in a form useful both for the course and for revision, but a more detailed account has been given of

(*a*) molecular ideas,
(*b*) waves,
(*c*) Physics from 1880 to 1920.

There are 275 diagrams, most of which are labelled in detail. This is perhaps a surprisingly large number for such a comparatively small book, but we are convinced of the value of well-labelled diagrams as an aid to revision.

We have felt able to leave out some topics hitherto taught at O Level (such as details of the method of mixtures, the chemistry of electric cells, and colour) but have, in keeping with the intentions of the new syllabuses, included more of the *ideas of Physics* than is usual in a concise text.

Some details

(1) We have given definitions of quantities in the form of equations (as explained on page 20), because we think this method
   (*a*) is more rigorous,
   (*b*) makes definitions easier to quote and to remember,
   (*c*) emphasizes the fundamental nature of a relation (e.g. $R = V/I$).
(2) Units are written in the form which we think most helps pupils to appreciate the significance of the quantities: e.g. m^3, $\frac{\mathrm{m}}{\mathrm{s}}$, $\frac{\mathrm{J}}{\mathrm{kg\ K}}$.
We also believe that this form will help them in numerical work and in checking the correctness of equations.
(3) Wherever possible, explanations of phenomena have been given in terms of the behaviour of molecules and electrons.
(4) In such a concise text we have sometimes felt the need to use ideas before they have been fully explained. For example, the ideas of kinetic and potential energy are used in Chapter 2 before they are formally dealt with in Chapter 3.
(5) *We feel that a sound understanding of the idea of* **force** *is essential.* We have therefore introduced this subject with some care, and have throughout been precise in our use of language and in our drawing of diagrams where forces are involved.

Acknowledgements

We should like to thank the publisher and his reader for their interest in the book, and Mr. J. K. Hodgson who drew the diagrams. And we owe a great deal to the encouragement and inspiration of Frank Stanger, sometime head of the Physics department of The King's School, Canterbury. He had no direct part in the production of the book but we could not have produced it without him.

April 1970 T.B.A. C.J.M. P.M.W.

Contents

1 Fundamental ideas

2 The structure of matter

3 Principles of mechanics

4 Applications of mechanics

ELECTRICAL MEASUREMENTS

A note to students

The nature of Physics

Learn what has to be learned (e.g. the definitions, and other matter enclosed in boxes) but also *understand what has to be understood.* Physics is not a collection of independent facts and results but an explanation of the natural world: therefore to be good at Physics you have to *understand explanations* more than you have to *learn facts.*

Unfamiliarities

We have used

(*a*) symbols and abbreviations to conform to the latest internationally agreed system,
(*b*) equations to define quantities,
(*c*) units in quotient form: e.g. $\frac{\text{N}}{\text{m}^2}, \frac{\text{kg}}{\text{C}}$.

These may not be familiar to you, but if you understand the work they should not cause you any trouble. (*a*) is the right thing to do; (*b*) and (*c*) we have explained in Chapter 1, and we think they will help you.

1 Fundamental ideas

1.1 NUMBERS

Numbers in Physics are often, and should often be, expressed using powers of 10: for example,

67 000	is written as $6{\cdot}7\times10^4$,
273	is written as $2{\cdot}73\times10^2$,
0·000 089	is written as $8{\cdot}9\times10^{-5}$.

Notice that they are in the form $N\times10^n$, where N is a number between 1 and 10. We say that N then has its decimal point in the **standard position.** The advantages of this are that

(*a*) it is often quicker to write the number down in this way,
(*b*) it is always easier to judge its size,
(*c*) it is often simpler to make calculations when the numbers are in this form.

As examples to illustrate (*c*), note the following:

(i)
$$\frac{5000\times0{\cdot}000\,36}{0{\cdot}009}=(5\times10^3)\times(3{\cdot}6\times10^{-4})\div(9\times10^{-3})$$
$$=2\times10^{3-4+3}$$
$$=2\times10^2.$$

(ii) The antilogarithm of 3·6990 is $5{\cdot}00\times10^{-3}$. The *index* of the '10' is the *characteristic* of the logarithm, so the correct positioning of the decimal point presents no problem. Further examples:

$$\text{antilog}\,(2{\cdot}6021)=4{\cdot}00\times10^2,$$
$$\text{antilog}\,(5{\cdot}8808)=7{\cdot}60\times10^5,$$
$$\text{antilog}\,(\bar{4}{\cdot}5315)=3{\cdot}40\times10^{-4}.$$

1.2. MEASUREMENTS AND RESULTS

Any calculation in Physics, whether based on data supplied in a problem, or on data acquired in practical work, gives an *estimate* of the correct answer.

For example, the area of a carpet which measures 2·3 m by 3·6 m could be calculated as being 8·28 m^2. But is it justified to quote as many figures in the answer? No – if by 2·3 m is meant a length which is 2·3 m correct to the nearest 0·1 m: that is, a length whose value is between 2·26 m and 2·34 m. For in an extreme case, the sides of the carpet could actually have measured 2·26 m by 3·56 m, and this gives an area of 8·05 m^2. Or it could have measured 2·34 m by 3·64 m, which gives an area of 8·52 m^2. So to give 8·<u>28</u> m^2 is to imply an accuracy of measurement which simply is not justified, and it would be better to leave the result as 8·3 m^2, which implies that the area is 8·3 m^2 to the nearest 0·1 m^2, a result which is probably true.

The estimation of the *possible error* in a result is often a complicated process: at this stage it will be enough to judge the number of figures that it is justifiable to quote from the number of figures given in the data of a problem, or obtained from a laboratory measurement.

1.3 QUANTITIES

The three **primary quantities** in mechanics are usually taken to be **length, mass** and **time.** They are indefinable: that is, they cannot be expressed in terms of each other or of other quantities. There are other **derived quantities** (for example, speed, force, energy) which are then defined in terms of these primary quantities.

Scalar quantities are completely specified when their size is given, and these can be added or subtracted simply. Some of these are:

mass, length, speed, energy.

Vector quantities need to have their direction and sense specified: the statement 'a velocity of 10 m/s' is not complete. Some of these are:

displacement, velocity, acceleration, force, momentum.

The *addition* and *subtraction* of vector quantities is more difficult than that of scalars since the directions of vector quantities must also be considered. Whereas a mass of 5 kg plus a mass of 3 kg is always a mass of 8 kg, a displacement of 80 m plus a displacement of 60 m may be anything between a displacement of 20 m and a displacement of 140 m: the result depends on the direction of the displacements.

Vector quantities are represented by arrows with size, direction and sense, and the **parallelogram law** is used to add them. The tails of two arrows are placed together, and the sum of the vectors is represented by the diagonal (drawn from where the tails meet) of the parallelogram of which the vectors form two sides. So the sum of the displacements shown in Fig. 1.1 is a displacement of 72 m in a direction and sense E 44° N. This sort of result can be found by scale drawing as well as by calculation.

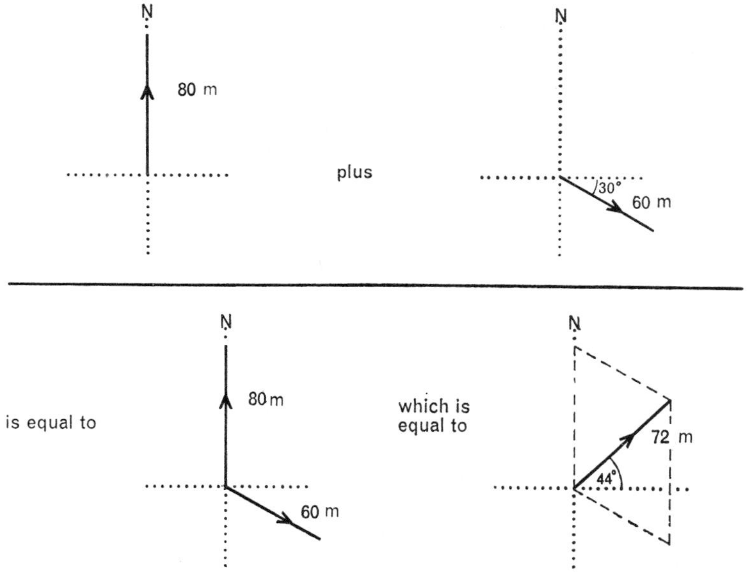

Fig. 1·1

We can also think of **negative vector quantities:** for example, a displacement of 20 m South is the same as a displacement of -20 m

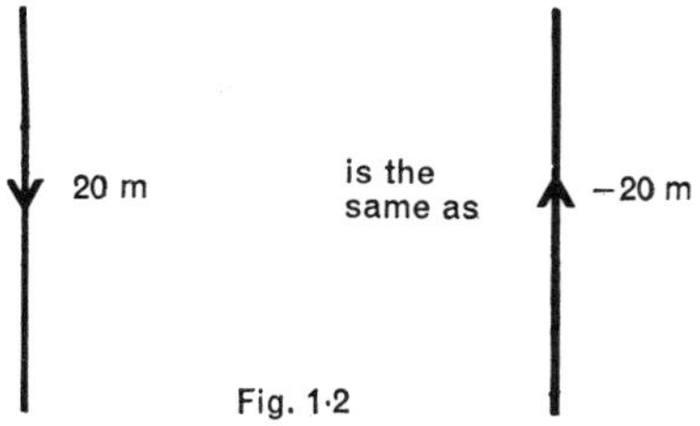

Fig. 1·2

North. Thus the displacements shown in Fig. 1.2 are the same. This idea helps us to subtract vector quantities since, for example,

$$\begin{aligned} &50 \text{ m North} - 30 \text{ m SE} \\ = &50 \text{ m North} + (-30 \text{ m SE}) \\ = &50 \text{ m North} + 30 \text{ m NW}, \end{aligned}$$

and thus a subtraction problem becomes an addition problem, as in Fig. 1.3.

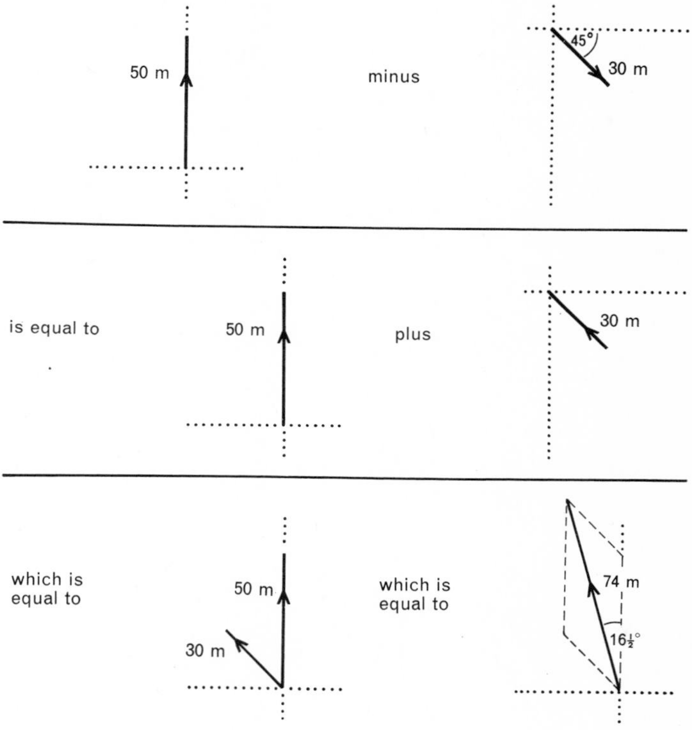

Fig. 1·3 Subtracting vectors

1.4 UNITS

The measurement of nearly all quantities involves using **units.** Something is selected and chosen as a standard for the primary quantities:

For **length:** originally the length of a bar of platinum, but now the wavelength of a particular kind of light.

For **mass:** the mass of a platinum cylinder.

For **time:** originally a particular fraction of the length of a particular year, but now in terms of the frequency of a particular kind of electromagnetic wave.

The primary quantities have the following units:

Quantity	*Unit*
Mass	kilogramme (kg)
Length	metre (m)
Time	second (s)

The unit of a derived quantity is found from the defining equation of that quantity: for example, for velocity,

$$\text{average velocity} = \frac{\text{change of displacement}}{\text{time taken}},$$

so that the unit of velocity is the m/s.

In the metric system, the following **prefixes** are used:

mega-	kilo-	milli-	micro-	nano-
$10^6 \times$	$10^3 \times$	$10^{-3} \times$	$10^{-6} \times$	$10^{-9} \times$

Thus a microsecond is 10^{-6} second.

1.5 SYMBOLS AND EQUATIONS

A symbol that represents a physical quantity will be assumed to stand for both a number and a unit. For example, in the equation for density,

$$\rho = \frac{m}{V},$$

m might stand for $5{\cdot}2\,\text{kg}$, V for $4{\cdot}0\,\text{m}^3$, and therefore ρ for $1{\cdot}3\,\text{kg/m}^3$. When listing data, or giving an answer, we write down, for example, $t = 10\,\text{s}$, or $s = 15\,\text{m}$.

Thus the equation will be satisfied not only by the numbers but also by the units. In the example quoted,

$$1{\cdot}3\,\frac{\text{kg}}{\text{m}^3} = \frac{5{\cdot}2\ \text{kg}}{4{\cdot}0\ \text{m}^3}$$

we can see that this is so. This provides a useful check on the possibility of an equation being correct: the equation

$$\rho \left[\frac{\text{kg}}{\text{m}^3}\right] = \frac{V\,[\text{m}^3]}{m\,[\text{kg}]}$$

is obviously not correct. All the terms in the equations must have the same units (or else we cannot equate, add or subtract them).

As another example, consider

$$s[\text{m}] = u\left[\frac{\text{m}}{\text{s}}\right].t[\text{s}] + \tfrac{1}{2}.a\left[\frac{\text{m}}{\text{s}^2}\right].t^2[\text{s}]^2$$

1.6 DEFINITIONS AND DESCRIPTIONS

A **definition of a quantity or a unit** is a precise statement about that quantity or unit. In this book we often use equations to define quantities: for example, we define electrical resistance by saying that

$$\text{electrical resistance of a device} = \frac{\text{potential difference between the ends of the device}}{\text{current flowing through the device}}$$

and it will help to remember that certain equations are **defining equations.** (For example,

$$c = \frac{Q}{m(\theta_2 - \theta_1)}$$

is used to define specific heat capacity.)

The definition of a *unit* of a quantity is often associated with the defining equation of the quantity itself: for example, '1 ohm is the resistance of a conductor when a potential difference of 1 volt produces a current of 1 ampere' (if **1** volt produces **1** ampere, the equation

$$R = \frac{V}{I}$$

shows that the resistance must be **1** unit – and it only remains to give the unit a name – the **ohm**). Again the power P of a force is defined by the equation

$$P = \frac{W}{t},$$

where W is the work done in time t. That is the definition of the quantity 'power', and the definition of the unit of power follows from this: if **1** joule of work is done in **1** second, the rate of working is **1** unit, and we call this unit the **watt.**

We must note whether we are being asked to *define* or *explain what is meant by* a quantity. We have already given a definition of resistance: if we have to explain what is meant by the resistance of a metal, we are asked to explain *as to someone who does not know much about the subject,* and a definition, although precise, may not much help a person to understand. We might *explain* by describing the structure of a metal, mentioning that the conduction electrons collide with the ions, and that these collisions are the cause of the resistance.

So there are three related questions: define resistance, define the ohm, and explain what is meant by resistance, and we must be careful to give the appropriate answer to each.

1.7 PROPORTION

In any physical situation there are usually at least two quantities which **vary,** and we call these quantities **variables.** For example, in an electrolysis experiment, we can vary the amount of electric charge that passes, and then the mass of a substance deposited varies. Or, in a gas kept at a steady temperature, the pressure may vary and then so will the volume.

Sometimes these variables are **directly proportional** to each other: that is, when one is doubled, the other is doubled; when one is halved, the other is halved. We can express this relationship by a **law of proportion.** In the first of the examples given above,

$$\text{mass deposited} \propto \text{electric charge passed,}$$

or

$$m \propto Q.$$

If two variable quantities *are* directly proportional to each other, then the ratio of one to the other will always be the same: that is, the ratio will be *constant.* Thus we might find that

$2{\cdot}7 \times 10^{-4}$ kg of copper are deposited when 819 C pass,
$6{\cdot}5 \times 10^{-4}$ kg of copper are deposited when 1970 C pass,
$7{\cdot}8 \times 10^{-4}$ kg of copper are deposited when 2360 C pass,

but always m/Q is *constant*: $\dfrac{2{\cdot}7 \times 10^{-4}\,\text{kg}}{819\,\text{C}}$, $\dfrac{6{\cdot}5 \times 10^{-4}\,\text{kg}}{1970\,\text{C}}$, and $\dfrac{7{\cdot}8 \times 10^{-4}\,\text{kg}}{2360\,\text{C}}$, are all equal to $3{\cdot}3 \times 10^{-7}\,\dfrac{\text{kg}}{\text{C}}$. We usually express this by saying $m/Q =$ constant. In this particular case the constant is given the symbol z, so that $m = zQ$ is the law that relates the two variables m and Q.

Some quantities are *not* directly proportional: for example, in the second situation already mentioned, the pressure of a gas is **inversely proportional** to its volume. p is **not** $\propto V$, but p **is** $\propto 1/V$: that is,

$$p = k \times 1/V, \text{ or } pV = k.$$

Thus, for a certain mass of gas, we might find that when:

$$\text{the pressure} = 1{\cdot}21 \times 10^5 \ \frac{\text{N}}{\text{m}^2}, \text{ the volume} = 1{\cdot}25 \times 10^{-3} \text{ m}^3;$$

$$\text{the pressure} = 1{\cdot}34 \times 10^5 \ \frac{\text{N}}{\text{m}^2}, \text{ the volume} = 1{\cdot}13 \times 10^{-3} \text{ m}^3;$$

$$\text{the pressure} = 1{\cdot}57 \times 10^5 \ \frac{\text{N}}{\text{m}^2}, \text{ the volume} = 0{\cdot}96 \times 10^{-3} \text{ m}^3.$$

Always pV is constant:

$$1{\cdot}21 \times 10^5 \ \frac{\text{N}}{\text{m}^2} \times 1{\cdot}25 \times 10^{-3} \text{ m}^3,$$

$$1{\cdot}34 \times 10^5 \ \frac{\text{N}}{\text{m}^2} \times 1{\cdot}13 \times 10^{-3} \text{ m}^3,$$

and $$1{\cdot}57 \times 10^5 \ \frac{\text{N}}{\text{m}^2} \times 0{\cdot}96 \times 10^{-3} \text{ m}^3$$

are all equal to $1{\cdot}51 \times 10^2$ joules.

1.8 GRAPHS

So that we can find out what the proportion constant is, or so that we can find out if two variables *are* directly proportional, we sometimes **plot** these variable quantities on a **graph.** One variable is usually thought of as the **independent variable,** because it is this one whose values we have chosen ourselves (we plot this along the horizontal axis). The other is then the **dependent variable,** because its value depends on the values we have chosen for the other variable (this dependent variable is plotted along the vertical axis). In the example first given, we would be likely to pass a *known* current for a *known* time, and then *find out* what mass of copper had been deposited: we would have *chosen* the value of the charge that had passed, and the mass deposited would have *depended* on what we had chosen. In this case we get a graph like the one shown in Fig. 1.4.

In the other case (where the pressure and volume of a gas are varying) we would *not* get a 'straight-line' graph by plotting p along one axis and V along the other: the graph would instead be a curve. But we could think of p being directly proportional to $1/V$, and if we plot p

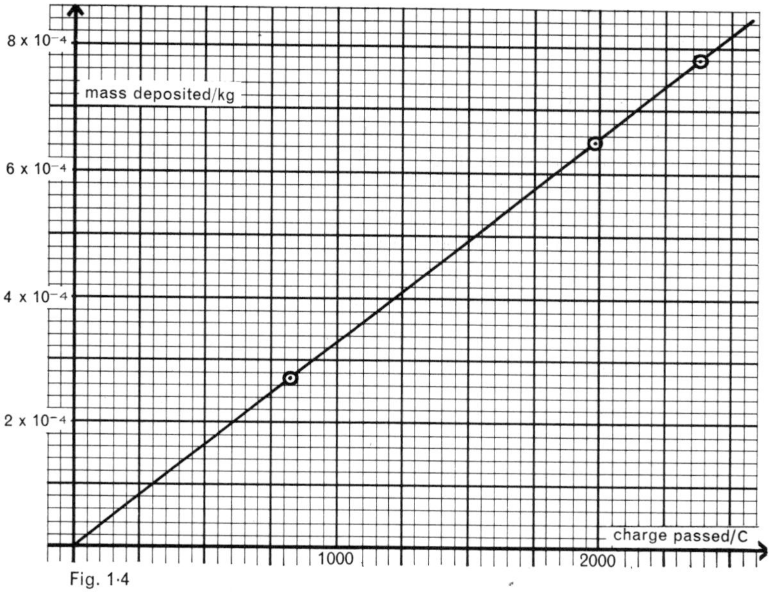

Fig. 1·4

along one axis, and $1/V$ along the other, a straight line *will* result. This line will pass through the origin.

Similarly, if we know that, for an object moving from rest with constant acceleration,

$$s = \frac{1}{2}at^2,$$

we see that $s \propto t^2$: thus, if we plot s against t, we shall not get a straight line, but we shall do so if we plot s against t^2.

We can use these straight-line graphs to find the values of the constants of proportion, since the **slope** of the graph is equal to this constant: in each case, the slope measures the average values of m/Q, $p/(1/V)$, or s/t^2. Thus we can find from the slope of the graph the values of z, k and $\frac{1}{2}a$.

Whenever an experiment is done to measure the constant of proportion it is best to take several pairs of readings and plot them on a graph. The advantages are:

(*a*) we see at once if there is any obvious mistake, because the point corresponding to that pair of readings will not lie on the line of the other points,

(*b*) when we choose which line to draw through the points we are averaging the readings, and automatically giving more importance to those which lie nearest the best possible line.

Some practical points

(*a*) Each axis must have a label which specifies the quantity and the unit in which it is being measured. It is convenient and consistent to use a label of the form (for example) mass/kg when we are plotting mass on that axis, and expressing the mass in kg. Then we are plotting pure numbers. For clarity, the axes should be ruled, even if we are using graph paper.

(*b*) The scales should be chosen so that

(*i*) the points are not bunched up in one corner of the paper,
(*ii*) the **origin** is on the paper.

In practice a compromise may have to be made, but both aims should be considered.

1.9 THE READING OF SCALES

In practical work all readings taken should be written down at once. Care must be taken to interpret the scales correctly: for example, some measuring cylinders are marked every $2\,cm^3$, some every $5\,cm^3$.

The distance between a pointer and the scale it moves over should ideally be very small. If it is not, we must make sure that one eye is directly above the correct scale graduation: in Fig. 1·5, the reading is actually 4 units though it does not seem to be. In some instruments we are helped to do this by

(*a*) there being a mirror beneath the pointer, so that an image of the pointer is formed directly beneath it,

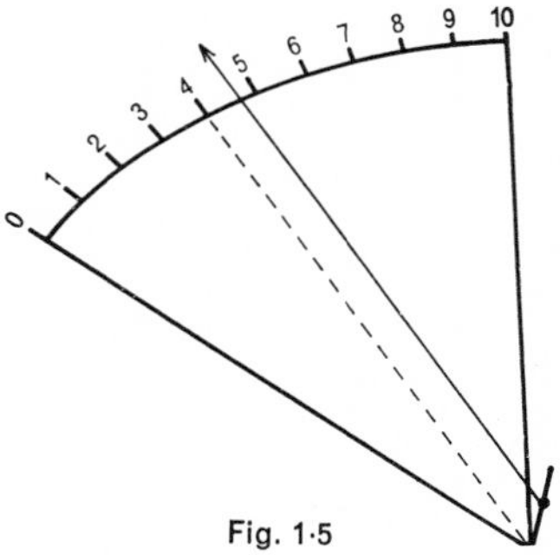

Fig. 1·5

(*b*) the pointer being made of thick Perspex, with lines marked on the front and back.

In each case the direction in which the eye should look is defined.

1.10 MODELS

Some of the ideas of Physics are so hard to understand that we explain them to ourselves by imagining what objects and processes are like. For example, we imagine that the molecules of a gas are like small hard elastic spheres colliding with each other and rebounding from each other – like billiard balls. To some extent this **model** helps us, but we must always remember that it is only a model, and we must not press the similarity too far. If, for example, we think that light travels in definite and distinct 'rays', we shall find it hard to accept that it is possible for light to spread round corners: thinking of light as consisting of rays helps us at one stage in our learning, but there comes a time when we have to modify or abandon that idea, and form another model for ourselves.

We use models for nearly every part of every branch of Physics, and it is important that we should realize how greatly we rely on them, and, therefore, how very different from our imaginings the real world of Physics is likely to be.

2 The structure of matter

Atoms and molecules

2.1 THE ATOM: ELECTRONS, PROTONS AND NEUTRONS

Electrons and **protons** have electric charges of the same size but of different kinds: electrons have a negative charge, protons a positive charge. **Neutrons** have no charge. One simple model of an **atom** suggests that a **nucleus** of protons and neutrons attracts a number of electrons, which move round the nucleus. For example, an atom of aluminium consists of 13 electrons, circling round a nucleus consisting of 13

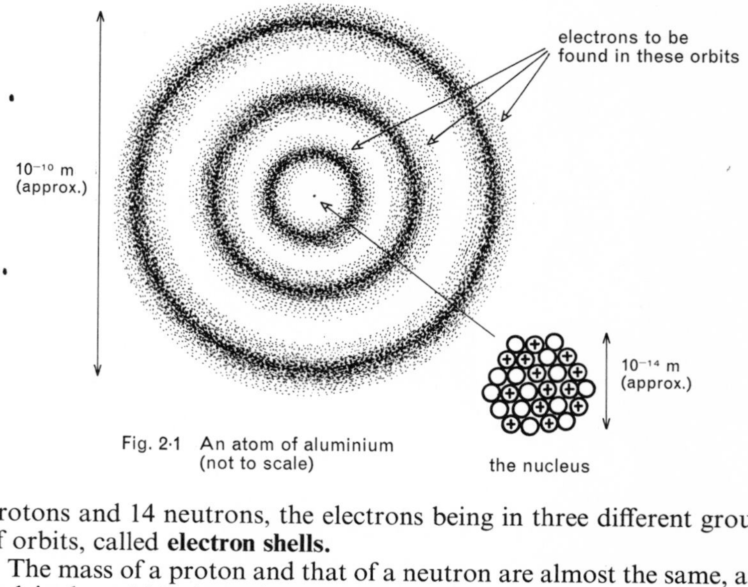

Fig. 2·1 An atom of aluminium (not to scale)

protons and 14 neutrons, the electrons being in three different groups of orbits, called **electron shells.**

The mass of a proton and that of a neutron are almost the same, and each is about 1840 times the mass of an electron (which is $9{\cdot}1 \times 10^{-31}$ kg) so that the mass of an atom is almost equal to the mass of its nucleus.

The simplest atom is that of hydrogen, which consists of one electron and one proton: the most complicated have about 100 electrons, and nuclei consisting of about 100 protons and 150 neutrons.

The diameters of nuclei vary very little, and are of the order of 10^{-14} m: the diameters of the atoms are about 10^4 times larger, that is, about 10^{-10} m. The chemical behaviour of an atom depends on the electrons in its outermost electron shell.

An **ion** is any charged particle: usually an atom or group of atoms which has lost or gained one or more electrons.

The **ionization** of gases can be increased by heating them, or by exposing them to radiation from X-rays: gases are always ionized to some extent.

2.2 MOLECULES

A **molecule** of a substance is the smallest particle of it which can exist under normal conditions.

For example, a molecule of hydrogen consists of two hydrogen atoms; a molecule of carbon dioxide consists of an atom of carbon and two

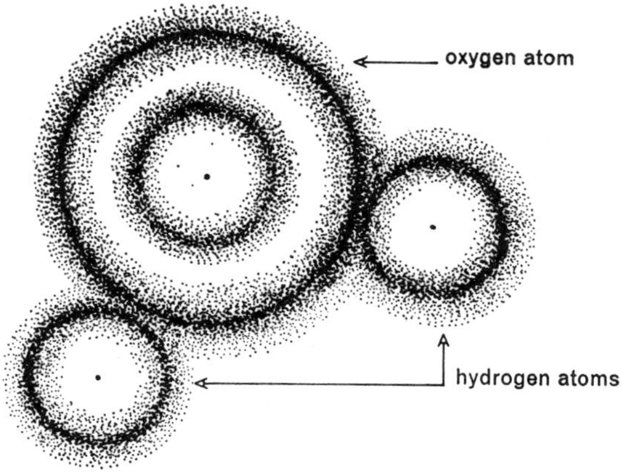

Fig. 2·2 A molecule of water (H_2O) (not to scale)

atoms of oxygen. Some substances, like argon, have a 'molecule' which consists simply of a single atom.

The idea of the 'molecule' sometimes breaks down: in crystalline structures, for example, the atoms are arranged in regular patterns, and it is impossible to say which atoms belong to particular 'molecules'.

2.3 THE SCALE OF MATTER

As we shall see, a substance in the solid state consists of molecules which are vibrating about fixed positions in a framework. We shall not see this if we look at a one-centimetre cube of copper. Even if we magnify the cube 1000 times, the cube will still appear to have smooth rigid surfaces. And if we magnify it further, 1000 times more, so that the cube now appears about 10 km wide, we shall not see this molecular motion clearly, though we may think the cube has an indistinct outline and that its surface shimmers. If the cube were magnified a further 100 times, we could perhaps see objects, apparently about one centimetre across, moving to and fro at very high speed. But the cube would now have sides of 1000 km. So normally we see nothing of the actual structure of substances.

An experiment to provide some evidence of the size of molecules

We use oleic acid, which dissolves in alcohol, but not in water. We

(*a*) prepare a solution of the acid in alcohol (1 part in 100);
(*b*) find the volume of one drop of the solution, and hence the volume of the acid in one drop;
(*c*) sprinkle lycopodium powder on the surface of some water in a large black-bottomed tray;
(*d*) place one drop of the solution on the water surface.

The alcohol is absorbed by the water, but the oleic acid spreads out over the water surface, to an extent shown by the limit to which the powder is pushed back.

$$\text{The thickness of the layer} = \frac{\text{volume of acid in the drop}}{\text{area of the layer}},$$

and in a typical experiment might be found to be 10^{-9} m. The thickness of the molecules in the layer cannot be greater than this.

The fact that it is oleic acid that remains in the layer on the surface can be shown by taking a freshly powdered water surface and placing a drop of alcohol on it. The alcohol sweeps the powder away, but this is then absorbed, and the powder now returns to cover the whole of the surface again. Thus in the original experiment the surface layer consisted only of oleic acid.

The smell of a very small amount of perfume spreads to all parts of a room, and the whole of the volume of a liquid may be coloured by the addition of a very small amount of another substance. For this to happen, the perfume, or the added substance, must be very finely divided: thus these facts are evidence that *if matter exists as particles, the particles must be very small.*

2.4 BROWNIAN MOVEMENT

If a microscope is used to view a strongly illuminated suspension of graphite particles in oil, or a suspension of particles of cigarette ash

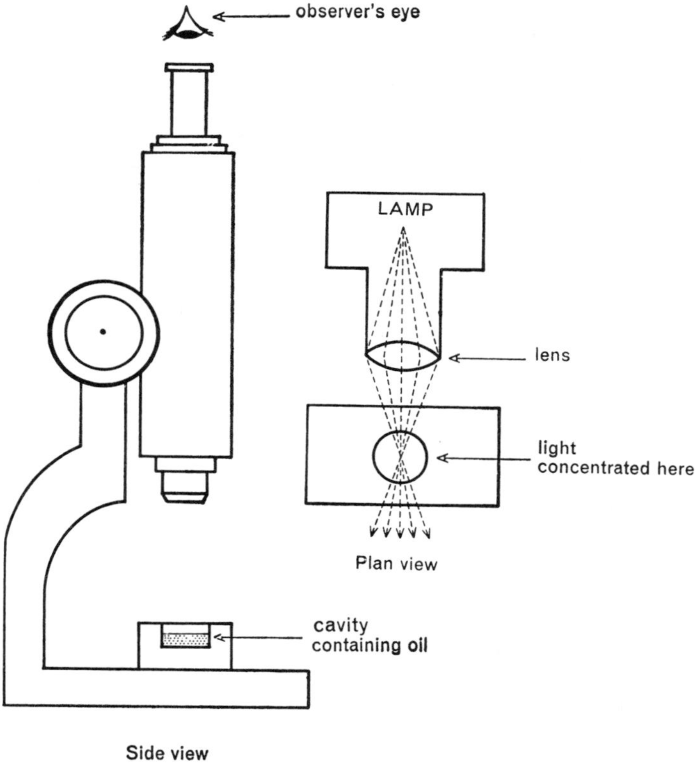

Fig. 2·3 Microscope being used to inspect Brownian movement

in air, it is observed that these particles are moving about *erratically,* as shown in Fig. 2.4. This figure does not show the actual paths the particles take: only their positions at intervals of $\frac{1}{20}$ second. For convenience, we join up these positions with straight lines. In fact the particles will undergo a very large number of changes of direction between the positions shown.

We assume that the *particles* (which may be 10^{-6} m across) are being pushed by the *molecules* of the oil, or of the air. Since we cannot see these molecules, they are presumably very small. To have this effect on

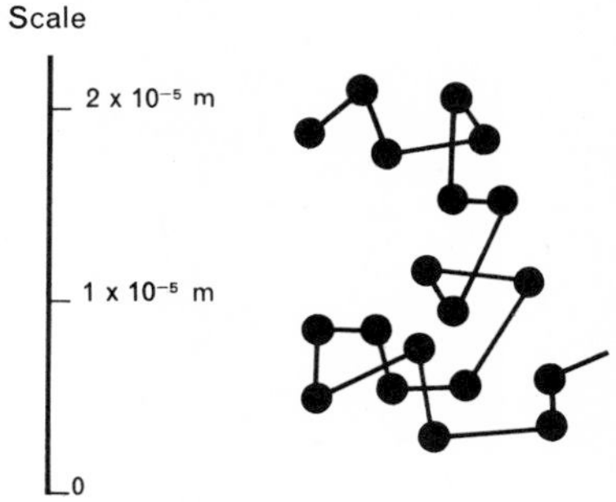

Fig. 2·4
A diagram of Brownian movement
The position of the particles is shown every 1/20 second: the lines joining the positions do not show the actual movements

the particles, therefore, the molecules must be moving very fast. This is more *evidence for the molecular nature* of liquids and gases. In fact (though the experiment does not show this) the particles are being bombarded, not by a few molecules, now and again, but by a very large number of molecules, continuously. At any one instant, there is probably one side of a particle which is receiving more hits than the others, and thus there is a resultant force on the particle: the next instant, the resultant force will almost certainly be in a different direction.

We may also observe convection currents in the oil or in the air, but we can distinguish these from the true Brownian movement, because the effect of the convection will be to superimpose a movement in *one* direction on *all* the particles.

2.5 THE FORCES MOLECULES EXERT ON EACH OTHER

Consider two molecules, A and B (for simplicity, single atoms) moving towards each other. Each is electrically neutral, but as they move closer and closer, their electron shells begin to penetrate each other, and the shape of the molecule becomes distorted. First A and B attract each

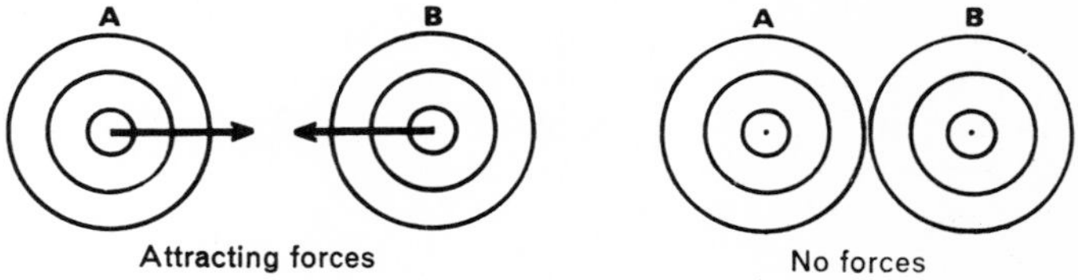

Fig. 2·5

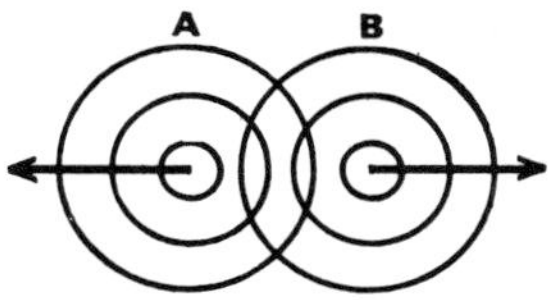

Repelling forces

Fig. 2·5 cont.

other, and then they repel each other, as shown in Fig. 2.5. The graph (Fig. 2.6) shows how the force which the molecules exert on each other changes as their distance apart changes.

It can be seen that there is a position of the molecules where they do not exert a force on each other, and where, therefore, they will be in

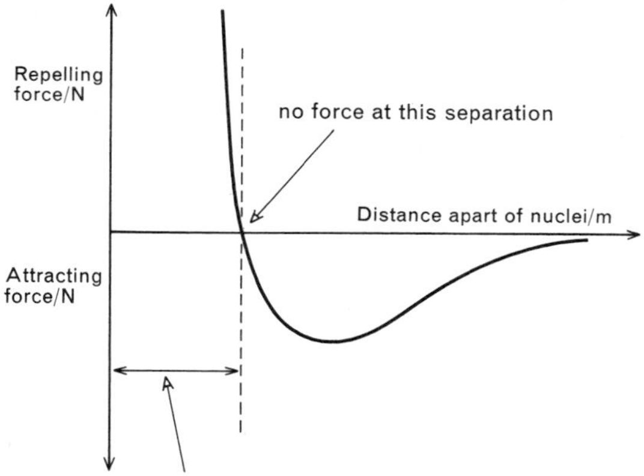

Fig. 2·6

equilibrium. If from this position they then move farther apart, they attract each other, and if they move nearer, they repel each other. Thus if a molecule begins to move in this situation, it acquires a continuing vibration.

For more complicated molecules, a similar situation exists.

The states of matter

2.6 THE GASEOUS STATE

A substance in the **gaseous state** has its molecules relatively far apart – probably at least 10 molecular diameters. The molecules are moving *at random*: that is, with unpredictable speeds and in all directions. The average speed is high – of the order of 10^3 m/s. They are continually colliding with each other and rebounding without the collision causing a lowering of the total energy: they are moving fast enough to be able to penetrate each other to such an extent that each exerts a large repelling force on the other, and thus each pushes the other so far away that neither can attract the other. (At a distance of a few molecular diameters, the attracting force is negligible.)

Thus individual molecules have different speeds, and the velocity of a particular molecule is continually changing in size, direction and sense, but the total energy of the molecules does not change.

2.7 THE LIQUID STATE

If a substance in the gaseous state is cooled (that is, loses energy) and so has its molecules slowed down, the collisions are less violent. The molecules do not then move in as far towards each other, so they do not experience such large repelling forces, and do not move out so far on the rebound – therefore they may keep within range of the attracting forces. Thus they become held in a state of vibration.

The substance is then said to be in the **liquid state:** such a substance has its molecules very much closer together (about one molecular diameter apart) than in the gaseous state. The molecules are still continually moving to and fro, but are now vibrating also.

The reverse process occurs if the molecules of a substance in the liquid state have their kinetic energies increased. The vibrations become more and more violent, until an outward-moving molecule has enough energy to overcome the forces with which the other molecules are attracting it, and the liquid then begins to become a gas.

2.8 THE SOLID STATE

When a liquid has energy taken from it, the vibrations of its molecules become less violent until the molecules lock into position in a regular arrangement, still vibrating, but now with fixed positions about which they vibrate. The substance is then in the **solid state,** and as the solid so formed is cooled, the vibrations become slower and slower. Thus, unlike a gas and a liquid, a solid has shape, because its molecules keep to a particular position. The shape of a particular solid in the crystalline state, and its resistance to change of shape, depend on the way in which the molecules lock together.

2.9 HEAT AND TEMPERATURE: LATENT HEAT

Since heat is a form of energy, the phrase 'giving heat to a body' is merely another way of saying 'increasing the energy of the molecules'. Their energy can also be increased by doing work on the body. In either case we say the **internal energy** of the body increases.

With a solid, giving heat results in an increase in the molecules' **potential and kinetic energy** as long as the substance remains in the solid state. When its temperature reaches the melting point it remains steady for a time: the supply of heat (which is continuing) is now being used to break down the orderly structure of the substance to get the molecules into the liquid state (and a little energy is being used to push the atmosphere back – since most solids expand on melting). During the process of melting, the molecules are gaining intermolecular *potential energy* but not kinetic energy.

When the substance has completely melted, further gains of heat result in further increases of *potential and kinetic energy*. During the change from liquid to gas, the substance again absorbs intermolecular *potential energy* but not *kinetic energy* until the liquid has completely vaporized: the molecules' *kinetic energy* is then again able to increase further. During this change, too, some energy is needed to push back the atmosphere, and this time a much larger proportion, since the expansion during the vaporization is much greater than during melting.

Thus *rises in temperature mean increases in kinetic energy:* in fact the absolute temperature of a substance in the gaseous state is *directly proportional* to the average translational kinetic energy of its molecules. Also, to a particular absolute temperature there corresponds a particular

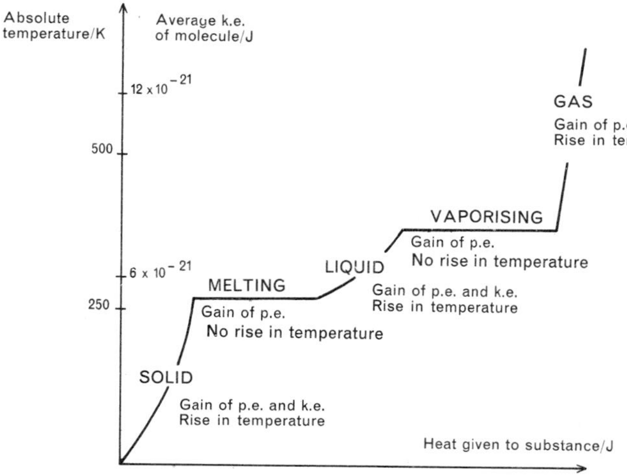

Fig. 2·7 Graph to show what happens to the heat energy absorbed by a typical substance: gains of p.e. and k.e. mean rises in temperature, gains of only p.e. mean changes in state.

average translational kinetic energy of the molecules, *irrespective of what the substance is,* if it is in the gaseous state.

For example, at 300 K the average translational kinetic energy of a hydrogen molecule is 6×10^{-21} J: at 600 K, it is twice as much, 12×10^{-21} J. Further, at 300 K, the average translational kinetic energy of a carbon dioxide molecule is 6×10^{-21} J also, despite its different mass, and at 600 K its molecules, too, have an average kinetic energy of 12×10^{-21} J.

The **latent heat** of fusion or vaporization of a substance is therefore another way of talking about the heat needed to do two things:

(*a*) provide the additional potential energy which the molecules need in their new states (which we have been calling intermolecular potential energy),
(*b*) push back the atmosphere.

When a gas is cooled, the work done by the molecules' attracting forces in pulling the molecules closer together is spare, since it is not used to increase the molecules' kinetic energy during the process of condensation. This spare energy appears as heat when the gas condenses; it is, of course, equal to the heat absorbed when the liquid evaporates. Both are what we call the **latent heat of vaporization** of the substance.

A similar process occurs when the liquid solidifies (see p. 32).

2.10 THE CHANGES OF STATE: A MODEL

It may help to picture the changes of state when a substance is heated as being similar to what would happen to some cube sugar at the bottom of a rectangular biscuit tin. Initially the cubes are arranged regularly,

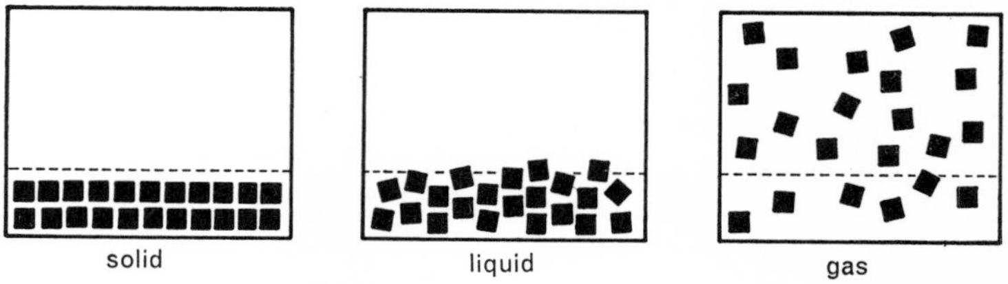

Fig. 2·8 A model for the three states of matter

but as the tin is shaken gently to and fro, the cubes vibrate. As the shaking becomes rougher, the cubes leave their regular arrangement, still vibrating, and change positions with their neighbours in the process. With even more vigorous shaking, the whole of the space in the tin is filled with sugar cubes bouncing around.

In reverse, as the shaking becomes again more gentle, the cubes first occupy only the bottom of the tin, vibrating and changing position, and finally settle down again, vibrating, in a regular pattern.

A molecular view of pressure

2.11 THE PRESSURE CAUSED BY GASES

The molecules of a gas collide with the walls of whatever contains them, are repelled by the molecules in the wall, and rebound: thus the wall exerts a force on them, and they exert a force on the wall. It is the forces produced by this continual bombardment by the molecules on the walls which cause the **pressure** produced by a gas.

If the gas is given heat, the molecules will move faster and make harder impacts on the walls. If we

(*a*) leave the volume the same, the pressure will increase. In fact the pressure varies directly as the absolute temperature. This is the *Pressure Law* (see p. 129).

(*b*) want to keep the pressure the same, we must let the volume increase (so that the molecules have farther to travel, and make their harder impacts less often). In fact the volume will vary directly as the absolute temperature. This is *Charles's Law* (see p. 129).

We can change the pressure of a gas by changing its volume, without allowing its temperature to change. Reducing the volume increases the pressure (because the impacts occur more often): increasing the volume reduces the pressure. In fact, the product of pressure and volume is constant. This is *Boyle's Law* (see p. 129).

2.12 THE PRESSURE CAUSED BY LIQUIDS AND SOLIDS

Liquid molecules, like gas molecules, strike surfaces, and this bombardment is the cause of liquid pressure. Of course there are many more molecules striking 1 m^2 of a surface in this case, but the attractive forces exerted on these molecules by the molecules in the body of the liquid reduce the violence of the impacts, as is shown in Fig. 2.9*b*. Fig. 2.9*a* shows the comparative rarity of impacts, and the absence of attracting molecules, when a gas adjoins a solid surface.

A substance in the solid state can also be thought of as exerting a pressure, but in this case the net force exerted by the motion of the molecules is zero. This must be so, since two adjacent vertical solid surfaces do not exert a force on each other unless pressed together. The 'pressure' exerted when one solid body rests on another is simply caused

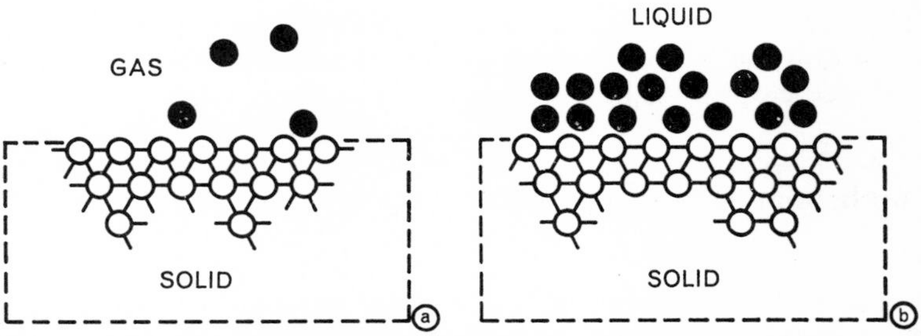

Only a few impacts on the solid surface, but the push of the gas molecule on the solid molecules is large

Many more impacts, but the liquid molecules near the solid surface are pulled by the other liquid molecules and so are not pushed as hard by the solid molecules – and hence (Newton's Law III) the push exerted in each impact by the liquid molecules on the solid molecules is smaller than in (a)

Fig. 2·9

by the forces of repulsion which the molecules in the two bodies exert on each other.

2.13 EVAPORATION

Upward-moving molecules of a liquid at or near its surface may

(*a*) have enough kinetic energy to escape completely from the liquid;
(*b*) have enough kinetic energy to escape from the surface, but may then strike another molecule (from the liquid or of the air) and be repelled, thus returning to the liquid;

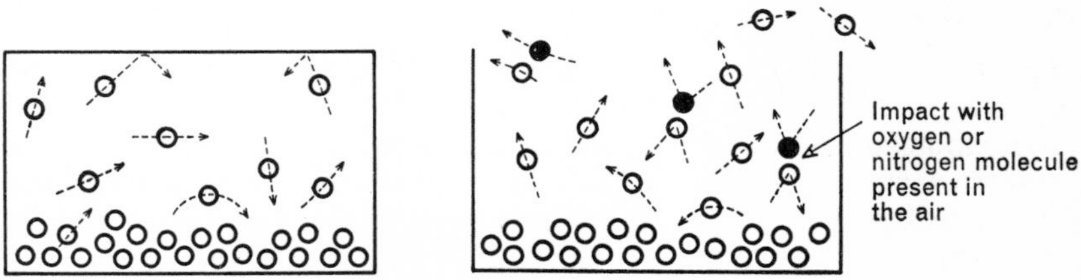

Evaporation from a liquid in a closed space: over a period of time, as many molecules enter the liquid as leave it. The space is saturated

Evaporation from a liquid open to the surroundings

Fig. 2·10

(Note that the containers are not drawn to the same scale as the molecules) (*c*) only have enough kinetic energy to move a little way before the other liquid molecules pull them back. In a draught these slower molecules may be swept away by the stream of air molecules, and will not then return. Thus the rate of **evaporation** is greater in a draught.

Evaporation occurs at all temperatures. The range of the speeds of the molecules is such that there will always be some which can escape, though the number will be greater (and therefore the rate of evaporation greater) at high temperatures. At all temperatures it will be the fastest molecules that will escape, and so the temperature of the remaining liquid will be lowered (see p. 135).

The molecules which have left the liquid exert a **vapour pressure.**

If some liquid is placed in an evacuated space, it will evaporate very quickly. But as more and more molecules occupy the space above the liquid, there will be more and more molecules in the space to strike and enter the surface of the liquid, until the rate at which molecules return to the liquid is equal to the rate at which they are leaving. When this happens, the space is said to be **saturated** with **vapour** (the name sometimes given to a relatively cool gas).

The number of molecules then in the space above the liquid is the maximum number, although they are not always the same molecules. At a higher temperature the rate of evaporation will be greater, and there will need to be more molecules in the space before the rate of returning can balance the rate of leaving.

The number of molecules in the space, when it is saturated, depends on the temperature, and the greater the temperature, the greater the pressure produced by a space-saturating vapour – or the greater the **saturation vapour pressure** (see p. 135).

Shape and volume

2.14 DENSITIES

The density of a substance in the *solid* state will depend on the mass of its atoms, and on how closely together they are packed, so we cannot at this stage predict what the density of a particular substance in the solid state will be.

In general the density of the same substance in the *liquid* state will be less, though not much less.

The density of the same substance in the *gaseous* state will be very much less. If the distance apart of the molecules is 10 times what it was in the liquid state, the density will be 10^{-3} times as much as it was in the liquid state.

2.15 CHANGES OF SHAPE AND VOLUME

The shape and volume of a *gas* can both easily be changed. The shape of a *liquid* can easily be changed, since the molecules have no fixed positions, but it is difficult to reduce the volume, since the molecules are already close together.

Gases and liquids **flow** easily and this is why they are called **fluids.** The ease with which the shape of a *solid* can be changed depends on the size of the forces keeping the molecules in position. In general, since the molecules of a solid are (nearly always) even closer together than those of a liquid, it is even more difficult to reduce the volume of a solid than that of a liquid. Solids can be distorted, however: a solid in the form of a rod, for example, can be pushed and pulled, and it will get shorter and longer as the molecules get closer together and farther apart. Fig. 2.11, which is an enlargement of part of Fig. 2.6, shows that the

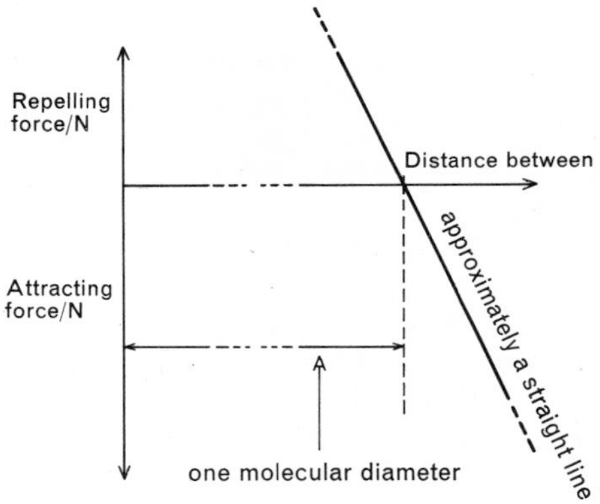

Fig. 2·11

An enlargement of part of Fig. 2·6. The straightness of this part of the graph shows that the force is proportional to the extension or compression

force needed is proportional to the distance of compression or extension, provided that the compression or extension is not too large. This is **Hooke's Law** (see p. 111).

If such forces are not too large, the solid behaves **elastically:** that is, it regains its original shape when the force is removed. A permanent distortion can be produced by large forces: this is the result of the planes of the regular arrangement of molecules slipping over each other and taking up some similar position, as in Fig. 2.12, and of course very large forces may pull the molecules apart altogether.

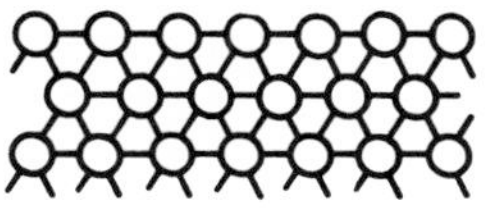

Solid before stretching forces are applied

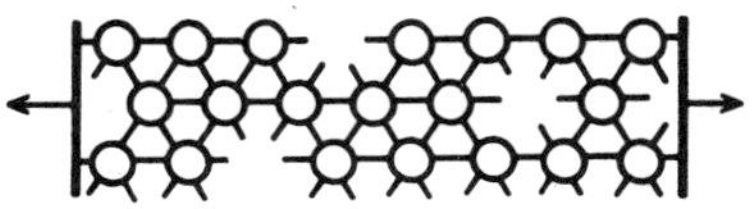

Solid after large stretching forces are applied: the planes of molecules slip over each other, and a permanent extension occurs

Fig. 2·12

2.16 THERMAL EXPANSION OF SOLIDS AND LIQUIDS

The molecules of a substance in the *solid* state will, when the substance is given heat, vibrate more violently. As a result their average positions become farther apart and they take up more space: thus the solid expands.

The average positions of a *liquid's* molecules will similarly become farther apart. Liquid expansion will be easier than solid expansion since the molecules are not held in a fixed arrangement, and a typical liquid may expand 10 times more than the same substance in the solid state.

2.17 SURFACE EFFECTS

The molecules in the body of a liquid have attracting and repelling forces exerted on them by other molecules from all sides. Those within one or two molecular diameters' distance of the surface, however, have more molecules influencing them from below than from above, and cannot easily move upward because attracting forces would pull them back. (A repelling force also acts on the surface molecules, but its effect is relatively short-range, so that if there were a molecule just above the surface it would experience a resultant downward force.)

If isolated, a mass of liquid would form itself into a spherical shape because this is the shape in which a certain volume has the least surface area: in practice other forces, such as gravitational forces, exist which modify this effect. The spherical shape would also have been achieved if the liquid had been surrounded by a rubber sheet, like a balloon, and this has led to the idea of a liquid having a **surface tension,** and to the idea of the boundary of a liquid pulling at whatever it joins. Examples are the formation of almost spherical drops of rain, and the pulling of a film of liquid on a wire frame which has been dipped into a liquid and then raised.

The situation is complicated by the force exerted on the liquid molecules by the molecules of the solid vessel containing the liquid: it is this **adhesion** between liquid and solid which pulls against the **cohesion** of the liquid molecules, and causes **meniscuses,** and accounts for the **capillary action** of liquid in a narrow tube (see p. 105).

Transfer phenomena

2.18 DIFFUSION

Diffusion is the spreading, on a molecular scale, of a substance into a region which it has not hitherto occupied. Thus if two fluids are placed in contact, each will diffuse into the other's region. We should expect this, since fluids consist of wandering molecules, but the process also occurs to a small extent with solids: gold and lead, placed in close contact, will show some diffusion after a period of years. This solid diffusion would not occur if it were not for imperfections in the arrays of ions in each solid.

We should also expect the rate at which diffusion occurs to depend in some way on the speeds of the molecules: in fact, the rate of diffusion through a small hole or group of holes into a vacuum is proportional to the average speed of the molecules of the gas. Thus, from the same container, hydrogen will diffuse four times faster than oxygen, since

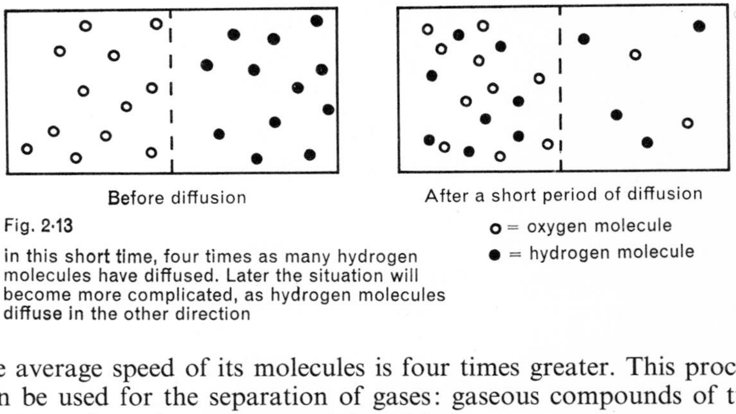

Fig. 2·13

in this short time, four times as many hydrogen molecules have diffused. Later the situation will become more complicated, as hydrogen molecules diffuse in the other direction

the average speed of its molecules is four times greater. This process can be used for the separation of gases: gaseous compounds of two isotopes of uranium are separated in this way.

Diffusion does not occur as rapidly as the very high speed of the molecules might lead us to expect: collisions between the molecules slow down the rate.

2.19 THE MECHANISM OF ELECTRICAL CONDUCTION

The 'molecules' of metals are usually single atoms, and these are held together by electrical forces. These forces involve the sharing of electrons, and these electrons are free to move at random within the metal much as do the molecules of a gas within a container. Thus we should think of a metal *as consisting of ions,* rather than of atoms.

Under the action of an electric field, the electrons **drift** through the metal (in a sense opposite to that of the field): it is not a steady motion, since the electrons are continually colliding with the vibrating ions that mainly constitute the metal. They start and stop, and start and stop again. Their motion is more like a ball rolling down a flight of stairs than that of a ball rolling down a chute. This drift of the electrons is superimposed on the electrons' random motion. The **drift speed** of the

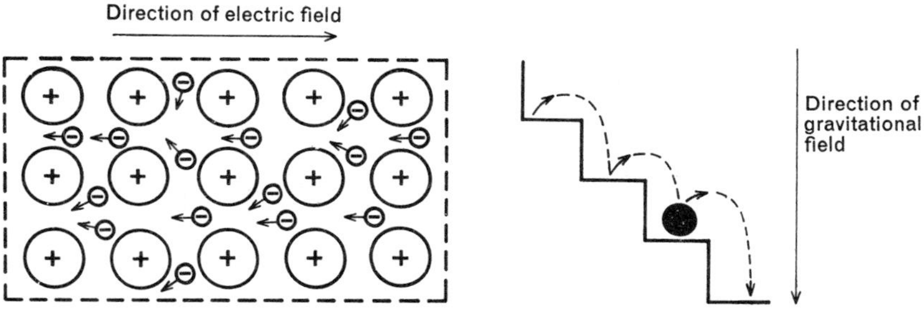

There is a drift to the left (if the direction of the electric field is to the right) superimposed upon the electrons' random motion

The electrons' motion is similar to that of a ball bouncing downstairs

Fig. 2·14 The mechanism of the electrical current

electrons is low (of the order of 10^{-4} m/s), though the speed of the electrons in their random motion is of the order of 10^6 m/s. The number of these **conduction electrons** or free electrons per atom depends on the metal: for copper, for example, there is one conduction electron per atom. This means that the total number of conduction electrons in a wire is very high: in copper, it is of the order of 10^{29} in each m^3.

It is this flow of electrons that carries charge in a metallic conductor: this is the mechanism of the **electric current.**

The collisions between the electrons and the ions give the ions more energy: the actual reasons are complicated, but we can think of the ions as causing the **resistance** of the metal. The impacts made by the electrons increase the energy of the ions and hence either raise the temperature of the metal or (if it is solid) make it melt.

There are some substances in which the number of conduction electrons per m^3:

(*a*) is very much lower: hence they are worse conductors than most metals, and are called **semiconductors,**

(*b*) varies greatly with temperature: hence they are used as **thermistors,** resistors whose resistance varies greatly with temperature.

These substances may be metallic compounds (e.g. lead telluride), metals (e.g. germanium) or non-metals (e.g. silicon). In germanium the number of conduction electrons per m^3 is as small as 5×10^{19} at 300 K but is 30 times greater at 400 K and this produces a very large *decrease* in resistivity.

In moving round a circuit, electrons lose electric potential energy, temporarily gain kinetic energy, and then give this to the ions. This process occurs about 10^5 times for each electron in each millimetre of its travel along the wire.

2.20 THERMAL CONDUCTION

The conduction electrons which serve as the mechanism for the conduction of electric charge also serve as one mechanism for the conduction of heat. If one end of a metal bar is heated, the conduction electrons there are given extra kinetic energy: some move along the bar and take this energy with them. Other slower electrons take their place and are in their turn given more energy, and themselves move along the bar. Thus the fast and slow electrons are diffusing into regions which they did not originally occupy. In this way heat is transmitted from place to place without any apparent movement of the transmitting substance.

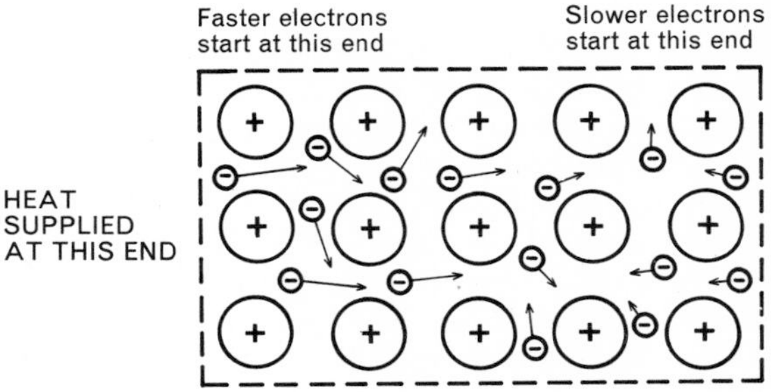

The faster electrons (indicated by the longer arrows) diffuse into the region occupied by the slower electrons (indicated by the shorter arrows), and vice-versa. Thus energy is transmitted

Fig. 2·15

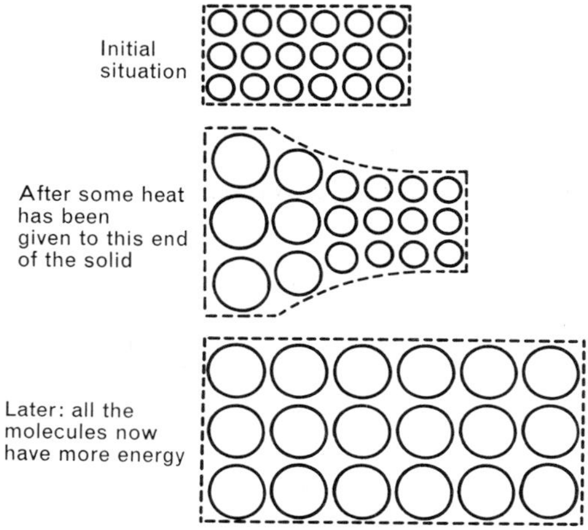
Initial
situation
After some heat
has been
given to this end
of the solid
Later: all the
molecules now
have more energy

Fig. 2·16

The mechanism of heat conduction in non-metals
The circles represent the regions in which the molecules vibrate: they vibrate faster and with greater amplitude as their kinetic energy is increased. Note the expansion which occurs

The vibrating ions are responsible for some thermal conduction: if they jostle each other, energy can be passed from one part of the solid to another. This second conduction mechanism cannot be very effective, since high rates of conduction of heat are only possessed by substances with conduction electrons. There are exceptions, however: some non-metals (i.e. substances without conduction electrons) are as good conductors as some metals.

As the conduction electrons can transfer both electric charge and internal energy, we see why the same substances are good conductors of both electricity and heat.

3 Principles of mechanics

Kinematics

3.1 DEFINITIONS

The **distance** a particle moves is the length of the path it follows between its initial and final positions.

The **displacement** of a particle is the length, direction and sense of the line drawn from its initial to its final position.

The **change** of a physical quantity which varies with time is its final value minus its initial value.

Speed

$$\textbf{Average speed} = \frac{\text{distance moved by particle}}{\text{time taken}}$$

$$v\left[\frac{\text{m}}{\text{s}}\right] = \frac{s\ [\text{m}]}{t\ [\text{s}]}$$

$$v = \frac{s}{t}$$

Velocity

$$\textbf{Average velocity} = \frac{\text{change of displacement of particle}}{\text{time taken}}$$

$$v\left[\frac{\text{m}}{\text{s}}\right] = \frac{s\ [\text{m}]}{t\ [\text{s}]}$$

$$\boxed{v = \frac{s}{t}}$$

Displacement and velocity are **vector** quantities (see p. 16). Distance, time and speed are **scalar** quantities.

The velocity of a particle will alter if the speed, direction or sense of its motion alters. This means that a particle moving along a curved path has a varying velocity.

The **speed,** v, of a particle at a particular moment is defined by the equation

$$v = \frac{s}{t},$$

where t represents a very short time interval which contains the moment, and s represents the (small) distance moved in the time.

The velocity of a particle at a moment is similarly defined.

Acceleration

$$\textbf{Acceleration} = \frac{\text{change of velocity of a particle}}{\text{time taken}}$$

$$a\left[\frac{\mathrm{m}}{\mathrm{s}^2}\right] = \frac{(v-u)\left[\frac{\mathrm{m}}{\mathrm{s}}\right]}{t\ [\mathrm{s}]}$$

$$\boxed{a = \frac{v-u}{t}}$$

where u is the initial velocity and v is the final velocity of the particle.

As acceleration is a vector quantity, this equation means that the direction of a particle's acceleration *need not* be that of its initial or final velocity; e.g. see p. 49, where the acceleration of a body moving in a circle is considered.

3.2 VELOCITY

Velocities are *added* and *subtracted* using the parallelogram law (see p. 16).

The **relative velocity** of two particles is calculated as follows:

The velocity of particle A relative to particle B is the velocity which A *seems* to have to a person *moving with* B.

As the person will *think* himself to be at rest (as we do on the Earth), the relative velocity is found by subtracting the velocity of B, v_b, from the velocity of A, v_a.

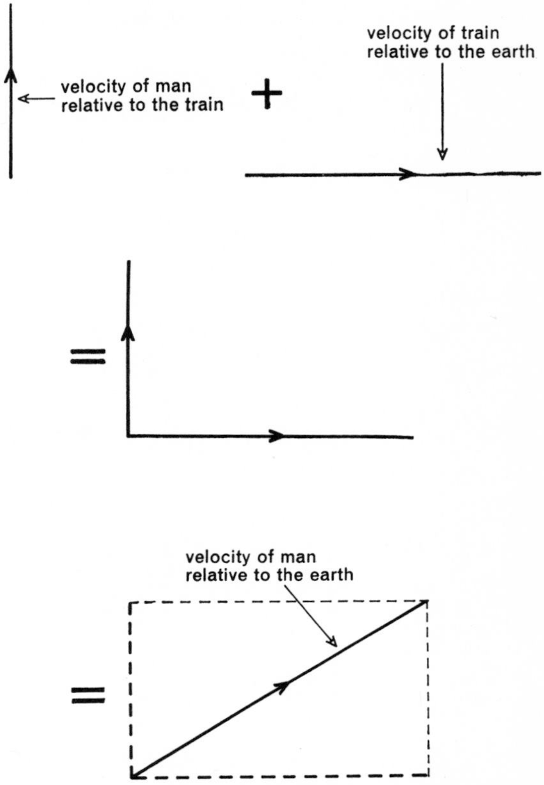

Fig. 3·1 A man crosses a train

$$\text{Velocity of A relative to B} = v_a - v_b$$
$$= v_a + (-v_b)$$

Note that A and B may be two points on the same body.

3.3 MOTION IN A STRAIGHT LINE

If a particle moves in a straight line, the direction in which it moves is constant. We can show the magnitude and sense of the displacement and velocity most conveniently on a graph.

Displacement-time graphs

The *slope* of the graph represents the *velocity* of the particle.

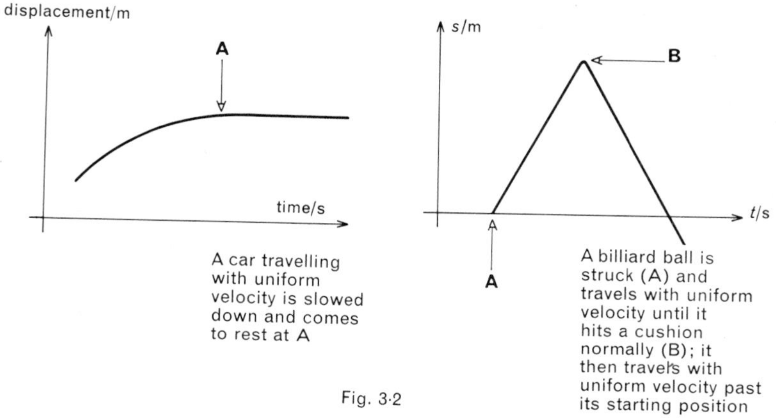

displacement/m
A
time/s
A car travelling with uniform velocity is slowed down and comes to rest at A
s/m
B
t/s
A
A billiard ball is struck (A) and travels with uniform velocity until it hits a cushion normally (B); it then travels with uniform velocity past its starting position

Fig. 3·2

Velocity-time graphs

(*a*) The *slope* of the graph represents the *acceleration* of the particle.

(*b*) The area between the time axis and the line of the graph, counted positive for positive velocities (i.e. above the time axis) represents the displacement of the particle.

If the motion is not in a straight line then similar (1) distance-time, and (2) speed-time graphs can be drawn, from which similar deductions can be made.

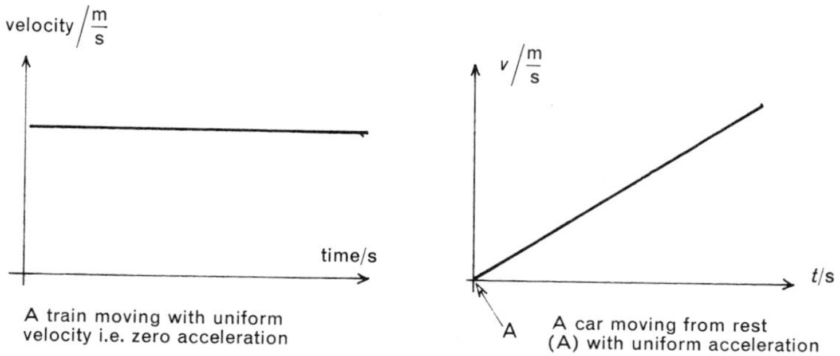

Fig. 3·3

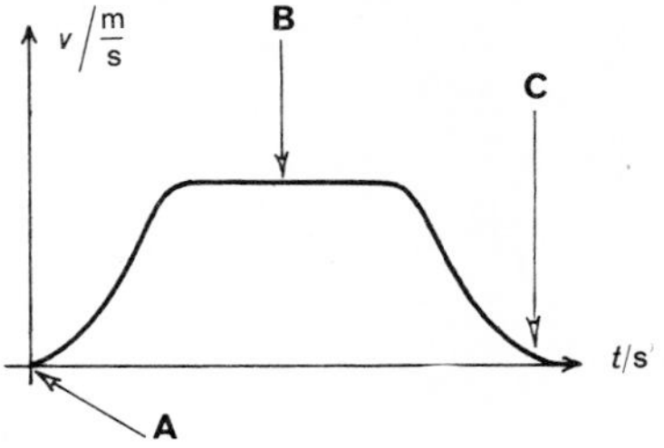

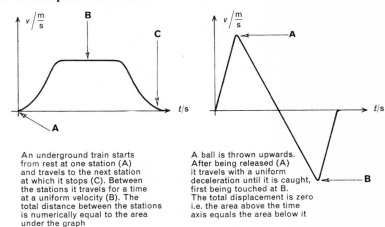

An underground train starts from rest at one station (A) and travels to the next station at which it stops (C). Between the stations it travels for a time at a uniform velocity (B). The total distance between the stations is numerically equal to the area under the graph

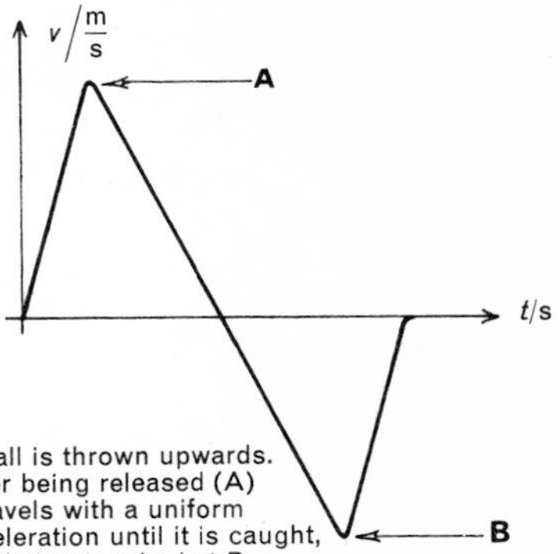

A ball is thrown upwards. After being released (A) it travels with a uniform deceleration until it is caught, first being touched at B. The total displacement is zero i.e. the area above the time axis equals the area below it

Fig. 3·3 cont.

3.4 UNIFORM ACCELERATION IN A STRAIGHT LINE

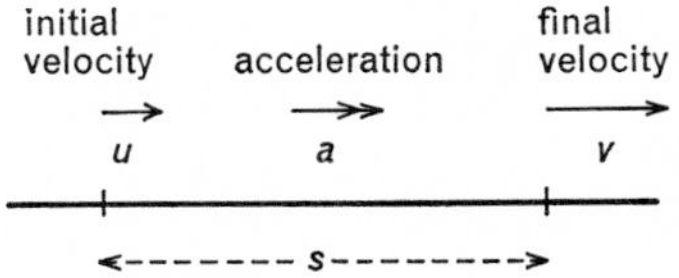

time taken t

Fig. 3·4

In Fig. 3.4,
$$a = \frac{v-u}{t} \qquad (1)$$

$$\text{The average velocity} = \frac{v+u}{2}$$

$$\text{and thus } \frac{s}{t} = \frac{v+u}{2} \qquad (2)$$

From these two equations any one of u, v, a, t and s can be found if:

(*a*) three of them are known,
(*b*) due care is taken to check the sense of the vector quantities,
(*c*) a consistent set of units is used.

For example, a train is moving at 30 m/s when the driver suddenly applies the brakes. If the train slows to 15 m/s in the next 20 s, how far will it have travelled during the application of the brakes, and what will have been its average deceleration?

If a *velocity-time* graph for this situation is drawn then the acceleration and the distance travelled can be quickly deduced by calculating the slope of the graph and the area between the graph and the time axis respectively.

Alternatively we can say:

$$a = \frac{v-u}{t} = \frac{15\,\frac{\text{m}}{\text{s}} - 30\,\frac{\text{m}}{\text{s}}}{20\text{ s}} = -0{\cdot}75\,\frac{\text{m}}{\text{s}^2}$$

and $$\frac{s}{t} = \frac{v+u}{2},$$

therefore $$\frac{s}{20\text{ s}} = \frac{15\,\frac{\text{m}}{\text{s}} + 30\,\frac{\text{m}}{\text{s}}}{2}$$

$$= \frac{45}{2}\,\frac{\text{m}}{\text{s}},$$

therefore $$s = 450\text{ m}.$$

Thus the deceleration of the train is $0{\cdot}75\,\text{m/s}^2$, and it travels 450 m in slowing down.

When, as often happens, an object is released from rest and travels a distance s in t with a constant acceleration a, the relation between s, t and a can again be deduced by drawing a velocity-time graph, or as follows:

$$u = 0,$$

therefore $$a = \frac{v-0}{t} \quad \text{and} \quad \frac{s}{t} = \frac{0+v}{2}$$

Eliminating v: $$s = \tfrac{1}{2}at^2$$

and $$a = \frac{2s}{t^2}$$

3.5 MOTION IN A CIRCLE WITH UNIFORM SPEED

A particle moving in a circle of radius r with speed v will complete one revolution in time T, where

$$v = \frac{2\pi r}{T} \quad \text{or} \quad T = \frac{2\pi r}{v}$$

T is called the **period** of the motion.

The **frequency** of the rotation is the number of times the particle describes a circle in one second:

$$n\left[\frac{1}{\text{s}}\right] = \frac{1}{T[\text{s}]}$$

$$\boxed{n = \frac{1}{T}}$$

The velocity of the particle is *continually changing*.

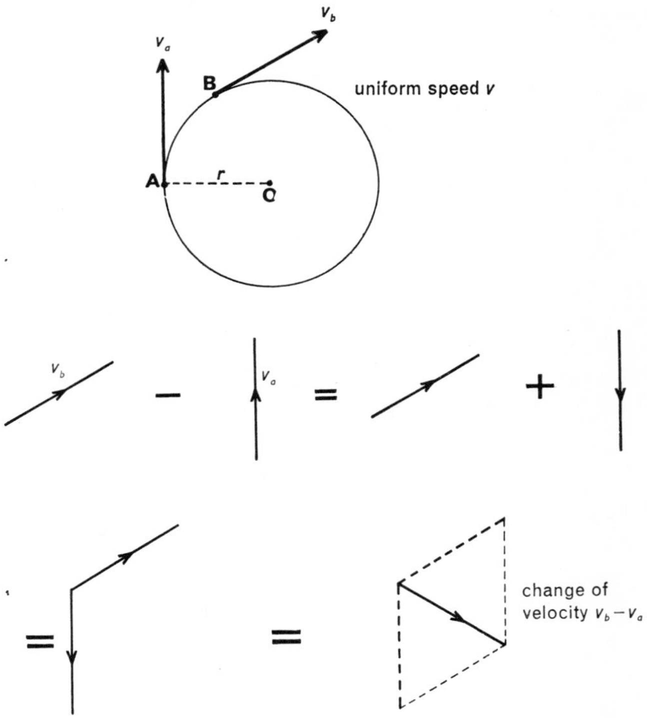

Fig. 3·5

E.g. between A and B the change of velocity $= v_b - v_a$
$= v_b + (-v_a)$

If this is repeated for the case when B is very close to A, the **direction** and **sense** of the change of velocity is found (using the parallelogram law) to be inwards along the radius, i.e. **towards the centre of the circle.** Thus the **acceleration** of the particle is **centripetal.** Its magnitude is given by

$$a\left[\frac{\text{m}}{\text{s}^2}\right] = \frac{v^2\left[\frac{\text{m}}{\text{s}}\right]^2}{r\,[\text{m}]}$$

$$\boxed{a = \frac{v^2}{r}}$$

3.6 THE ACCELERATION DUE TO GRAVITY (g)

Any *direct* method of measuring g involves measuring small time intervals, for if a body is allowed to fall for many seconds, its velocity will increase to a stage where the resistance of the air through which it is moving destroys the condition that it is falling freely, that is under gravity alone. (It would eventually reach a **terminal velocity,** when it would be in equilibrium.)

Experiment

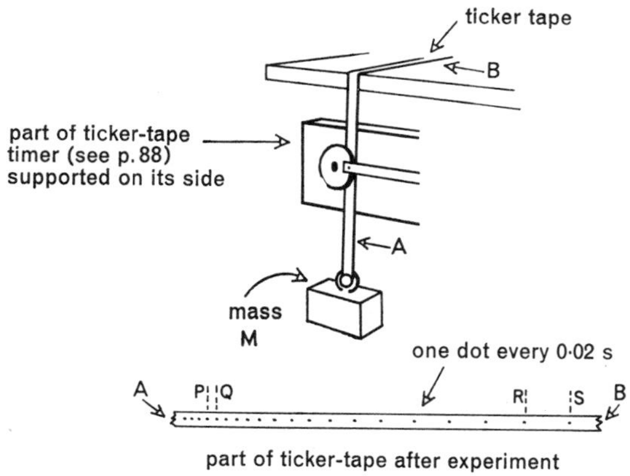

Fig. 3·6

Release M from rest. The ticker-tape will become marked as shown (see p. 88). Ignoring air resistance, the upthrust of the air, and the small pull of the ticker-tape on M, its acceleration will be constant and equal to g. Considering the tape:

$$u = \text{average speed over PQ} = \frac{PQ\ \text{m}}{0{\cdot}02\ \text{s}},$$

$$v = \text{average speed over RS} = \frac{RS\ \text{m}}{0{\cdot}02\ \text{s}},$$

$$\therefore \qquad g = a = \frac{v-u}{t},$$

and t between the middle of PQ and the middle of RS $= 0{\cdot}02 \times 15$ s.

$$\therefore \qquad g = \frac{\dfrac{RS\ \text{m}}{0{\cdot}02\ \text{s}} - \dfrac{PQ\ \text{m}}{0{\cdot}02\ \text{s}}}{15 \times 0{\cdot}02\ \text{s}}$$

$$= \frac{RS - PQ}{6 \times 10^{-3}} \frac{\text{m}}{\text{s}^2}.$$

Different positions of PQ and RS should be taken and an average value of g found.

The value of g depends upon where it is measured. To two significant figures, however, it is found to be

$$9{\cdot}8\ \frac{\text{m}}{\text{s}^2},$$

at any point *on the Earth's surface*.

The value of g to three significant figures varies from

$$9{\cdot}78\ \frac{\text{m}}{\text{s}^2} \quad \text{to} \quad 9{\cdot}83\ \frac{\text{m}}{\text{s}^2}.$$

The value of g decreases as one moves away from the Earth, falling to half of its average surface value at a height of 2600 km above the Earth's surface.

Forces

3.7 FORCES

A **force** can only be thought of in terms of the effect that it can have on a material body. A *single* force may

(1) alter the *speed* of a body,
(2) alter the *direction of motion* of a body.

In order to use this idea of force, it is essential to consider:

(*a*) a body,

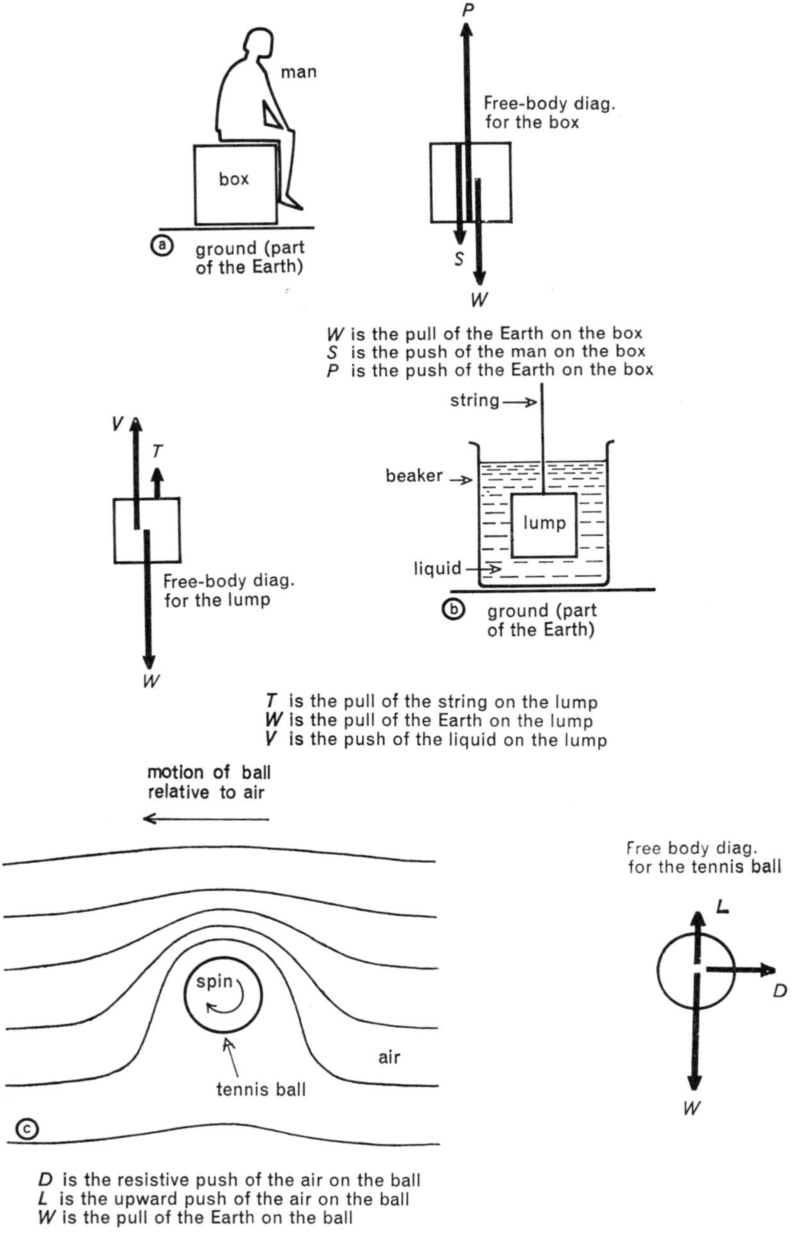
P
man
Free-body diag.
for the box
box
ⓐ ground (part
of the Earth)
S
W
W is the pull of the Earth on the box
S is the push of the man on the box
P is the push of the Earth on the box
string
V
T
beaker
lump
liquid
Free-body diag.
for the lump
ⓑ ground (part
of the Earth)
W
T is the pull of the string on the lump
W is the pull of the Earth on the lump
V is the push of the liquid on the lump
motion of ball
relative to air
Free body diag.
for the tennis ball
L
spin
D
air
tennis ball
W
ⓒ
D is the resistive push of the air on the ball
L is the upward push of the air on the ball
W is the pull of the Earth on the ball

Fig. 3·7

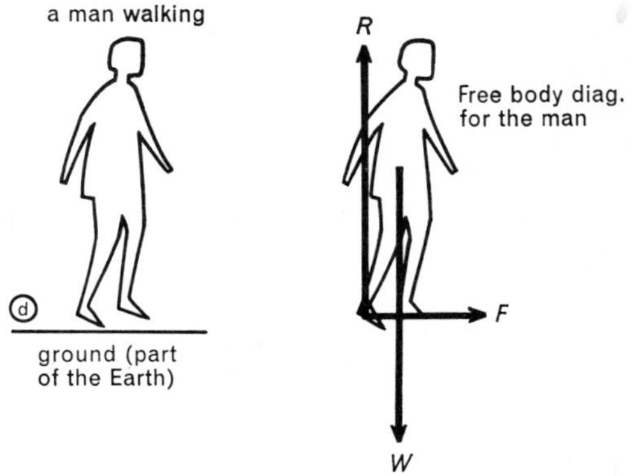

R is the normal push of the Earth on the man
F is the frictional push of the Earth on the man
W is the pull of the Earth on the man

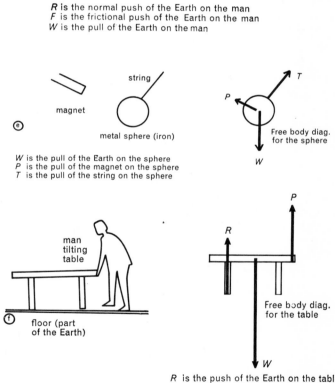

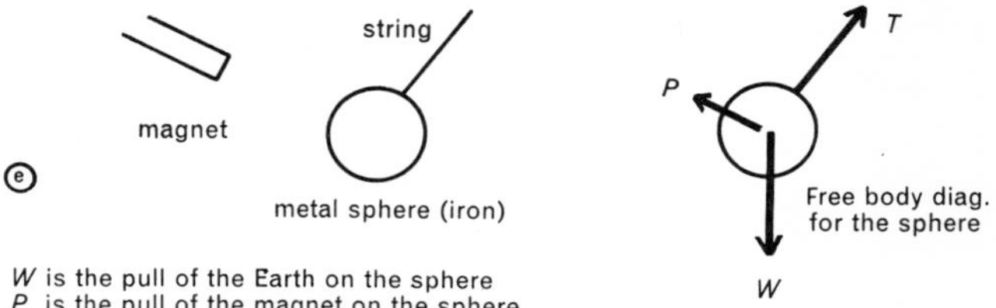

W is the pull of the Earth on the sphere
P is the pull of the magnet on the sphere
T is the pull of the string on the sphere

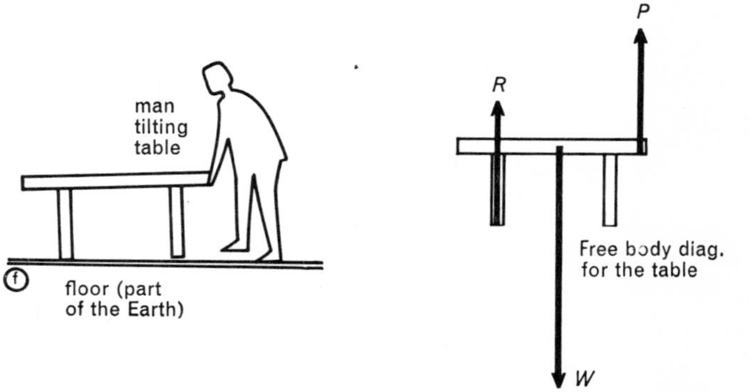

R is the push of the Earth on the table
P is the pull of the man on the table
W is the pull of the Earth on the table

Fig. 3·7 cont.

(*b*) the nature of the force acting on the body (is it a **push,** a **pull,** a **drag,** an **upthrust,** etc.?)
(*c*) the **cause** of the force. Is it caused by the Earth, the air, a man? That is, what material body causes it?

(*a*) *cannot be stressed too much.* By 'consider a body' we mean choose *one* body and draw a picture of it isolated from its surroundings. This diagram, on which we represent the forces decided by (*b*) and (*c*), we will call a **free-body diagram.** Any diagram or sketch drawn to obtain a general view of a problem should not contain forces.

Force is a *vector* quantity. We will represent the direction and sense of a force by a thick arrow which will usually be drawn emerging from the chosen body.

Types of force

In Fig. 3.7 several types of forces are illustrated. Though they can all be classified as *pushes* or *pulls*, particular types of force appear so often that they are given special names, e.g.,

gravitational forces – **weights** (W in all parts of Fig. 3.7),
fluid **upthrust** forces (V in (*b*)),
frictional forces (F in (*d*)),
normal contact forces – **reactions** (R in (*d*) and (*f*)),
inter-molecular forces,
tension forces (T in (*b*) and (*e*)),
magnetic forces (P in (*e*)),
electrostatic forces,
lift forces and **drag** forces (L and D in (*c*)).

These are further discussed at various places in the text, and reference should be made to the index.

A force should always be thought of as

the push (or pull) of the . . . (A) . . . on the . . . (B) . . .,

where A represents the body which *causes* the force
and B represents the body *on* which the force is *acting*.

Normal contact forces (sometimes called reactions)

When a body is acted on by a force which presses it against another body, the molecules in the surface repel each other and keep the bodies apart (see p. 35).

Note that it is the push of the body on the surface (and *not* the pull

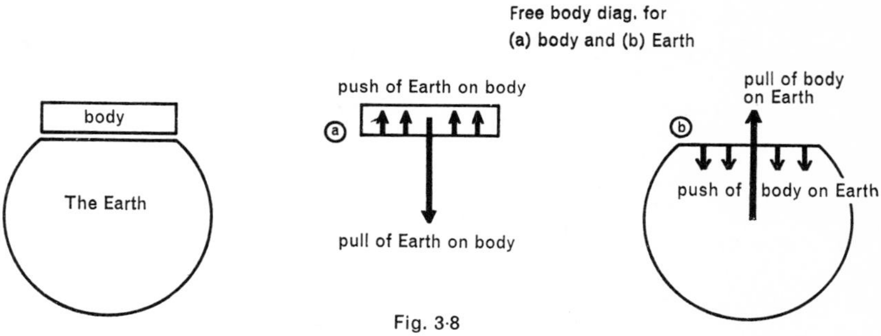

Fig. 3·8

of the Earth on the body – its weight) that acts on the surface in Fig. 3.8.

Pressure

The pressure which exists between two surfaces in contact is defined by the equation:

$$\textbf{pressure} = \frac{\text{normal contact force}}{\text{area in contact}}$$

$$p\left[\frac{\mathrm{N}}{\mathrm{m}^2}\right] = \frac{F\,[\mathrm{N}]}{A\,[\mathrm{m}^2]}$$

$$\boxed{p = \frac{F}{A}}$$

In practice situations arise where

(*a*) a *high pressure* is deliberately produced, as with knives, chisels, nails;

(*b*) a *low pressure* is deliberately produced, as with skis, snow-shoes, cups placed under the feet of heavy furniture, large tyres for motor vehicles;

(*c*) an object has parts of it designed to produce *both high and low pressures*, as with shooting-sticks and caterpillar tracks. There the sharp point and the ridges, respectively, create high pressures which enable the body to sink until the disc and the tread rest on the surface of the ground. Then the low pressure there is not enough to let the object penetrate the ground further.

Friction

Consider a body A resting on a horizontal surface B, as in Fig. 3.9.

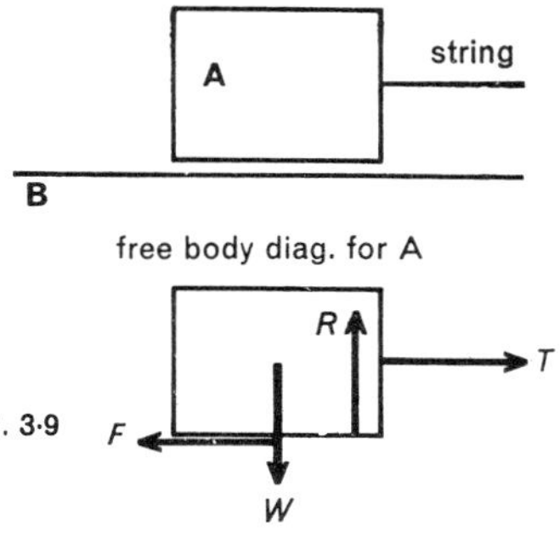

Fig. 3·9

Suppose we exert a horizontal force on A: B will exert an opposing *frictional force* on A.

There is a limit to the size of the frictional force which B can exert on A: this maximum value depends on

(*a*) the material and state of the surfaces in contact,
(*b*) the normal contact force which each body exerts on the other.

In symbols,

$$F_{max} = \mu R,$$

where μ is the **coefficient of friction** for that pair of surfaces, and R is the normal contact force (or reaction). μ is a number without units.

In general the frictional force is not equal to μR and is only as large as is necessary. The following table refers to Fig. 3.9 and shows the possibilities:

Value of T	*Value of F*	*What happens to A?*
Zero	Zero	A is in equilibrium
P } all less than μR	P } all equal to T	A is in equilibrium
Q } all less than μR	Q } all equal to T	A is in equilibrium
S } all less than μR	S } all equal to T	A is in equilibrium
$U = \mu R$	μR	A is in equilibrium
$V > \mu R$	μR	A accelerates to the right

F can never be greater than T.

In practice

(*a*) we often assume that at least one of the surfaces is frictionless: then $F = 0$;

(*b*) when motion occurs, the value of the frictional force decreases. Nevertheless, we usually assume that when a body is sliding, the frictional force is equal to μR.

Note that there is also a frictional force exerted on B by A.

Newton's Laws: II

3.8 NEWTON'S LAWS: II

A moving body possesses **momentum.**

The **momentum** of a body = (mass of body) . (velocity of body)

$$\text{momentum}\left[\frac{\text{kg m}}{\text{s}}\right] = m\,[\text{kg}]\,.\,v\left[\frac{\text{m}}{\text{s}}\right]$$

$$\boxed{\text{momentum} = mv}$$

The unit $\frac{\text{kg m}}{\text{s}}$ can also be written N s, since $1\text{ N} = 1\,\frac{\text{kg m}}{\text{s}^2}$, as shown later.

Momentum is a *vector* quantity, as velocity is a vector and mass is a scalar. The direction and sense of a body's momentum are those of its velocity.

Changes of momentum are calculated by the same method as are changes of velocity (see p. 50).

Thus change of momentum between A and B

$$= (\text{momentum})_B - (\text{momentum})_A$$
$$= (mv)_B - (mv)_A$$
$$= (mv)_B + (-mv)_A$$

Consider a ball bouncing against a wall: although the numerical value of (mass of body).(velocity of body) may be the same before and after the ball bounces, the momentum *does* change.

Newton's Law II states that:

$$\frac{\text{the change of momentum of a body}}{\text{time taken}} \propto \text{the resultant force on the body.}$$

The change of momentum is in the same direction and sense as the resultant force on the body.

$$\frac{mv-mu}{t} \propto F_{\text{resultant}},$$

$$\therefore \qquad m\left(\frac{v-u}{t}\right) \propto F_r,$$

$$\therefore \qquad ma \propto F_r$$

where a is the acceleration of the body.

$$\therefore \qquad ma = (\text{constant}) \,.\, F_r \qquad \text{(See p. 21.)}$$

Choosing the constant to be unity *defines* our unit of force:

$$m\,[\text{kg}]\,.\,a\left[\frac{\text{m}}{\text{s}^2}\right] = \text{F}_r\,[\text{newtons}],$$

i.e. 1 newton is that force which will cause a mass of 1 kg to accelerate at 1 m/s^2, or a mass of 2 kg to accelerate at $\frac{1}{2}$ m/s^2, etc.

The **newton** (N) is called an **absolute unit of force** and is defined by the above relationship.

$$1\ \text{N} = 1\ \text{kg} \times 1\ \frac{\text{m}}{\text{s}^2}$$

$$= 1\ \frac{\text{kg m}}{\text{s}^2}.$$

The equation $ma = F_{\text{resultant}}$ also tells us that a force can be measured by measuring the acceleration it produces in a standard mass.

3.9 MASS AND WEIGHT

Different bodies exhibit different resistances to a change in their motions. Each body is said to possess a different **inertia.**

Mass

The numerical measure of inertia is called the **mass** of a body.

Thus two bodies of different mass will experience different accelerations when acted upon by the same force.

Weight

The pull of the Earth on a body is called the **weight** of that body.

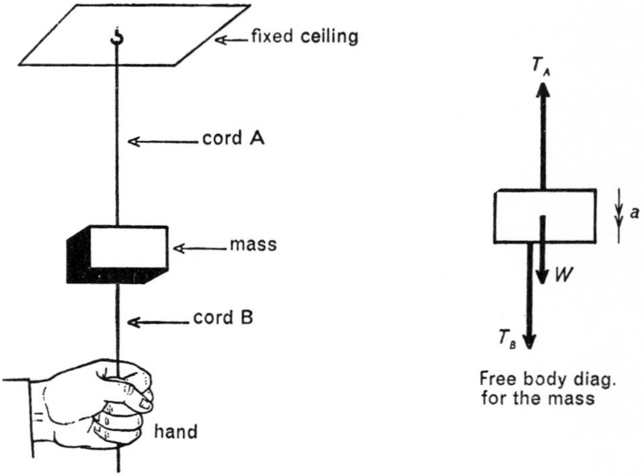

Fig. 3·10 Mass and weight

To illustrate the difference between mass and weight, consider the mass and the cords A and B shown in Fig. 3.10. If the person holding the cord

(*a*) exerts a *steady pull* – the cord A breaks,
(*b*) gives a *sudden jerk* – the cord B breaks.

To explain (*a*) and (*b*) consider a free-body diagram for the mass.

Suppose the mass accelerates as shown, then, applying Newton's Law II to it,

$$ma = W + T_B - T_A.$$

In case (*a*): $a = 0$ (a steady pull),
so $T_A = T_B + W$ and $T_A > T_B$
∴ A will break first.

In case (*b*): a is high (a jerk);
thus $T_B - T_A$ is large, and $T_B > T_A$,
each being so large that W can be neglected.
∴ B will break first.

The resistance of the mass to a change in its motion, i.e. its *inertia*, is demonstrated by the cord B breaking in (*b*).

Gravitational units of force

One kilogramme weight (kgwt) is a force equal in size to the pull of the Earth on a mass of one kilogramme.

The **kilogramme weight** is called a **gravitational unit of force.**

The weight of a body *is dependent* on the location of the body. For this reason a physicist always uses an absolute force unit, whose value

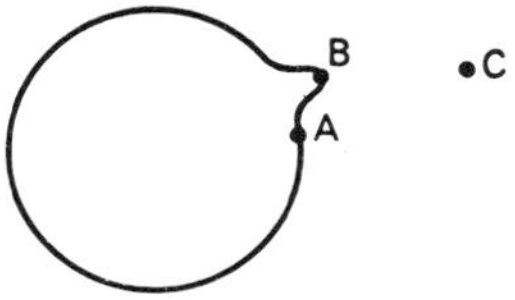

Fig. 3·11 For a given body:
mass at A = mass at B = mass at C
weight at A > weight at B > weight at C
i.e. mass of body is constant, weight of body varies

is invariable, rather than a gravitational unit, since the value of the latter varies from place to place. On the Earth's surface the variation in the weight of a body is small but noticeable. When one tries to measure the weight of a body the rotation of the Earth complicates the experiment.

One **kilogramme force** (kgf) = 9·806 65 N by definition: it is a unit of constant size which must not be confused with the kilogramme weight.

3.10 FREE FALL

Consider a body of mass m accelerating under the action of one force, the pull of the Earth on it (its weight). The body is said to be in a state of **free fall.**

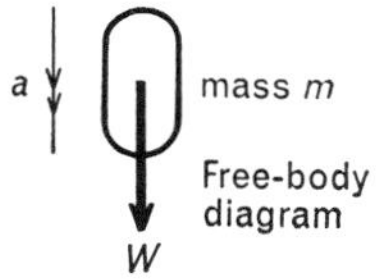

Fig. 3·12 A falling body

By Newton's Law II:

$$ma = W.$$

The acceleration is the acceleration due to gravity, g.

$$\therefore \qquad mg = W.$$

If the value of g is known, this relationship enables us to evaluate the weight of the body. Thus a body of mass 1 kg has a weight of about 10 N, or, to two significant figures, 9·8 N.

Weightlessness

A body in a state of free fall is sometimes described as being **weightless.** Weightlessness does *not* mean 'there is no Earth pull', and the word should be avoided if possible. The word 'weightless' is particularly popular in circumstances where the free fall lasts for long periods of time. Some examples of weightlessness are as follows:

(*a*) An Earth satellite (see below).
(*b*) A person in a car who leaves his seat when the car goes over a humped-back bridge at a high speed.
(*c*) A ball thrown upwards. Note that the ball is in a state of free fall when moving *up* as well as when moving down.
(*d*) A chair in a lift just after the chain which supports the lift has broken.
(*e*) A bullet fired horizontally by a gun (ignoring air resistance).

Satellites

If a body is projected horizontally above the surface of the Sun or a

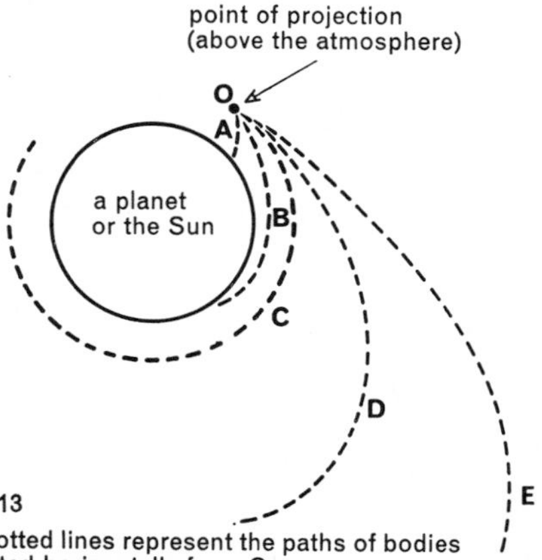

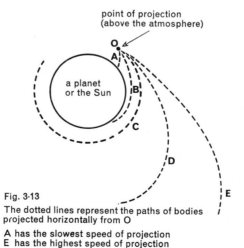

Fig. 3·13
The dotted lines represent the paths of bodies projected horizontally from O

A has the slowest speed of projection
E has the highest speed of projection

planet, then in the absence of air resistance the body will follow one of the paths shown in Fig. 3.13. The exact path depends on its initial speed. When the body follows a path which keeps it in **orbit** around the planet or the Sun, it is called a **satellite** of that planet or the Sun. *Satellites are in a state of free fall.*

The universal law of gravitation tells us that the force on a satellite is
(*a*) inversely proportional to the square of the body's distance r from the centre of the planet or the Sun,
(*b*) proportional to the mass m of the body,
(*c*) proportional to the mass M of the planet or the Sun.

i.e.
$$W \propto \frac{mM}{r^2}$$

When the satellite *moves in a circle* the acceleration of the satellite is radial and is numerically equal to v^2/r (see p. 51). It follows that

(*a*) a satellite at a certain distance from a planet or the Sun must have a particular speed;
(*b*) the farther away from its planet or the Sun a satellite is moving, the lower is its speed, and the longer it takes to complete one revolution.

For example, at 200 km from the Earth's surface a satellite requires about 90 minutes to complete one revolution, whereas the Moon, at about 4×10^5 km, requires about 28 days.

3.11 ACCELERATING BODIES

A body subject to a resultant force will accelerate according to Newton's Law II. To apply the law,

(*a*) pick a body,
(*b*) draw a free-body diagram for the body,
(*c*) mark *all* the forces on the body *in absolute units,*
(*d*) mark the acceleration a of the body,
(*e*) calculate the value of $F_{\text{resultant}}$, the magnitude of the resultant force on the body in the direction and sense of a, resolving the forces if necessary,
(*f*) apply Newton's Law II in the form

$$ma = F_{\text{resultant}}$$

For example:

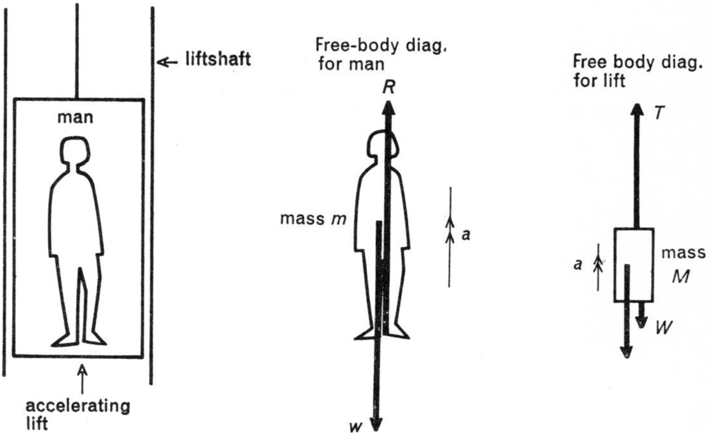

Fig. 3·14

Newton's Law II for man: $ma = R - w$,
Newton's Law II for lift: $Ma = T - R - W$.

The symbols have their usual meaning: the student should describe them fully. Note the forces, *R, one on each free-body diagram,* which are equal as Newton's Law III (see below) demands.

Newton's Laws: I and III

3.12 NEWTON'S LAWS: I AND III

Newton's Law I states that:

> A body on which no resultant force acts will move with a constant velocity. (This velocity is frequently zero.)

This law *seems* to be contrary to common sense, for a ball rolled along the ground comes to rest, and a cart only continues to move while the horse pulls on it. The difficulty in such cases is to 'see' *all* the forces on the body which produce the resultant force on it: some types of force, like friction, can easily go unnoticed. We do not attempt to verify this law, as our idea of force is dependent upon it: thus if we see a body apparently not acted on by a resultant force, but whose velocity is changing, our conclusion is not that Newton's Law I is untrue, but rather that there must be a resultant force acting on the body, and that the body which is causing the force is not obvious.

Newton's Law III states that:

> If a body A exerts a force F on body B, then body B exerts a force on body A which is equal in magnitude and direction but opposite in sense to F.

Note that the two forces in this law *always act on two different bodies.* It is this law which makes it so essential to identify the body causing a force to act, and to *avoid* referring to a force as 'gravity', 'reaction' or 'friction', for example.

Consider a boy landing on the ground (part of the Earth) after jumping off a wall.

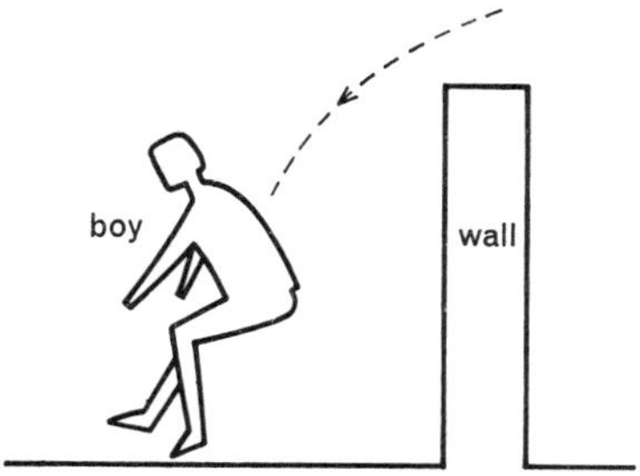

Fig. 3·15

ground (part of the Earth)

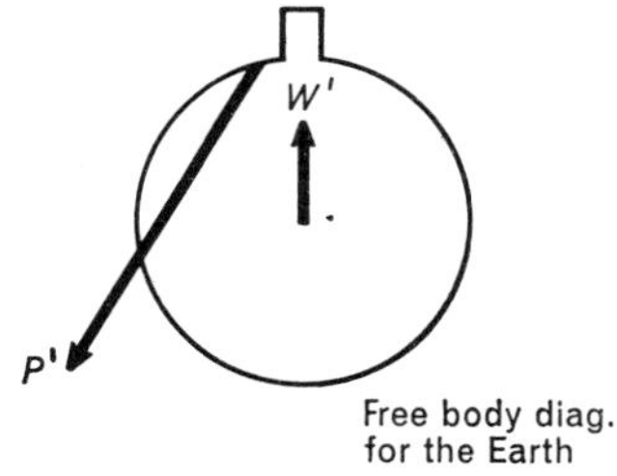

W' is the pull of the boy on the Earth
P' is the push of the boy on the Earth

W is the pull of the Earth on the boy
P is the push of the Earth on the boy

In Fig. 3.15,

$$P = P',$$
$$W = W'$$

This is so *at every instant.*

We could repeat this procedure on any of the examples in Fig. 3.7 by drawing further free-body diagrams. For example, in (*b*) 'the push of the liquid on the lump' will have a Law III force 'the push of the lump on the liquid', which would appear acting downward in a free-body diagram of the liquid.

3.13 IMPULSE

We define the **impulse of a force** by the equation

impulse = (force) . (time for which force acts)

i.e. $$\text{impulse [N s]} = F\text{[N]} . t\text{[s]}$$

$$\boxed{\text{Impulse} = Ft}$$

From Newton's Law III it follows that *the impulses of a pair of Law III forces are the same in size and direction, but opposite in sense,* even if the forces are not constant, since Newton's Law III states that the force of A on B and the force of B on A are equal in size and direction, but opposite in sense, at every instant. Thus if a hammer gives an impulse to a nail, the nail gives an impulse to the hammer which is the same in size and direction, but opposite in sense.

We naturally think of impulse as being associated with a sharp blow like a kick, or a tug, or a blow from a hammer. The idea of impulse is certainly useful in these situations, since the force itself is large and variable and cannot be measured (whereas we shall see that impulse *can* be measured). But the idea of impulse can also be used where a steady force acts for some time: for example, a man exerting a force of 4 N on a trolley for 5 s gives the trolley an impulse of 20 N s.

3.14 ROCKETS AND JETS

An understanding of Newton's Laws I and III enables us to explain both rocket and jet propulsion.

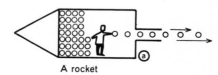

A rocket

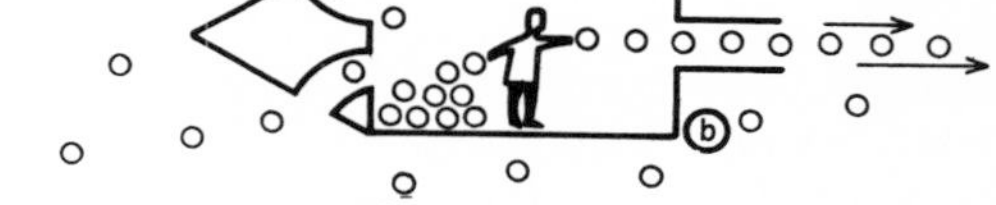

A jet engine

Fig. 3·16

The rocket

If bodies are to be projected out of the back of a rocket it is necessary for a force to be exerted on each body (Law I). An equal force in the opposite sense must be exerted by each body on the rocket (Law III). These forces propel the rocket.

In practice the bodies acquire their kinetic energy from combustion processes, and the machine is one designed to convert chemical energy into mechanical energy. A gun recoiling is a simple example of the rocket principle.

The jet engine

The *principle* is the same as for the rocket. The difference is the source of the bodies to be projected. The rocket carries all its own bodies: the jet engine carries some of the bodies it projects, but most of what it projects has been picked up from the atmosphere.

Both rockets and jet engines are *hindered* by the resistance of the atmosphere: long distance jet-engined airliners are flown high up in the Earth's atmosphere where the air resistance is low, but where there is still enough air to be picked up.

3.15 IMPULSE AND MOMENTUM

Momentum has already been defined (see p. 58). For a constant force F acting on a body of mass m for a time t, and changing the velocity of the body from u (initially) to v (finally),

$$F = \frac{mv - mu}{t} \quad \left(\frac{\text{change of momentum of body}}{\text{time taken}}\right)$$

(see p. 59);

so

$$\boxed{Ft = mv - mu}$$

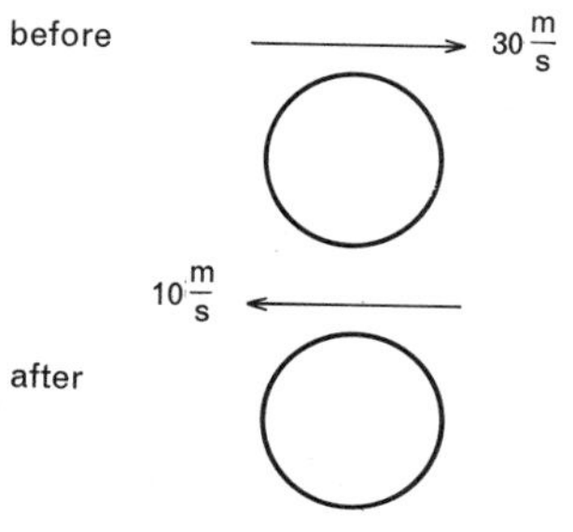

Fig. 3·17 Ball of mass 0·15 kg

Thus the **impulse of the force** is equal to the **change of momentum of the body.** This statement is true even if the force is not constant. In situations where we cannot measure F or t, we can nevertheless measure the impulse Ft if we can measure the change of momentum.

For example, a cricket ball of mass 0·15 kg is struck by a bat. It was travelling at 30 m/s before the blow, and travels at 10 m/s afterwards, in the opposite sense.

Momentum before = 0·15 kg × 30 m/s (to the right)
= 4·5 N s (to the right).
Momentum after = 0·15 kg × 10 m/s (to the left)
= 1·5 N s (to the left).

Hence
change of momentum = 1·5 N s (to the left) −4·5 N s (to the right)
= 6·0 N s (to the left).

So impulse = 6·0 N s (to the left).

3.16 CONSERVATION OF MOMENTUM

Suppose two bodies exert forces on each other (and no other forces are exerted on them): as we saw on page 66, the impulse that each exerts on the other are equal in magnitude and direction but opposite in sense.

If body A gains x units of momentum in one sense, body B gains x units of momentum in the opposite sense: the total momentum remains constant. Of course other forces (e.g. the pull of the Earth) do usually act on the bodies, but the result is still useful if there is a direction in which no external forces act.

The **principle of the conservation of momentum** states that if there is a direction in which no external forces act on a system, the total momentum of that system in that direction is constant, even if the bodies act on each other.

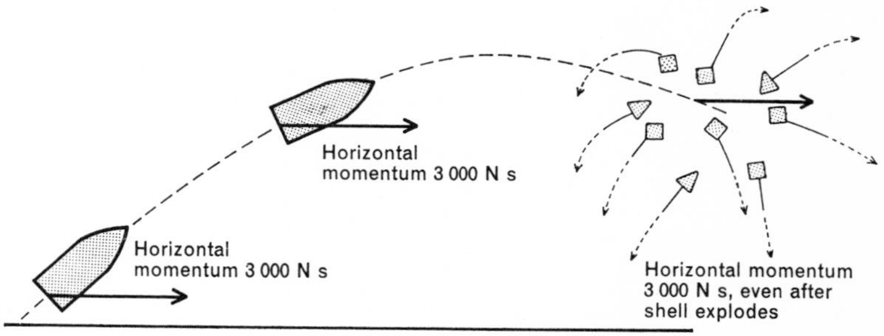

Fig. 3·18 In the absence of any horizontal external force, the horizontal momentum does not change

Fig. 3.18 shows a situation where the momentum of a body is conserved: the forces produced by the explosion are internal forces.

Solving problems using the principle of the conservation of momentum

The principle can be used in any problem involving two or more bodies where there is a direction in which no external forces act on the bodies during their interaction: this interaction may be their collision or an explosion involving only them. The *technique* is as follows:

(*a*) Draw diagrams of the situation, marking the masses on the bodies and their velocities (*i*) before, and (*ii*) after, the interaction.
(*b*) Choose the sense of a particular direction as positive, write down the total momentum of the bodies (*i*) before, and (*ii*) after, the interaction, and equate them.

An example is given on page 85.

Collisions in which there is no loss of kinetic energy are called **perfectly elastic:** most molecular collisions are of this type.

Equilibrium

3.17 ADDING AND RESOLVING FORCES

The parallelogram law

Force is a *vector* quantity. Two forces can thus be added by the parallelogram law (see p. 16).

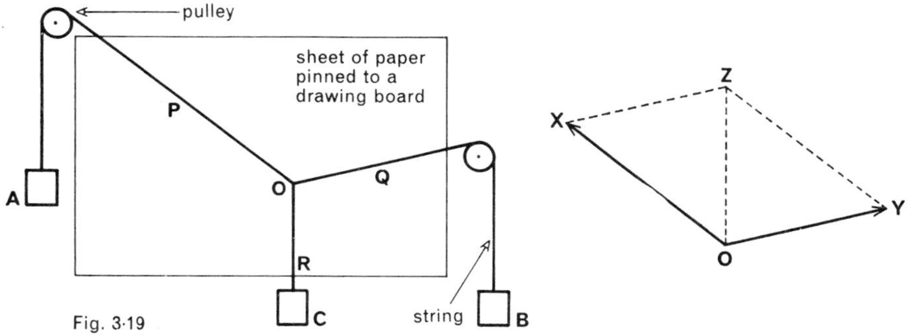

Fig. 3·19

Experiment to verify parallelogram law for forces

Find a position of equilibrium for the knot at O, using known masses A, B and C. Mark the directions OP, OQ and OR on the paper, and construct a parallelogram OXYZ with OX and OY proportional to the weights of A and B, and thus proportional to the pulls of the strings on the knot. If the resultant OZ is proportional to the weight of C, and parallel to OR, then the parallelogram law is verified.

The triangle of forces

If three coplanar forces act on a body and keep it in equilibrium, then when the forces are represented in size, direction and sense they will form a triangle, the sense of each force being such as to place the forces head to tail.

For example, for the body shown in Fig. 3.7*e*, the forces are drawn (*i*) to scale in Fig. 3.20*a*, and (*ii*) forming a triangle in Fig. 3.20*b*. This

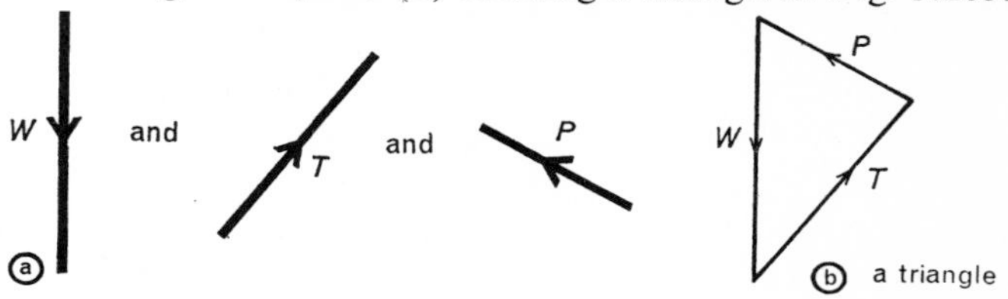

Fig. 3·20

result is called **the triangle of forces,** but the idea will be equally useful for other *vector* quantities such as velocity. The direction and sense of each force will be known from a free-body diagram: if the size of any one force is known, then the sizes of the other two can be found from the triangle.

It is important to realize that this is a geometrical construction: it cannot represent the points of application of the forces.

Resolving forces

The **resolved part** of the force F in the direction Ox is $F.\cos\theta$. If AO represents F in magnitude, direction and sense, then OB represents the resolved part of F in the direction Ox on a scale diagram. $F.\cos\theta$ represents the **effect of the force** in the chosen direction. Clearly, if θ is equal to 90°, the force has zero resolved part, i.e. no effect.

If a force is resolved in *two perpendicular directions,* e.g. Ox and Oy in Fig. 3.21, to give two resolved parts represented by OB and OC,

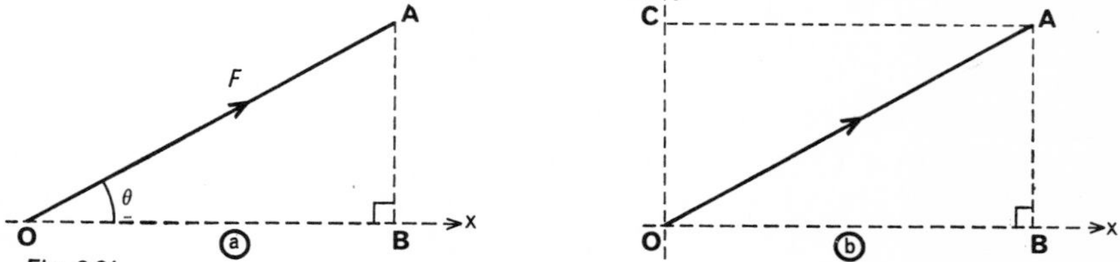

Fig. 3·21

then the sum of the two resolved parts will, when added by the parallelogram law, have a resultant represented by OA. This means that OB and OC are together *equivalent* to OA.

When more than two forces require adding it is inconvenient to use the parallelogram law as its repetition is arduous. The forces are best resolved in two perpendicular directions, each set of resolved parts added, and then these two forces added to give a single **resultant force.** In this way the parallelogram law is used only once, and with the forces at right angles. All vector quantities can be similarly resolved.

3.18 THE EQUILIBRIUM OF PARTICLES

We use the word *particle* to describe objects whose size is negligible. So far we have taken no account of the size of bodies and have therefore been treating them as particles. From now on we shall sometimes recognize that bodies have size.

A particle is said to be in equilibrium when it has *zero acceleration.* According to Newton's Law II the resultant force on the particle must then be zero.

To prove *that a particle is in equilibrium,* we must prove that the sums of the resolved parts of the forces on the particle in *any two* directions are each zero.

If *a particle is in equilibrium,* it follows that the sums of the resolved parts of the forces on the particle in *all* directions are each zero.

In solving problems we are usually asked 'What can be deduced from the fact that a given particle is in equilibrium?' The procedure to be followed is:

(*a*) draw a free-body diagram for the particle with all the forces acting on it,
(*b*) resolve twice in two *convenient* directions.

For example, consider a stone of weight 30 N resting on a slope without slipping.

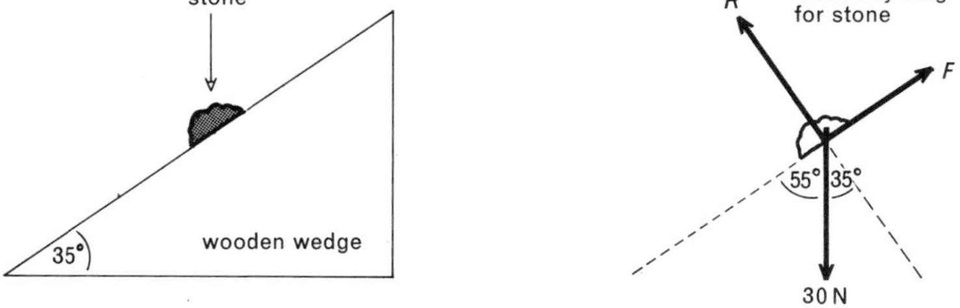

Fig. 3·22 *R* is the normal push of the wedge on the stone
F is the frictional push of the wedge on the stone
30 N is the pull of the Earth on the stone

Resolving parallel to the slope:

$$F - 30\ \text{N}.\cos 55^\circ = 0.$$

Resolving perpendicular to the slope:

$$R - 30\ \text{N}.\cos 35^\circ = 0.$$

Therefore

$$F = 30\ \text{N}.\cos 55^\circ = 17\ \text{N},$$
$$R = 30\ \text{N}.\cos 35^\circ = 25\ \text{N}.$$

3.19 THE MOMENT OF A FORCE

For **particles,** the forces acting on them must (obviously) pass through one point. All we need consider are such things as the resultant of the forces, or the sum of the resolved parts in a particular direction.

For **bodies** (i.e. objects with size), the forces acting on them need not pass through one point. In this case we shall need to consider also whether the forces tend to *turn* the body. We call the turning effect of a force about a particular axis the **moment of the force about that axis.**

$$\begin{pmatrix}\textbf{Moment of force}\\ \textbf{about an axis}\end{pmatrix} = (\text{force}) . \begin{pmatrix}\text{perpendicular distance from axis}\\ \text{to line of action of force}\end{pmatrix}$$

$$\text{Moment [N m]} = F\,[\text{N}] . d\,[\text{m}]$$

$$\boxed{\text{Moment} = Fd}$$

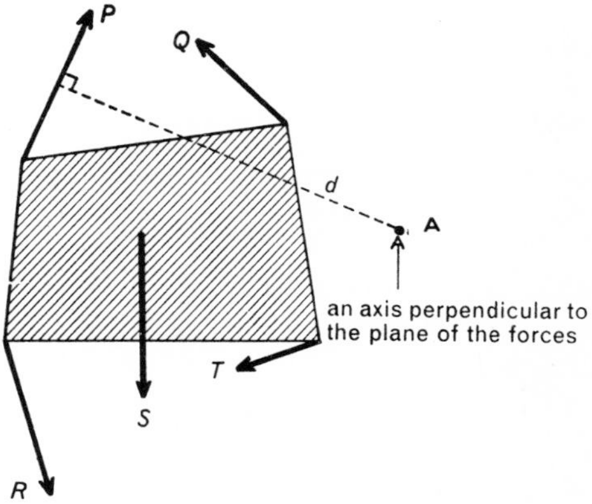

Fig. 3·23 Object acted upon by forces ***P***, *Q*, *R*, *S*, *T*, all of which are in the same plane

In Fig. 3.23 the moment about the axis A of the force P is Pd in a clockwise sense.

Note the following:

(*a*) *The moment of a force has a sense* (clockwise or anti-clockwise), and if we give one of these senses a positive sign and the other a negative sign (it does not matter which) moments can be added algebraically.

(*b*) If we are thinking of forces whose lines of action are all in the same plane (i.e. **coplanar** forces) we can speak of finding the moments of the forces (i.e. **taking moments**) 'about a point' rather than 'about an axis', since an axis appears as a point in the diagrams.

3.20 THE EQUILIBRIUM OF BODIES

We can now consider the equilibrium of *bodies,* and need not restrict ourselves to particles, but we shall at this stage confine ourselves to coplanar forces.

To prove that a body is in equilibrium, we must prove that

(*a*) the sums of the resolved parts of the forces on the body in *any two* directions are each zero, *and*

(*b*) the sum of the moments of the forces on a body about *any one* axis is zero.

If a body is in equilibrium, it follows that

(*a*) the sums of the resolved parts of the forces on the body in *all* directions are each zero, *and*

(*b*) the sums of the moments of the forces on the body about *all* axes are each zero.

The technique for solving problems is similar to that for dealing with problems about particles, but in addition to resolving, we can now also take moments. A very large number of equations can be formed. However:

(*a*) When we have resolved twice, and taken moments once, and thus formed three equations, there is nothing more we can do. Further resolving and moment-taking give us equations which contain no further information.

(*b*) It is wise to think carefully about the *directions* in which we choose to resolve and the *axes* about which we choose to take moments, because some choices give us equations with few terms in them, or equations which are easily solved.

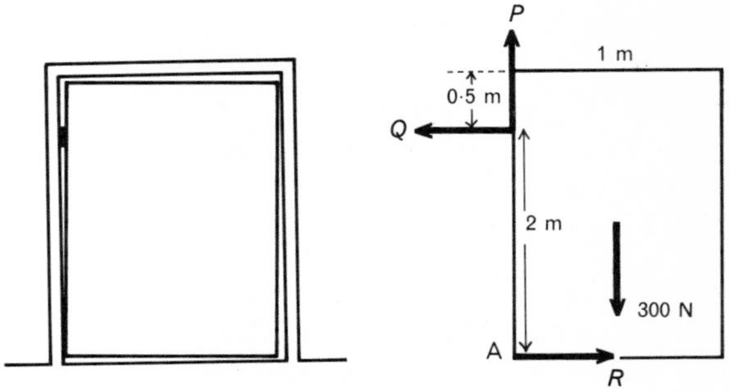

Door supported on one hinge

Free body diag. for door

Fig. 3·24

The following example gives some idea of the techniques required.

A door (shown in Fig. 3.24) is hung by one hinge, and also has a horizontal force exerted on it by the door frame lower down. Its weight is 300 N. The problem is to find the unknown forces. We first resolve the force at the hinge into forces P and Q.

Resolving horizontally: $Q - R = 0$.

Resolving vertically: $300\,\text{N} - P = 0$.

Taking moments about A: $0{\cdot}5\,\text{m} \times 300\,\text{N} - 2\,\text{m} \times Q = 0$.

Hence $Q = R = 75\,\text{N}$, $P = 300\,\text{N}$.

(If we wish, we can now add (vectorially) P and Q to find the size and direction of the total force exerted on the door by the hinge.)

3.21 THE PRINCIPLE OF MOMENTS

On page 73 we saw that

> if a body is in equilibrium, the sums of the moments of the forces on the body about all axes are each zero.

This is sometimes isolated and called the **principle of moments.**

An experiment to verify the principle

A metre rule has at least two threads tied to it: some of these support slotted-weight holders directly, others pass over pulleys and then support weight holders. The positions of the threads, and the sizes of masses placed on the weight holders are adjusted until equilibrium is achieved. Then, having drawn a free-body diagram for the rule, moments are taken about any point (on or off the rule) for all the

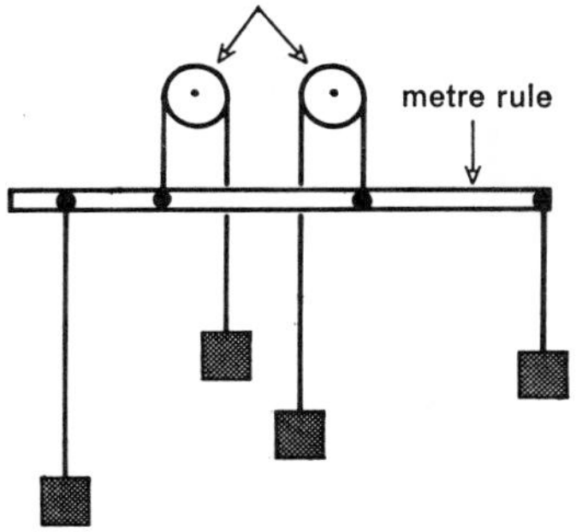

Fig. 3·25 An experiment to verify the principle of moments

forces acting on the rule (not forgetting its own weight). If the sum of these moments is zero, the principle has been verified. (See Fig. 3.25.)

3.22 TORQUES

If two forces, equal in size, parallel to each other, but with different lines of action and different senses, act on a body, the body will tend to turn, since two such forces do not produce equilibrium, even though the sums of the resolved parts (in all directions) of the forces are zero. Such a pair of forces is called a **couple.**

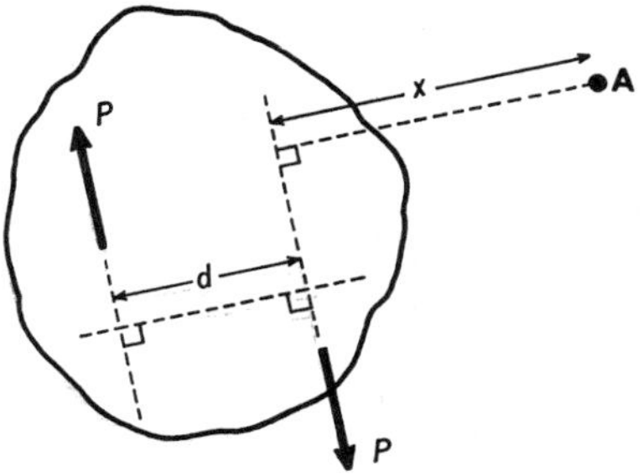

Fig. 3·26 The moment, about A, of the forces $= P(x+d) - Px = Pd$

If we take moments for two such forces, as in Fig. 3.26, about any point A, we find that the sum of the moments (i.e. the **torque**) is Pd; *the torque, about any axis, of two such forces is the product of one of the forces and the perpendicular distance between them.*

A tendency to turn is sometimes caused by a couple, but as in Fig.

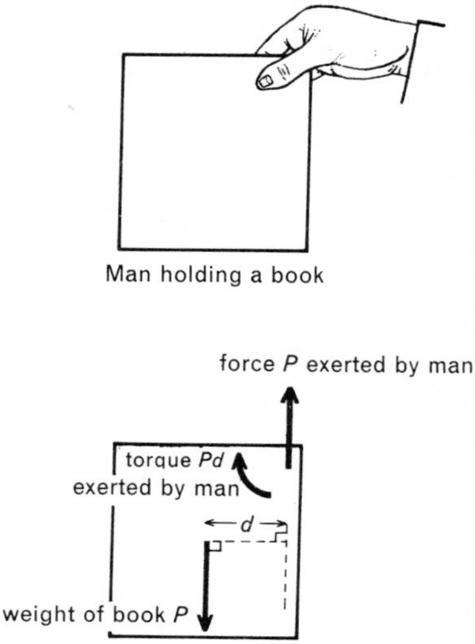

Fig. 3·27

3.27, where a man is holding a book by one corner, this need not be so. The weight of the book is *P*, so the man must exert an upward force *P* on the book. These forces constitute a couple whose torque is *Pd* (anti-clockwise), and so the man must, by the grip of his fingers, exert a torque of *Pd* (clockwise), although he does not exert *two separate* equal and opposite forces.

Other examples of torques not caused by two distinct forces:

(*a*) the torque exerted on the lid of a jar to unscrew it,
(*b*) the torque exerted by one clutch-plate on another in a motor-car clutch.

3.23 CENTRES OF GRAVITY

The pulls of the Earth on different parts of a body have a resultant which passes through a point called the **centre of gravity** of the body. This resultant force is called the weight of the body.

Methods of finding the centre of gravity

(*a*) A *plane* body can be hung freely from two different points and the point of intersection of the vertical lines through the points of

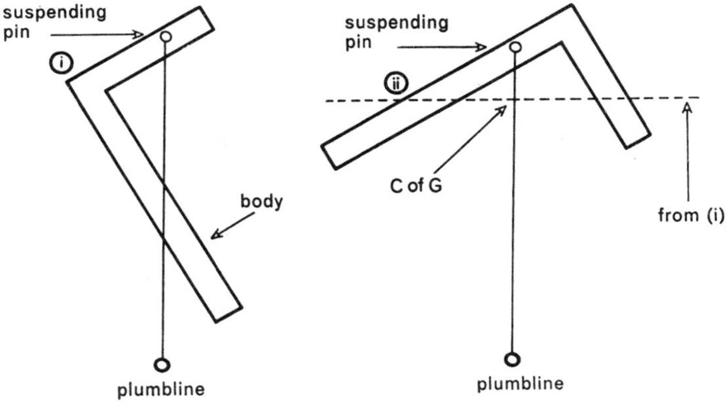

Fig. 3·28

suspension found. Hanging it from a third point will check that the correct point has been found.

(*b*) For bodies of simple shapes and uniform densities, it is possible to calculate the position of the centre of gravity by using the principle of moments. For example, for a uniform rod the centre of gravity is at the mid-point of the rod.

Stability

A body which is in equilibrium can be in a state of stable equilibrium, unstable equilibrium, or neutral equilibrium. To decide which, one imagines the body to be given a *small* displacement. If the centre of gravity is

(*a*) *raised* by this displacement, the equilibrium is **stable;**
(*b*) *lowered* by this displacement, the equilibrium is **unstable;**

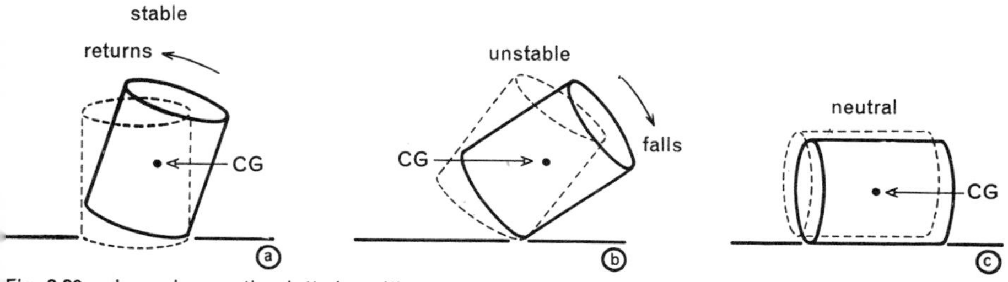

Fig. 3·29 In each case the dotted position represents a position of equilibrium (*c*) *remains at the same level* during this displacement, the equilibrium is **neutral.**

In practice the stability of a body is made evident by whether it

(*a*) returns to its original position (stable),
(*b*) continues to move away from its original position (unstable), or
(*c*) remains in the displaced position (neutral) after a small displacement.

To make a body stable for large displacements away from a position of stable equilibrium, it is necessary to make its base dimensions as *large* as possible and to keep its centre of gravity as *low* as possible.

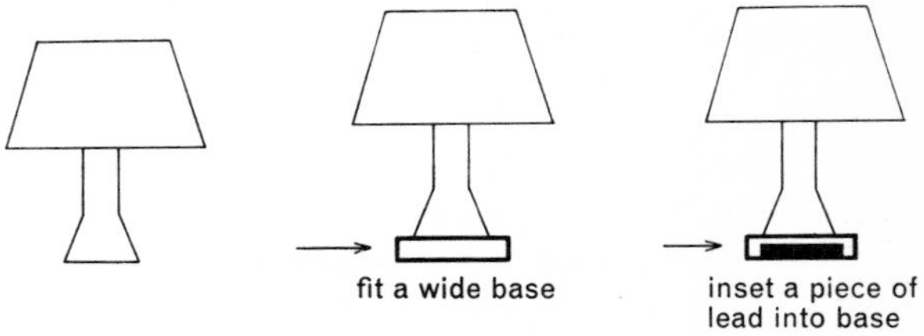
fit a wide base
inset a piece of lead into base

Fig. 3·30 How to improve the stability of a lamp

Care must be taken to distinguish between

(*i*) a body which is in *unstable* equilibrium,
(*ii*) a body which is *not* in equilibrium.

Energy

3.24 WORK

A force may do **work:** we define the *work done by a force* by

$$\begin{pmatrix}\text{work done}\\ \text{by force}\end{pmatrix} = (\text{force}) \begin{pmatrix}\text{distance moved in direction and sense}\\ \text{of force}\end{pmatrix}$$

$$W\,[\text{joules}] = F\,[\text{N}].s\,[\text{m}]$$

$$\boxed{W = Fs}$$

1 joule (J) is the work done by a force of 1 N when it moves a distance of 1 m (in the direction and sense of the force).

Using the definition to calculate the work done by a force

Consider the following cases:

(*i*) The force *does not move:* the work done is *zero:* e.g. the push of a man on a wall, the pull of a man on a suitcase he is holding still.

(*ii*) The force *is perpendicular to the movement of the body:* the work done is *zero:* e.g. the pull of the Earth on a satellite moving in a circular orbit, the normal push of a table on a book sliding on it.

(*iii*) The force *is in the direction and sense of the movement:* the work done is positive: e.g. a stone of weight 20 N falls down 2 m, then +40 J of work is done by the weight.

(*iv*) The force *is in the same direction as the movement but is in the opposite sense:* the work done is negative: e.g. a frictional force of 30 N opposes the motion of a book sliding on a horizontal table. In 3 m, −90 J of work are done by the frictional force.

Fig. 3.31 shows examples of these calculations in particular situations:

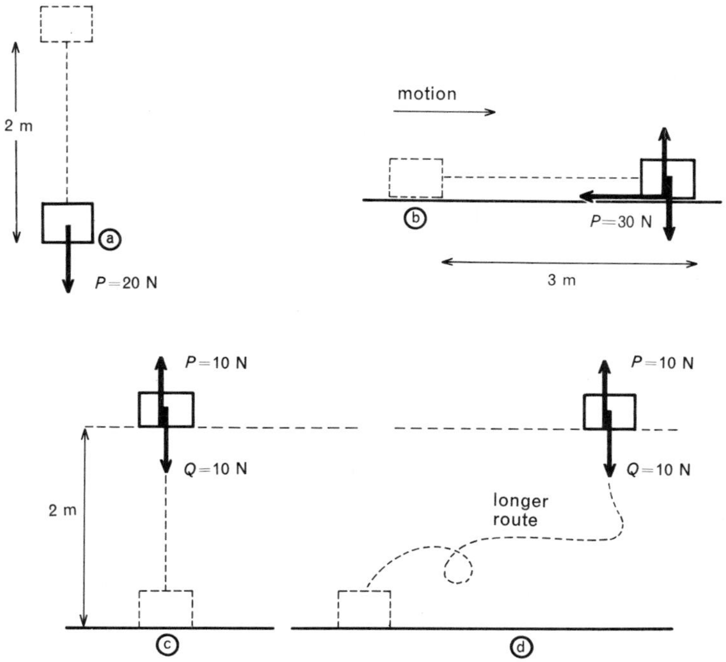

Fig. 3·31

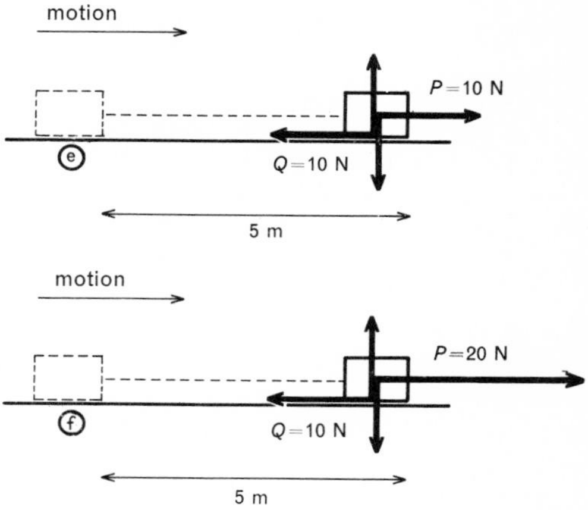

Fig. 3·31 cont.

Figure	*Situation*	*(Work done by force P)/ joules*	*(Work done by force Q)/ joules*	*(Total work done)/ joules*
3.31*a*	A stone falling down	+40		+40
3.31*b*	A stone sliding on a rough table	−90		−90
3.31*c*	A block raised vertically	+20	−20	0
3.31*d*	A block raised by a longer route	+20	−20	0
3.31*e*	A block pulled along a rough table	+50	−50	0
3.31*f*	A block pulled along a rough table	+100	−50	+50

3.25 ENERGY

Suppose body A exerts a force on body B and does work: the work done is a measure of the **interchange of energy** between A and B. A loses energy equal to the work done by the force it exerts on B: B gains that amount of energy.

Thus we say:

a body which can do work has **energy**.

Because there are many different reasons why a body may be able to do work, we say there are different forms of energy:

(*a*) kinetic energy,
(*b*) gravitational potential energy,
(*c*) internal energy,
(*d*) elastic potential energy,
(*e*) heat,
(*f*) chemical energy,
(*g*) radiant energy,
(*h*) electric and magnetic potential energy,
(*i*) nuclear energy.

Here we shall be concerned only with **kinetic energy,** gravitational potential energy (called **potential energy** from now on) and **internal energy,** but we should note in passing that energy is **conserved.**

The Principle of the **Conservation of Energy** states that

there is no change in the total energy in the universe.

Changes may occur between different forms of energy and the amounts possessed by different bodies. Some examples of these changes are given on pp. 82 and 83.

3.26 KINETIC ENERGY

Suppose a number of forces act on a body, and they have a resultant: the body accelerates, the forces do work and the body gains energy in a form which we shall call *kinetic energy* (k.e.), the *energy it possesses because of its motion.* Thus

$$\begin{pmatrix}\text{the work done by the forces}\\ \text{acting on the body}\end{pmatrix} = \begin{pmatrix}\text{the change in the body's}\\ \text{k.e.}\end{pmatrix}$$

Thus, in Fig. 3.31*a*, where +40 J of work are done on the body, the body gains 40 J of k.e. Where there is no resultant force, as in Figs. 3.31*c–e*, the total work done is zero, and there is no change in the body's k.e. Finally, in Fig. 3.31*f*, the total work done is +50 J, and the body gains 50 J of k.e.

It can be shown (though at this stage you would not be expected to prove) that a particle which has mass m and velocity v has a kinetic energy of $\frac{1}{2}mv^2$.

3.27 POTENTIAL ENERGY

It often happens that the pull of the Earth on a body (its weight) does work on it. When this work is positive, we call this the decrease in the body's *potential energy* (p.e.): when this work is negative, we call it the increase in the body's p.e. Thus, when bodies move up, their p.e. increases: when they move down, their p.e. decreases.

The **potential energy** of a body is the energy it possesses because of its position. Thus, in Fig. 3.31*c–d*, the work done by Q (the pull of the Earth) is negative (-20 J) and thus the body's p.e. increases by 20 J.

3.28 INTERNAL ENERGY

Since frictional forces *always* oppose motion, the work they do is always negative. They produce an amount of internal energy equal to the amount of work done. (Some sound may also sometimes be produced, but so little that we shall ignore this.) Thus, in Fig. 3.31*b*, 90 J of internal energy are produced because the frictional force does -90 J of work. The block loses the k.e. associated with its bodily motion, but the speeds of vibration of the molecules increase as they gain internal energy, and therefore so does the k.e. associated with these vibrations.

3.29 INTERCHANGES BETWEEN DIFFERENT FORMS OF ENERGY

(*a*) A bullet is fired into a block and becomes embedded in it. Suppose the bullet had 10 J of k.e. Since it loses this k.e., because it comes to rest, the frictional forces which the block exerts on the bullet must do -10 J of work, and therefore 10 J of internal energy are produced.

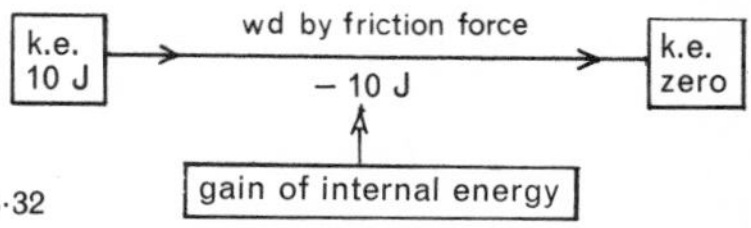

Fig. 3·32

(*b*) Consider water of weight 5 N falling down 30 m in a waterfall. Its weight does $+150$ J of work on it, and so

(*i*) it loses 150 J of p.e., and
(*ii*) it gains 150 J of k.e.

At the bottom it loses this k.e., because it comes to rest, and so the resistance forces must do -150 J of work on the water, and therefore 150 J of internal energy are produced.

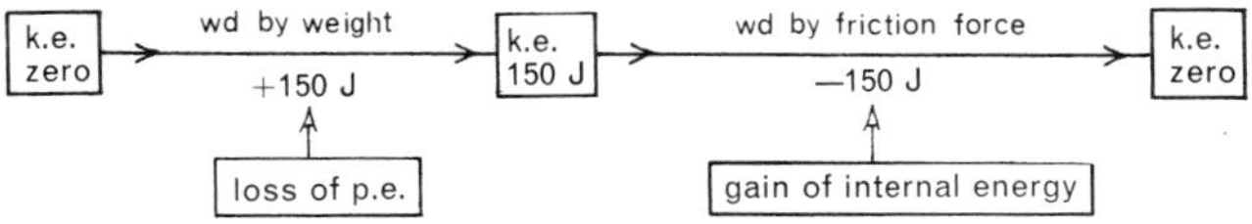

Fig. 3·33

(*c*) Consider a pendulum bob of weight 0·2 N which, as it swings (in a vacuum) rises and falls a vertical distance of 0·1 m. When it falls, its weight does +0·02 J of work, so

(*i*) it loses 0·02 J of p.e., and
(*ii*) it gains 0·02 J of k.e.

in reaching the lowest point of its swing. The reverse process then occurs as it rises, and so on.

If the pendulum swings in air, the frictional forces of the air resistance will do negative work on the bob, and eventually 0·02 J of internal energy will have been produced in the bob and the surrounding air when the bob has come to rest.

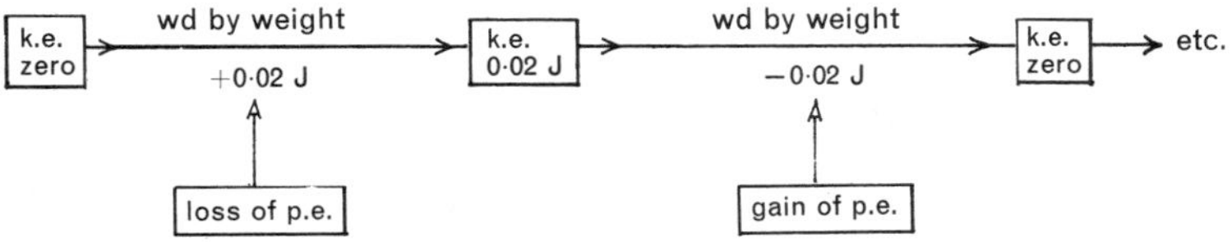

Fig. 3·34

3.30 POWER

When a force does work, its rate of working is called its **power.**

$$\textbf{Power} = \frac{\text{work done by force}}{\text{time taken to do work}}$$

$$P\,[\text{watts}] = \frac{W\,[\text{joules}]}{t\,[\text{seconds}]}$$

$$\boxed{P = \frac{W}{t}}$$

1 **watt (W)** is the rate of working when one joule of work is done in 1 second.

1 kilowatt = 1000 watts.

4 Applications of mechanics

Basic measurements

4.1 MEASUREMENT OF FORCE, WEIGHT AND MASS

(a) Measuring force. Spring balances *measure* forces: the spring stretches until it exerts forces equal to the forces exerted on it. Thus a spring balance can be used to measure **weight.**

(b) Comparing forces and thus measuring mass. Beam balances and lever balances *compare* forces. Since, in a particular place, the weight of a body is proportional to its mass, each balance can compare the mass of two bodies, and thus is used to measure the mass of a body in terms of known masses.

Suppose a body X is placed on one scale pan of a beam balance, and is balanced by a mass of 10 g in the other: wherever the operation is performed, a mass of 10 g will be found necessary for balance. A similar argument holds for the lever balance. However, body X placed on a spring balance will stretch the spring by different amounts in different places: thus a calibrated spring balance will give different readings for the mass of X if it is taken from place to place. Thus

beam balances and lever balances measure mass,
spring balances measure weight.

(c) Measuring mass. The previous three instruments depend for their working on the body being pulled by the Earth. Trolleys provide a way of measuring mass without relying on the body having a weight. The experiment is as follows:

(1) Two trolleys of masses m_1, m_2 are tied together, with a spring compressed between them.
(2) The body whose mass (M) is to be measured is placed on one of them.

(3) A paper tape is attached to each trolley and led through a ticker-timer (see p. 88). (The tape and the timers are not shown in the diagram.)

(4) The string is burned through so that the trolleys are pushed apart by the spring: let their initial speeds be v_1, v_2.

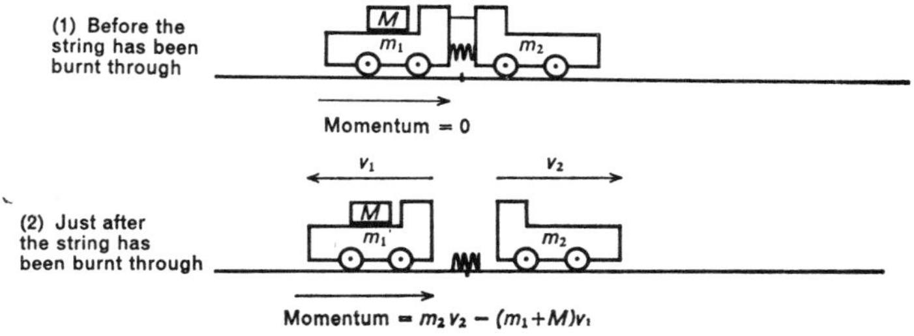

Fig. 4·1

(5) Afterwards the tapes are examined and the initial speeds v_1, v_2 calculated (ignoring the period while the trolleys were accelerating because the spring was still exerting forces on them).

Beforehand, momentum = 0,

afterwards, momentum (left-to-right)

$$= m_2v_2 - (m_1+M)v_1.$$

By the Principle of the Conservation of Momentum,

$$0 = m_2v_2 - (m_1+M)v_1.$$

Therefore $$(m_1+M)v_1 = m_2v_2,$$

and we can find M if we know m_1, m_2, and have measured v_1, v_2.

4.2 MEASUREMENT OF LENGTH, AREA AND VOLUME

Length: by ruler. Some instruments have a **vernier scale** so that we do not have to guess the final figure of the reading. Fig. 4.2 shows a ruler being used to measure the width of an object: the width is 17·( ) mm, and we have to guess that it is probably 17·6 mm. The vernier scale, in

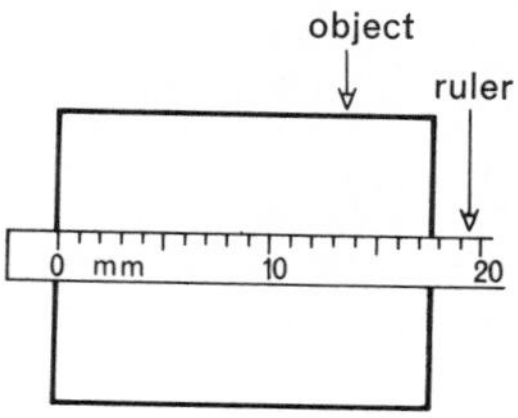

Fig. 4·2

Fig. 4.3. enables us to find the next figure without guessing. All vernier scales are used in the same way:

(*a*) We look opposite the '0' on the vernier scale and (as in Fig. 4.2) read 17·( ) mm.

(*b*) We see which of the vernier divisions is opposite a main-scale division, and the number of that vernier division gives the next figure. Thus this particular reading is 17·6 mm.

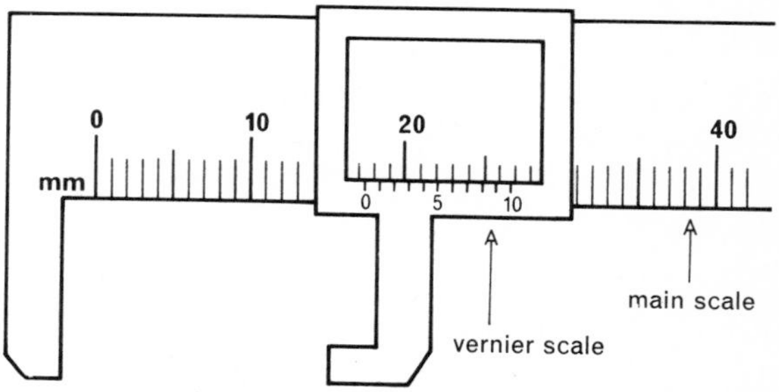

The vernier scale helps us to find that the reading is 17·6 mm

Fig. 4·3

A **micrometer screw gauge** is used to measure *small* distances. The measurements are *not* necessarily *accurate,* as the percentage accuracy depends on the size of the measurement: a measurement of 0·05 mm can be made, but is so small that it might be 0·04 mm or 0·06 mm, and so the error might be ± 1 in 5, or $\pm 20\%$. The particular instrument shown in Fig. 4.4 has divisions every half-millimetre along its barrel, and 50 divisions round its sleeve. The readings in Fig. 4.4 are $3\frac{1}{2}$ on the barrel, and 47 on the sleeve. Thus the reading it shows is $3{\cdot}50+0{\cdot}47 = 3{\cdot}97$ mm. In any case a little experimenting will usually show how the reading should be taken.

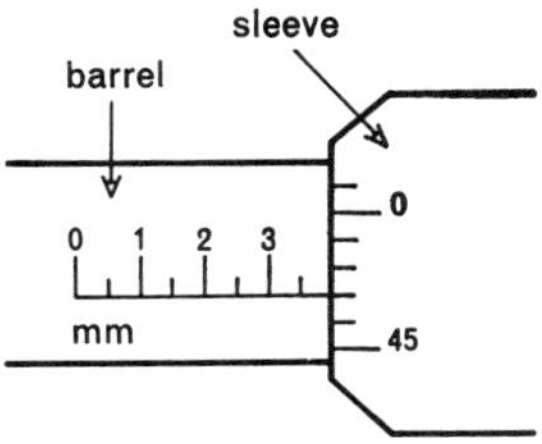

Part of a micrometer screw gauge which is reading 3·97 mm

Fig. 4·4

Area: by ruler, and calculation, if the area is regular. If the area is irregular, it can be estimated by dividing it into strips or triangles, and finding their areas.

Volume: by ruler, and calculation, if the object has a regular outline. But

(*a*) if liquid, by **measuring cylinder,**
(*b*) if an irregular solid, by **displacement methods:**

(*i*) the combined use of a **eureka can** (or spout can) and measuring cylinder, *or*
(*ii*) the use of a measuring cylinder alone, if the object is small enough.

Measuring flasks, pipettes, burettes, serve special purposes.

4.3 MEASUREMENT OF TIME

We measure *time intervals* in terms of the basic time interval, one *second,* which was defined on page 19, using a **clock.** This is a device which has a repetitive or periodic property and which has been graduated with reference to the standard.

(*a*) **Large** time intervals: radioactive decay processes can be used.
(*b*) **Ordinary** time intervals: pendula, or torsional balance wheels such as those in clocks and watches, can be used.
(*c*) **Small** time intervals:

(*i*) Devices employing the fact that the frequency of the electricity supply mains is 50 Hz can be used. Ticker-tape timers or special stop-clocks will both enable a time interval of $\frac{1}{500}$ s to be measured.
(*ii*) Stroboscopic devices can be used for measuring the size of a repeated time interval (see p. 166).

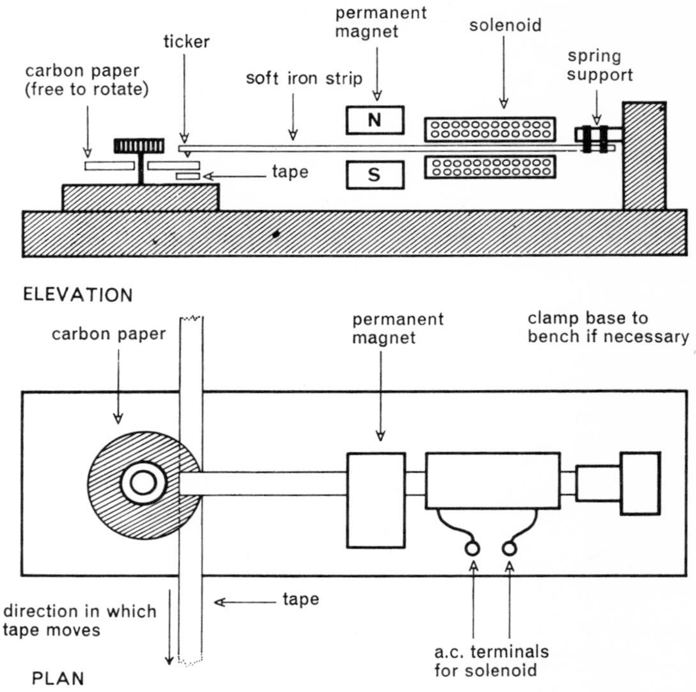

The dots on the tape are made every 0·02 second; thus if the tape moves, the time between events for bodies attached to the tape can be measured to 0·002 second by estimation

Fig. 4·5 Ticker-tape timer

4.4 MEASUREMENT OF DENSITY

The density of a substance is defined by the equation

$$\textbf{density} = \frac{\text{mass of substance}}{\text{volume of substance}}$$

$$\rho \left[\frac{\text{kg}}{\text{m}^3}\right] = \frac{m\,[\text{kg}]}{V\,[\text{m}^3]}$$

$$\boxed{\rho = \frac{m}{V}}$$

The g/cm^3 is another common unit of density: 1 g/cm^3 = 1000 kg/m^3.

Note that we refer to the density *of a substance,* not to that of a body: whatever the size and shape of a body made of aluminium, the density of aluminium is the same. Note also that the density of a substance (depending, as it does, only on *mass* and volume) is the same everywhere (for example, on Earth and in space) (see p. 59).

The **relative density** of a substance is defined by the equation

$$\textbf{relative density} = \frac{\text{density of substance}}{\text{density of water}}$$

For example, the density of mercury is 13 600 kg/m^3: its relative density is

$$\frac{13\,600\ \text{kg/m}^3}{1000\ \text{kg/m}^3} = 13{\cdot}6.$$

Relative density has no unit.

If we take the same volume of the substance and of water, the

$$\text{relative density} = \frac{\text{mass of substance}}{\text{mass of same volume of water}}$$

Measurement of density. We measure the mass and volume of as much of the substance as possible.

Measurement of relative density, using a density bottle. The density bottle can be used for liquids, or solids in finely-divided form. We take readings as shown in Fig. 4.6.

Fig. 4·6 (i)

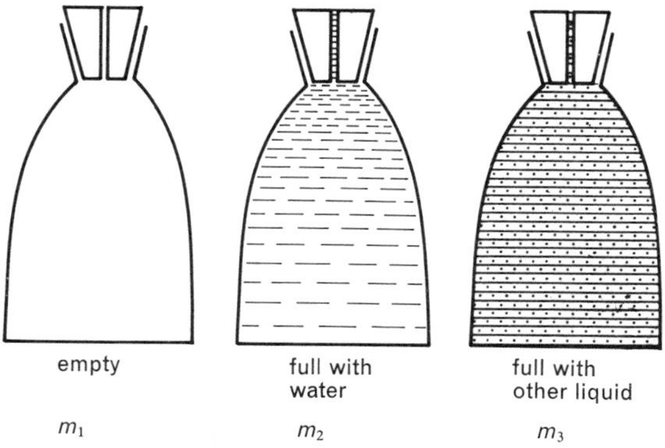

The density bottle
being used to find the relative density of a liquid

For a liquid

$$\text{relative density} = \frac{\text{mass of liquid}}{\text{mass of same volume of water}}$$

$(m_3 - m_1)$ gives the mass of the liquid.
$(m_2 - m_1)$ gives the mass of the same volume of water.

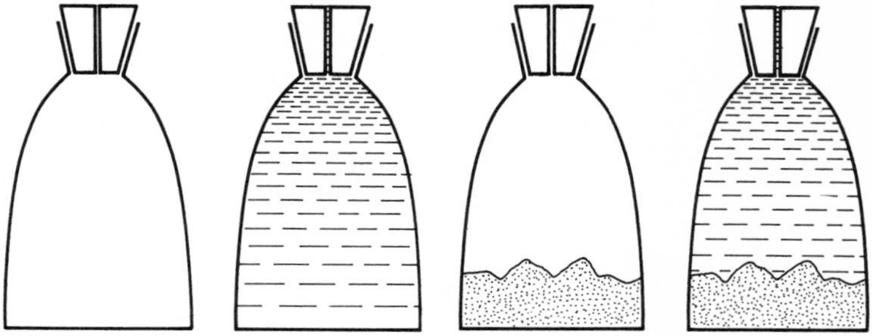

The density bottle being used to find the relative density of a finely-divided insoluble solid

Fig. 4·6 (ii)

For a finely-divided solid

$$\text{relative density} = \frac{\text{mass of solid}}{\text{mass of same volume of water}}$$

$(m_3 - m_1)$ gives the mass of the solid.
$(m_4 - m_3)$ gives the mass of the extra water,
and this subtracted from $(m_2 - m_1)$, gives the mass of water which has the same volume as the solid. Since we know the density of water (i.e. 1000 kg/m^3) we can find the density of the substance.

Properties of fluids

4.5 FLUID PRESSURE

As explained on p. 35, fluids exert forces on surfaces with which they are in contact. To define **the pressure at a point in a fluid,** we imagine a very small area in the fluid containing the point, and say:

$$\textbf{pressure at a point} = \frac{\text{normal force on the very small area containing the point}}{\text{the area}}$$

$$p\left[\frac{\mathrm{N}}{\mathrm{m}^2}\right] = \frac{F\,[\mathrm{N}]}{A\,[\mathrm{m}^2]}$$

$$\boxed{p = \frac{F}{A}}$$

The *pressure* has no direction: however, the *force* which it exerts is normal to the surface with which the fluid is in contact, irrespective of the orientation of the surface.

4.6 ATMOSPHERIC PRESSURE

The Earth's atmosphere is retained because the Earth pulls on the air molecules. The presence of the molecules, in random motion, causes the **atmospheric pressure** (see p. 35).

The atmosphere becomes less dense with increasing height above the Earth's surface: 50 per cent of the mass is within 6 km of the surface, 95 per cent within 20 km. The pressure of the atmosphere is greatest at the Earth's surface.

The existence of atmospheric pressure can be demonstrated by

(*a*) using model Magdeburg hemispheres,
(*b*) the collapsing of a can from which most of the air has been removed.

In each case the push of the atmosphere on one side of a surface is demonstrated when the atmosphere is removed from the other side of the surface.

4.7 THE PRESSURE IN A LIQUID

Consider, as in Fig. 4.7, a vertical column (of area A and height h) of a liquid of density ρ, and suppose the pressures at top and bottom are p_2 and p_1.

The volume of liquid in the column $= Ah\,[\mathrm{m}^3]$.
The mass of the liquid in the column $= Ah\rho\,[\mathrm{kg}]$.
The weight of the liquid in the column $= Ah\rho g\,[\mathrm{N}]$.

In equilibrium $F_1 = F_2 + W$,

so

$$p_1A = p_2A + Ah\rho g,$$
$$(p_1 - p_2)A = Ah\rho g,$$
$$p_1 - p_2 = h\rho g$$

or

$$\boxed{p = h\rho g}$$

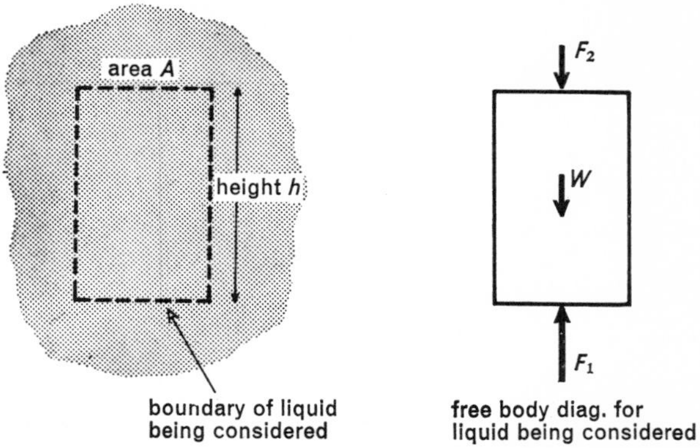

Fig. 4·7

where p is the *increase* in pressure which accompanies an *increase* in depth h in a liquid of density ρ. The increase in pressure in a particular liquid is directly proportional to the increase in depth, and to the local value of g. It follows that the pressure at two points *at the same level in the same liquid* is the same, provided that the points are connected by that liquid only.

Note that the increase in pressure depends on the distance moved *vertically* in the liquid, and does *not* depend on the cross-sectional area or shape of the vessel.

The densities of gases are so small that differences in height of a few metres have little effect on the pressure they exert: in an average room, the difference in pressure between ceiling and floor is about 0·05 per cent of the atmospheric pressure, so for all practical purposes the pressure of a gas is taken to be the same throughout its containing vessel. Situations do arise, however, where *Boyle's Law* (see p. 129) has to be used.

Pascal's Principle states that *pressure applied to an enclosed liquid is transmitted to every portion of the liquid,* whatever the shape of the liquid. Thus if the pressure at the surface of a liquid is atmospheric, as it very often is,

the pressure at a point in the liquid

$$= \begin{pmatrix}\text{atmospheric}\\ \text{pressure}\end{pmatrix} + \begin{pmatrix}\text{increase in pressure due to point}\\ \text{being below the surface of liquid}\end{pmatrix}$$

Fig. 4.8 shows the values of the pressure at different points in a **manometer,** which is being used to measure the pressure of the gas supply on a day when the atmospheric pressure is 102 000 N/m^2.

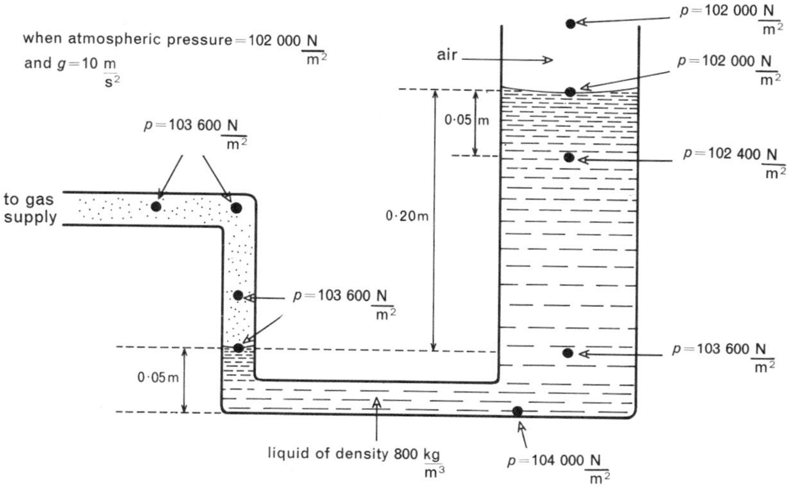

Fig. 4·8 A manometer being used to measure the pressure of the gas supply

4.8 MEASUREMENTS OF PRESSURE AND DENSITY

Density

The *manometer* can be used as in Fig. 4.9 to compare the densities of (*a*) miscible, or (*b*) immiscible, liquids. (In Fig. 4.9*a*, the second liquid is poured in until the points Q and Y are at the same level.)

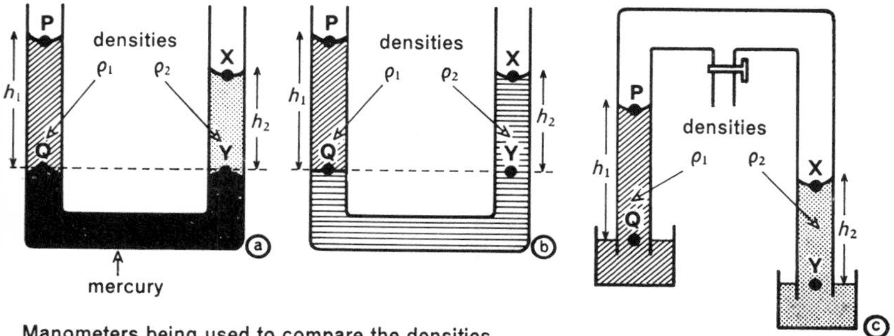

Manometers being used to compare the densities of (a) miscible, (b) immiscible, liquids

Hare's apparatus being used to compare the densities of two liquids

Fig. 4·9

Hare's apparatus can also be used to compare the densities of two liquids, as shown in Fig. 4.9*c*.

In each of these three diagrams:

$$\text{the pressure at P} = \text{the pressure at X},$$
$$\text{the pressure at Q} = \text{the pressure at Y},$$

so
$$\begin{pmatrix}\text{the increase of pressure}\\ \text{between P and Q}\end{pmatrix} = \begin{pmatrix}\text{the increase of pressure}\\ \text{between X and Y}\end{pmatrix}$$

Thus in each case $h_1\rho_1 g = h_2\rho_2 g$.

Pressure

The *manometer* can be used as in Fig. 4.8 to measure the pressure of a gas:

$$\begin{pmatrix}\text{pressure}\\ \text{of gas}\end{pmatrix} = \begin{pmatrix}\text{atmospheric}\\ \text{pressure}\end{pmatrix} + \begin{pmatrix}\text{quantity } h\rho g \text{ for the}\\ \text{liquid column}\end{pmatrix}.$$

There are some examples of this sort of calculation in Fig. 4.8.

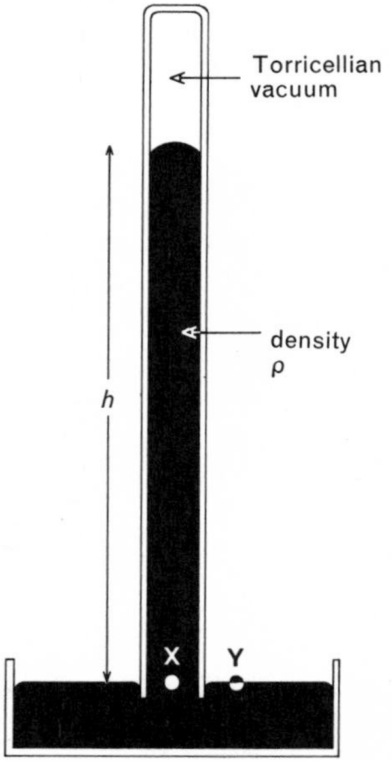

Fig. 4·10

The simple barometer:
the pressures at X and Y are equal

The **simple barometer** can be used to measure the pressure of the atmosphere. It consists of a tube (at least 800 mm long) closed at one end, which is first completely filled with mercury and then inverted with its open end under the surface of the mercury in a bowl. The mercury runs a little way down the tube, leaving a space above the mercury in which there is no air and very little mercury vapour (this

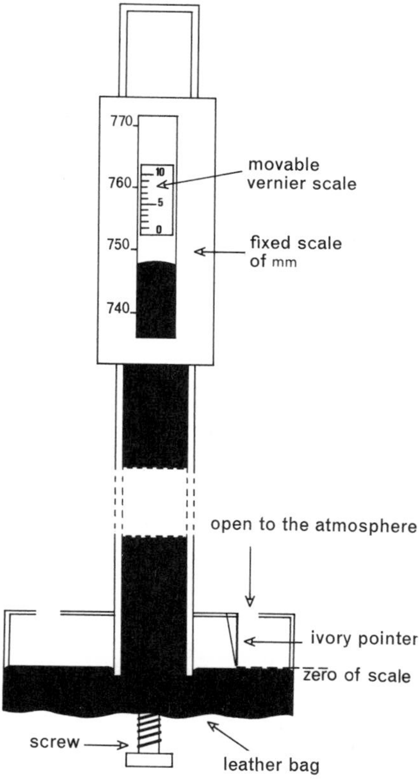

Fig. 4·11 The Fortin barometer

space is called a **Torricellian vacuum**), and so we say the pressure there is zero. Therefore

the pressure at X = $h\rho g$,

and the pressure at Y = atmospheric pressure.

But the pressure at X = the pressure at Y.

Therefore the atmospheric pressure = $h\rho g$.

The **Fortin barometer** is a more accurate version of the simple barometer. It has a fixed scale, and the mercury is contained in a leather bag which can be screwed up or down so that the mercury surface in contact with the atmosphere coincides with the zero of the scale. The scale has a vernier attachment at the top: the length of the column of mercury can be read to 0·1 mm.

The **aneroid barometer** consists essentially of a partially evacuated cylindrical tin whose ends move in and out as the atmospheric pressure (outside it) changes. In practice its movements are magnified, by a system of levers, to give direct readings of the atmospheric pressure on a circular scale.

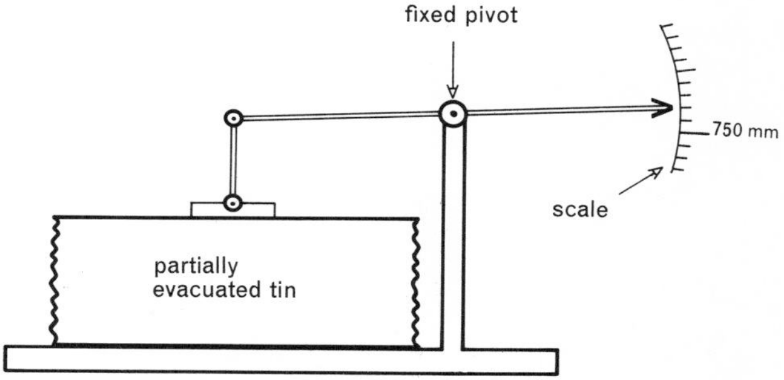

Fig. 4·12

The principle of the aneroid barometer: an increase in the atmospheric pressure makes the pointer move upwards

Standard atmospheric pressure is defined to be 101 325 N/m^2. Pressures are often given in heights, or **heads of liquid:** standard atmospheric pressure is roughly equivalent to 760 mm of mercury. These values can be converted to genuine units of pressure if the density of the liquid and the value of g are known. For example, the pressure exerted by 760 mm of mercury (using $p = h\rho g$)

$$= 0{\cdot}760 \times 13\,600 \times 9{\cdot}8\ \frac{\text{N}}{\text{m}^2},$$

$$\doteq 101\,000\ \frac{\text{N}}{\text{m}^2},$$

$$= 1{\cdot}01 \times 10^5\ \frac{\text{N}}{\text{m}^2}.$$

Places where the atmospheric pressure is the same are joined on weather charts by lines called **isobars.**

4.9 APPLICATIONS OF ATMOSPHERIC PRESSURE

(a) The sucker: some of the air is removed from the underside of the sucker; the difference in pressure on the two sides means that the resultant push of the air on the sucker is towards the surface. In most situations the air produces forces on *both* sides of objects, and these forces are only slightly (if at all) different, and can be ignored.

(b) The pipette: air is taken away from inside the pipette. The reduction in pressure allows the atmosphere to push the liquid up the pipette, to a height determined by the density of the liquid and the reduction of pressure. A straw works similarly.

(c) The siphon: part of the explanation is that the atmospheric pressure at level A (in Fig. 4.13) pushes the liquid up the tube and over the top

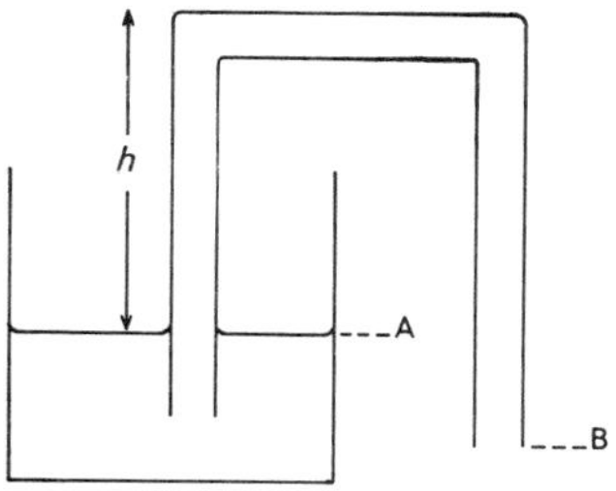

Fig. 4·13 The siphon

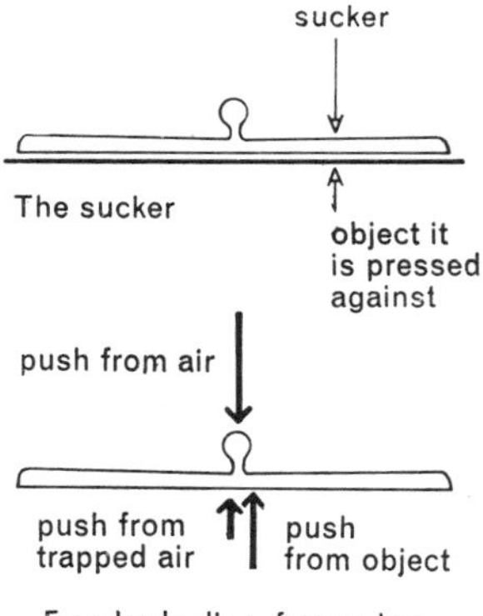

to come out at the end B. The height *h* must be less than the height of that liquid which the atmosphere can support, and the end B must be below the level A. In fact cohesive forces between the molecules of the liquid play a part in the siphon's working.

(d) Lift and force pumps: by reducing the air pressure above a liquid surface a **lift pump** allows the atmosphere to push liquids upwards. Obviously there is a limit to the possible height of rise (about 10 m, for water). In a **force pump** the downward strokes are used to increase the pressure on the liquid which has already been lifted, in such a way that this can be raised higher still.

(e) Altimeter: since the atmospheric pressure varies with height above the Earth's surface, the variation in pressure can be used to measure this height. *An altimeter is an aneroid barometer* calibrated directly in metres above sea-level. It has to be adjusted to compensate for changes in the atmospheric pressure at sea-level.

4.10 HYDRAULIC MACHINES

A hydraulic system consists of at least two cylinders, with pistons, connected by piping: the system is filled with a special fluid. A change in pressure in the master cylinder produces the same change in pressure throughout the system (by **Pascal's Principle**).

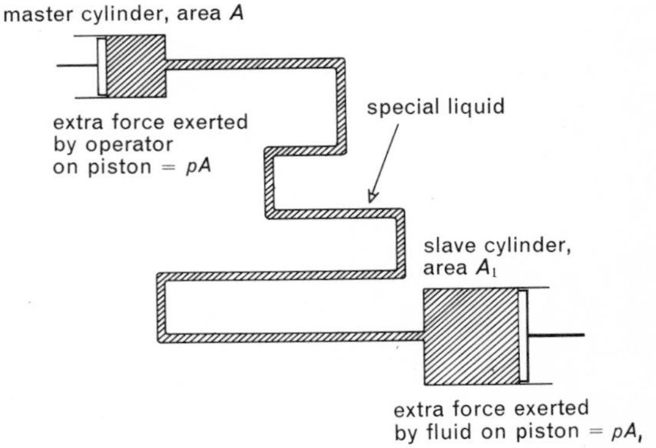

Fig. 4·14 A hydraulic system

If the area of the master cylinder is A, then an additional force pA will produce a change in pressure p. But if the area of the other cylinder is A_1, the additional force exerted on that piston by the change in pressure is pA_1, and if A_1 is greater than A, the force exerted by the change in pressure on the second piston is greater than the force exerted on the piston of the master cylinder. In hydraulic machines, the dimensions are usually small enough, and the additionai pressure often large enough, for us to be able to ignore differences in pressure caused by differences in height.

Hydraulic brakes are used because:

(*a*) the force is easily transmitted (the pipe may take any route),
(*b*) the force at each brake is necessarily the same.

The *hydraulic press* and *hydraulic jacks* and other hydraulic machines use the fact that the application of a small force to the machine will cause the machine to exert a very large force, if the areas of the pistons are sufficiently different (see Machines, p. 107).

4.11 ARCHIMEDES' PRINCIPLE

When a body is immersed in a *fluid* there is an upthrust on it equal to (but opposite in sense to) the *weight* of the fluid displaced. This is **Archimedes' Principle.**

The upthrust exists because a body immersed in a fluid has forces exerted on it from all sides: these forces are caused by the pressure in the fluid surrounding it. The pressure in the fluid increases from top to bottom of the body. At each level the horizontal resolved parts of the forces have zero resultant, but the vertical upward force at the bottom is greater than the vertical downward force at the top, so that *the differences in pressure produce a resultant upward vertical force.*

The proof of Archimedes' Principle is given in Fig. 4.15.

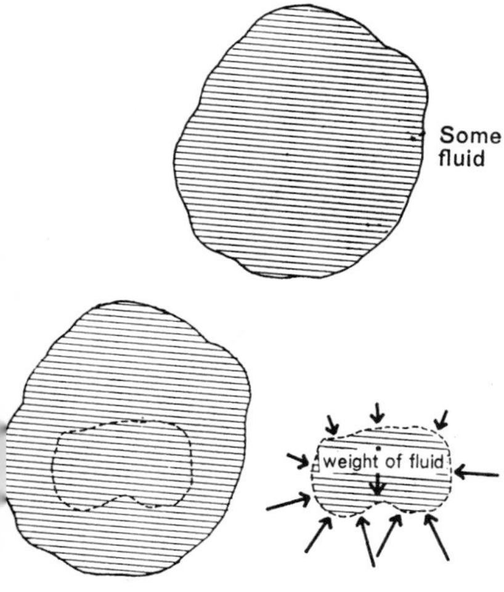

'e consider some of the fluid and draw
free-body diag. for that fluid. The pressure
rces have a resultant which must be equal
ut opposite in sense) to the weight of the fluid

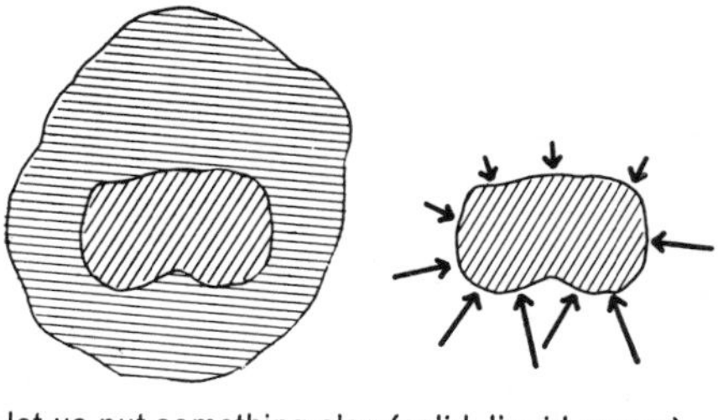

Now let us put something else (solid, liquid or gas) into the space once occupied by the fluid. The same pressure forces act on this body, and this provides an upthrust which, as we saw above, is equal (though opposite in sense) to the weight of the fluid which would have been there. Thus the upthrust = the weight of the fluid displaced

Fig. 4·15 Proof of Archimedes' Principle

Note that:

(*a*) the upthrust still acts even when the body rests on some support (such as the bottom of a vessel) provided the space between the body and the support is not evacuated;
(*b*) whenever a fluid exerts an upthrust on a body, the body exerts an equal but downward thrust on the fluid.

4.12 EXPERIMENTAL VERIFICATION OF ARCHIMEDES' PRINCIPLE

A body is weighed, W_1, on a spring balance, and again, W_2, when immersed in a liquid contained in a eureka can. The **apparent loss in weight** ($W_1 - W_2$), is equal to the upthrust. If the upthrust is found to be equal to the weight of the liquid displaced from the eureka can, Archimedes' Principle has been verified.

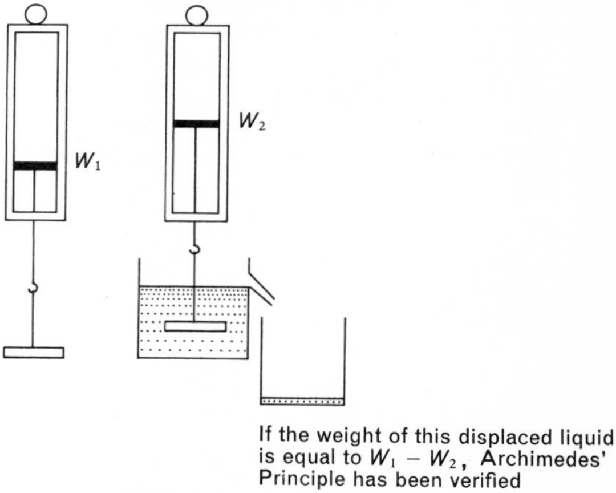
W_1
W_2
If the weight of this displaced liquid is equal to $W_1 - W_2$, Archimedes' Principle has been verified

Fig. 4·16 Experimental verification of Archimedes' Principle

4.13 FLOTATION

Whether a body immersed in a fluid rises or sinks depends on whether the pull of the Earth on it (W) is less or greater than the push of the fluid on it (U). This is illustrated in Fig. 4.17.

The **Principle of Flotation** states that *when a body floats, its weight and the upthrust of the fluid on it are equal.*

Variable weight and constant upthrust

A **submarine** has a weight which can be varied (because it can take in or let out water), but because its external volume is constant, there is a constant upthrust on it.

If $W > U$, it accelerates downwards;
if $W < U$, it accelerates upwards;
if $W = U$, it (*a*) can remain stationary (at any depth),
(*b*) will continue to move if initially moving, though it may be slowed down by resistance forces.

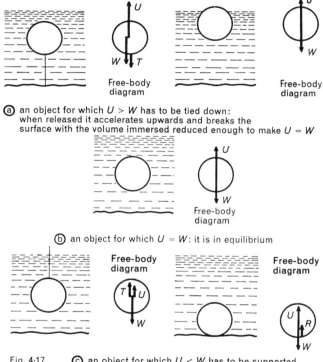

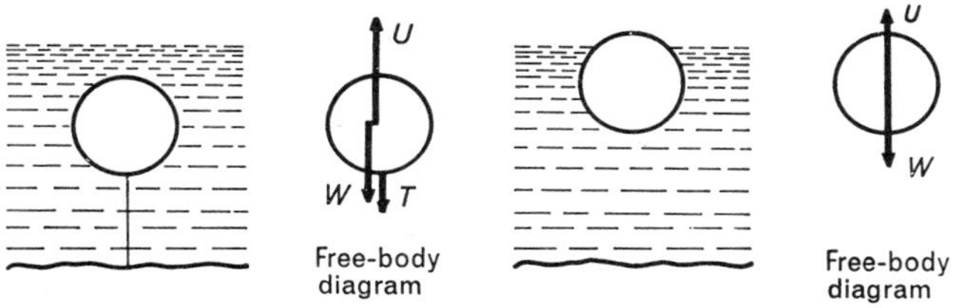

ⓐ an object for which $U > W$ has to be tied down: when released it accelerates upwards and breaks the surface with the volume immersed reduced enough to make $U = W$

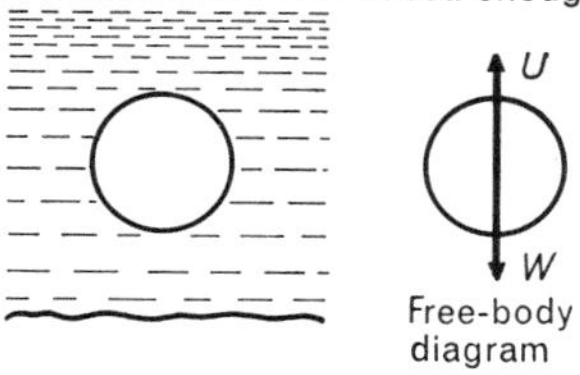

ⓑ an object for which $U = W$: it is in equilibrium

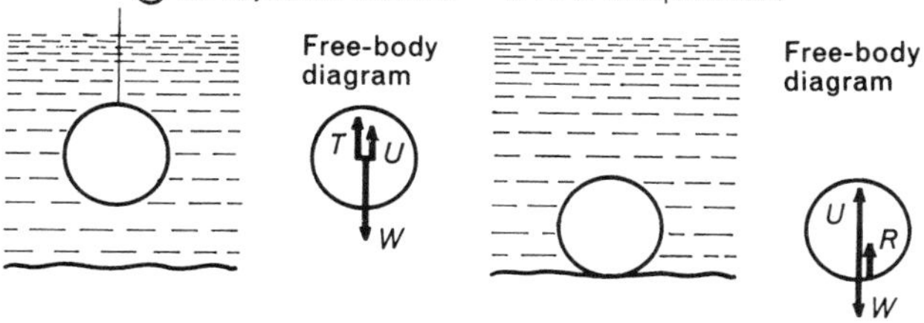

Fig. 4·17 ⓒ an object for which $U < W$ has to be supported. When released it accelerates downwards until the floor of the vessel supports it instead

Constant weight and variable upthrust

Balloons and **hydrometers** have a constant weight, but

(*a*) a balloon, in the atmosphere, has a different upthrust at different heights because (*i*) the density of the air varies, (*ii*) the external volume of the balloon varies;

(*b*) a hydrometer (which consists of a narrow tube fixed to a weighted bulb), if totally immersed in different liquids, has different upthrusts.

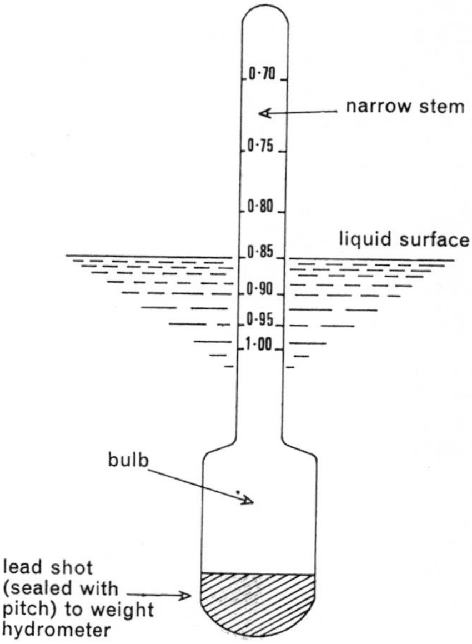

Fig. 4·18 A hydrometer floating in a liquid whose relative density is 0·85

Therefore

(*a*) a balloon reaches equilibrium *at a particular height,* where its weight is equal to the upthrust on it;
(*b*) a hydrometer reaches equilibrium *with a particular volume immersed,* where its weight is equal to the upthrust on it.

The narrow tube of the hydrometer has a scale marked directly in relative densities, so arranged that the level of the liquid in which it floats indicates the relative density on the scale. The narrower the tube the greater the spacing of the graduations, and this gives greater sensitivity. But the greater the spacing of the graduations, the larger (and more cumbersome) the hydrometer, so in practice a set of four or five short hydrometers is used, of different weights, each covering a different range of relative densities.

Hydrometers are used to measure the relative density of (*a*) acid and alkali in accumulators, (*b*) milk, (*c*) alcohol (for Customs purposes).

4.14 MEASUREMENT OF DENSITY, USING ARCHIMEDES' PRINCIPLE

(a) For a solid

A piece of the substance is weighed in air and in water.

$$\textit{weight of object} = W_1$$
$$\text{weight of object in water} = W_2$$
$$\therefore \quad \text{upthrust of water on object} = (W_1 - W_2).$$

Hence, by Archimedes' Principle,

$$\textit{weight of water displaced} = (W_1 - W_2)$$

and relative density

$$\left(= \frac{\text{mass of object}}{\text{mass of equal volume of water}}\right)$$
$$= \frac{\text{weight of object}}{\text{weight of water displaced}}.$$

The procedure is more complicated if

(*i*) the solid floats in water: a **sinker** is tied to the object to keep it completely immersed in this case;
(*ii*) the solid is soluble in water: a non-solvent liquid is used instead.

In each case additional weighings have to be made, but the principle is the same.

(b) For a liquid

A solid object, which does not float or dissolve in water or in the liquid, is weighed in water and in the liquid.

$$\text{weight of object} = W_1,$$
$$\text{weight of object in water} = W_2,$$
$$\text{weight of object in liquid} = W_3.$$
$$\therefore \quad \text{upthrust of water on object} = (W_1 - W_2)$$
$$\text{and} \quad \textit{weight of water displaced} = (W_1 - W_2).$$
$$\therefore \quad \text{upthrust of liquid on object} = (W_1 - W_3)$$
$$\text{and} \quad \textit{weight of liquid displaced} = (W_1 - W_3).$$

Hence relative density

$$\left(= \frac{\text{mass of liquid}}{\text{mass of equal volume of water}}\right)$$
$$= \frac{\text{weight of liquid displaced}}{\text{weight of water displaced}}.$$

4.15 SURFACE TENSION

As explained on p. 39, the forces of attraction which molecules exert on each other produce effects which are similar to those which would be produced by a liquid surface being in a state of tension.

This can be demonstrated as follows:

(*a*) A light wire is rested on a horizontal rectangular wire frame which supports a liquid film. When the film is broken on one side of the wire, the wire is pulled from the other side: see Fig. 4.19*a*.

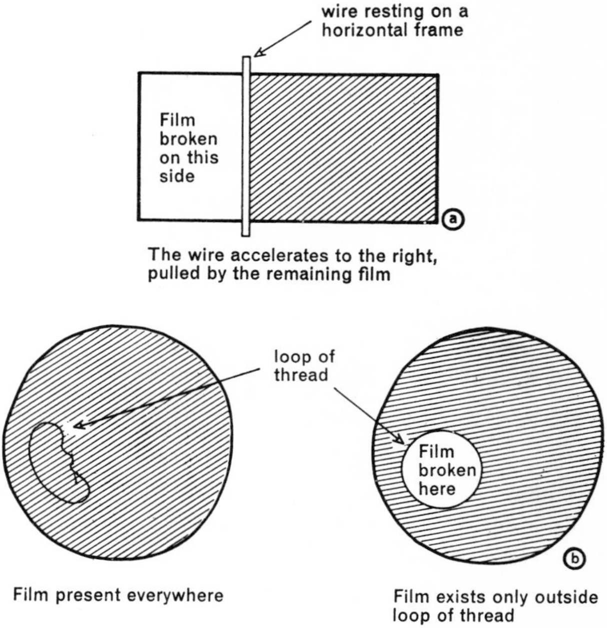

Fig. 4·19

(*b*) A loop of thread is placed on a film of liquid supported by a wire frame, as in Fig. 4.19*b*. When the film inside the loop is broken, the remaining film pulls the loop taut, into a circle. The circular shape shows that the surface tension force is *normal to the boundary*.

Some examples of the effects:

(*a*) The clinging together of paint-brush bristles.
(*b*) The supporting of light (though dense) objects – for example, razor blades – on liquid surfaces.
(*c*) The shape of soap bubbles, raindrops.

The **adhesive forces,** which attract the liquid molecules to solid molecules in solid surfaces, modify the simple surface tension effects. If it were not for these, water would form itself into spherical globules (as mercury does). In fact water and most other liquids spread over most other surfaces, though the extent to which they do so depends on the nature of both the liquid and the solid. For example, the spreading of water over a surface can be increased by

(*a*) heating,
(*b*) adding detergent to the water,

and can be reduced by greasing the surface. The cleansing effect of water depends on the ability to spread being increased.

(a) Capillary rise and fall, as shown in Fig. 4.20. The effect is greater

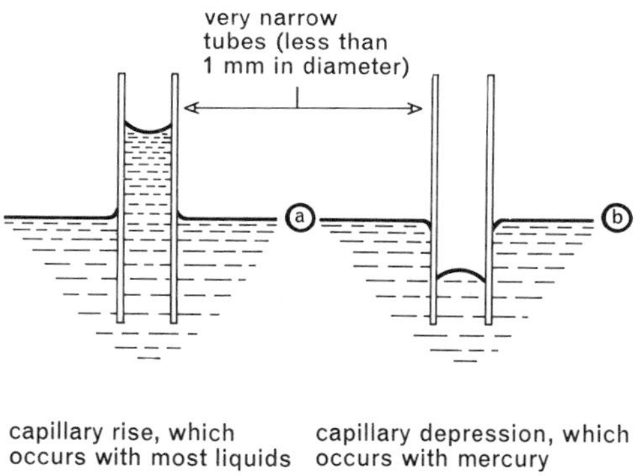

Fig. 4·20

(*i*) the narrower the tube,
(*ii*) the less dense the liquid,
(*iii*) the greater the surface tension of the liquid.

The action of blotting paper, and the rise of liquids in any porous substance, are forms of capillary rise.

(b) The formation of meniscuses, as is also shown in Fig. 4.20.

4.16 FLOWING FLUIDS

Consider a fluid flowing in a pipe whose cross-section becomes smaller: the mass per second flowing past A must be the same as the mass per second flowing past B, so *the speed of the fluid must be greater at B than at A*. If the fluid is thus to flow faster, there must be a force accelerating the fluid, and the cause of this is that *the pressure at A is*

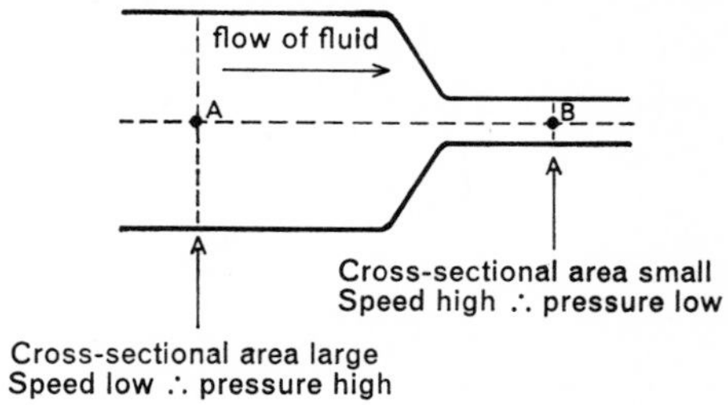

Fig. 4·21

greater than the pressure at B. In general, when the speed of a fluid increases, its pressure decreases **(Bernoulli's Principle).**

This can be demonstrated (as in Fig. 4.22) by:

(*a*) Blowing above a horizontal sheet of paper: the paper *rises,* because the reduced pressure above the paper produces a net upward force, exerted on the paper by the air.

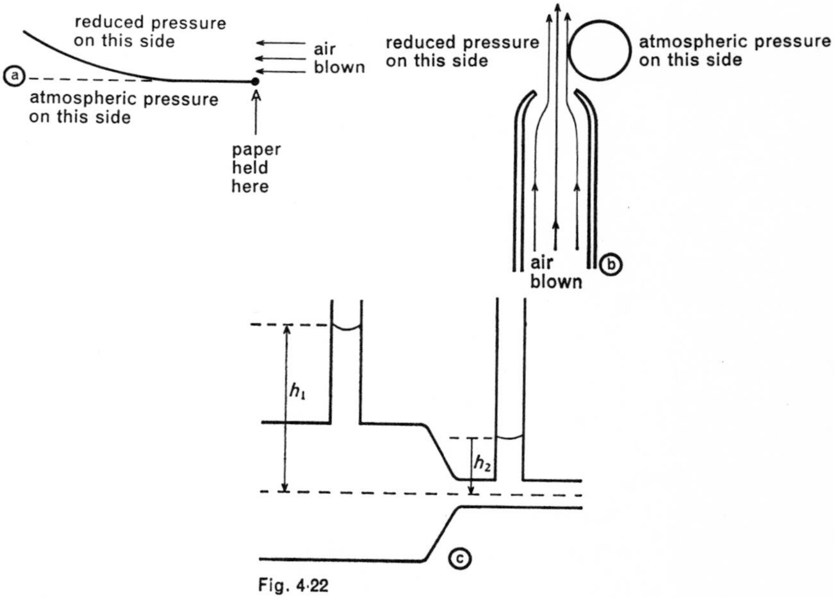

Fig. 4·22

(*b*) Balancing a ping-pong ball on a jet of air (for example, from a hair dryer). If the ball is pushed slightly to one side and released, it returns to the centre, because the atmospheric pressure is greater than the pressure in the air stream.

(*c*) Using a tube as shown in the diagram: h_1 is greater than h_2, because the pressure is less in the narrow part of the tube.

Bernoulli's Principle is applied:

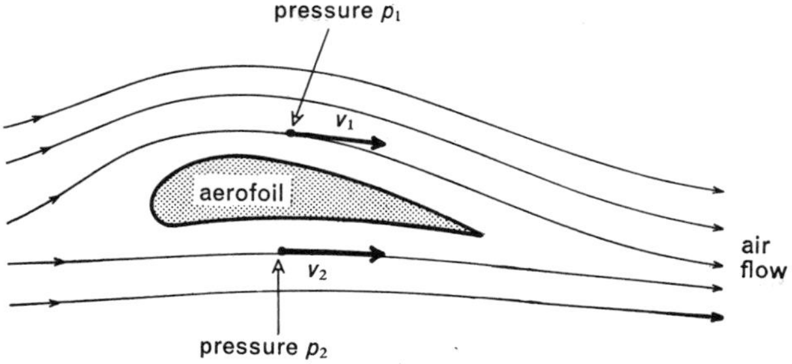

Fig. 4·23 An aerofoil: speed $v_1 > v_2$, so pressure $p_1 < p_2$. Thus there is a dynamic lift on the aerofoil

(*a*) In the construction of **aerofoils,** which are shaped so that air flows faster over the top than underneath: thus the pressure below is greater than the pressure above. Aeroplane wings are aerofoils, and the difference in pressure between top and bottom accounts for most of the force which supports the aeroplane.

(*b*) In the action of **bunsen burners, carburettors, filter pumps:** the fast-moving fluid (which has passed through a jet) has a reduced pressure, and so the atmosphere can push, respectively, air, petrol vapour, and air into the moving fluid.

(*c*) In the flight of **tennis and ping-pong balls,** by giving them top-spin or back-spin so that the relative velocities are different at the top and bottom of the ball. The ball then takes a different course *in the air,* quite apart from bouncing differently. A golfer's slice and hook produce similar effects.

Machines

4.17 MACHINES

A **machine** is a device which does work in a situation where we ourselves

(*a*) could not have done it at all, or
(*b*) could not have done it as conveniently.

The principle of all such machines is the same: an **operator** exerts a force which does work on some part of the **machine,** and the **machine** exerts a force which does work on an **object.**

Fig. 4.24 illustrates this: the operator exerts a force P on the machine (and the machine exerts a force P on the operator, but this is not important). The machine exerts a force Q on the object (and the object

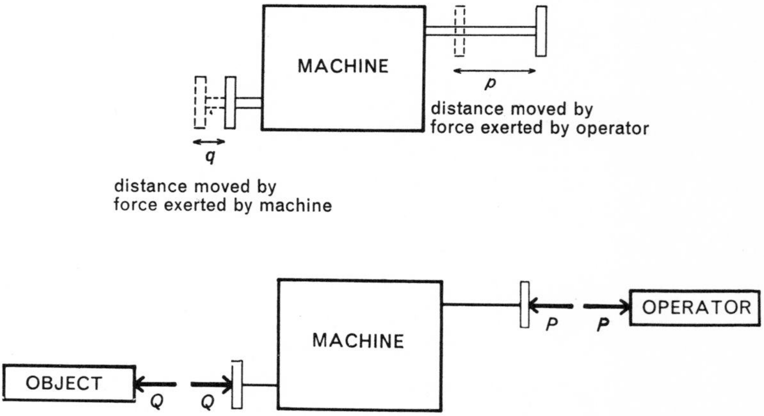

Fig. 4·24 The four forces which are important when we consider machines

exerts a force Q on the machine, but, again, this is not important – though we need to realize that these *four* forces exist).

The machine cannot do more work than the operator does: in practice, because frictional and other forces do work which is not useful, the machine does less work than the operator does. The efficiency of a machine is defined by the equation:

$$\textbf{efficiency} = \frac{\text{work done by machine}}{\text{work done by operator}} \times 100 \text{ per cent}$$

If there were a machine which was 100 per cent efficient, the work done by it and the work done by the operator would be equal.

A machine which 'goes into reverse' when the operator removes the force P is said to **overhaul:** overhauling may not occur if the frictional forces are large. A machine whose efficiency is less than 50 per cent will not overhaul: this can be an advantage of machines of low efficiency, such as a screw jack.

4.18 MECHANICAL ADVANTAGE AND VELOCITY RATIO

Mechanical Advantage(MA)

$$= \frac{\text{force exerted on object by machine}}{\text{force exerted on machine by operator}}.$$

In Fig. 4.24, the $MA = Q/P$. The MA is sometimes defined by

$$MA = \frac{\text{load}}{\text{effort}}.$$

An operator cannot tell in advance how large Q will be for a certain value of P, because frictional forces (among others) will affect the size of Q. Thus the MA can only be found by experiment.

Velocity Ratio (VR)

$$= \frac{\text{distance moved by force exerted by operator}}{\text{distance moved by force exerted on object}}.$$

In Fig. 4.24, the $VR = p/q$. The VR is sometimes defined by

$$VR = \frac{\text{distance moved by effort}}{\text{distance moved by load}}.$$

The VR depends entirely on the design of the machine: if we know the details of its construction we can calculate the VR.

In Fig. 4.24 work done by operator $= Pp$,
work done by machine $= Qq$.

So

$$\text{efficiency} = \frac{Qq}{Pp} \times 100\%$$

$$= \frac{Q}{P} \div \frac{p}{q} \times 100\%$$

$$\text{Efficiency} = \frac{MA}{VR} \times 100 \text{ per cent.}$$

Note that this is *not* a definition of efficiency: merely a useful relationship.

4.19 TYPES OF MACHINE

We show five simple types of machine: in the diagrams we simply state the expressions for the MA and the VR, and *only mark two relevant forces:* there are of course other forces acting on the bodies.

P represents the pull exerted *by* the operator, Q the force exerted *on* the object. (See Fig. 4.25.)

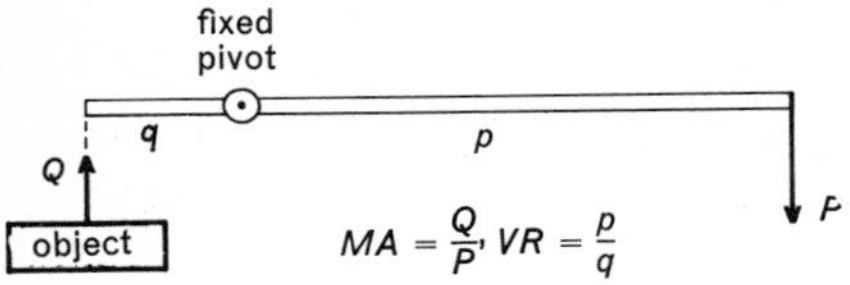

ⓐ a simple type of lever

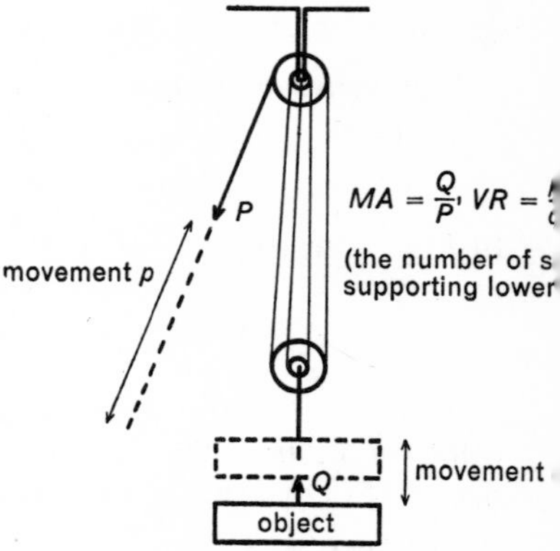

ⓑ a pulley block

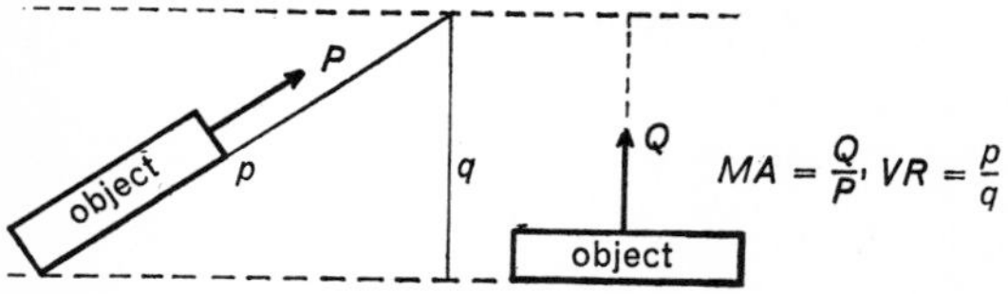

ⓒ an inclined plane: the object has to be lifted a height q. We compare what we have to do when we use the plane with what we have to do without it

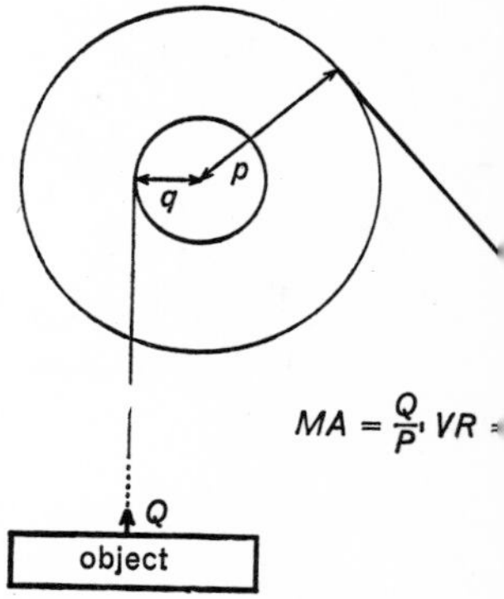

ⓓ a wheel and axle

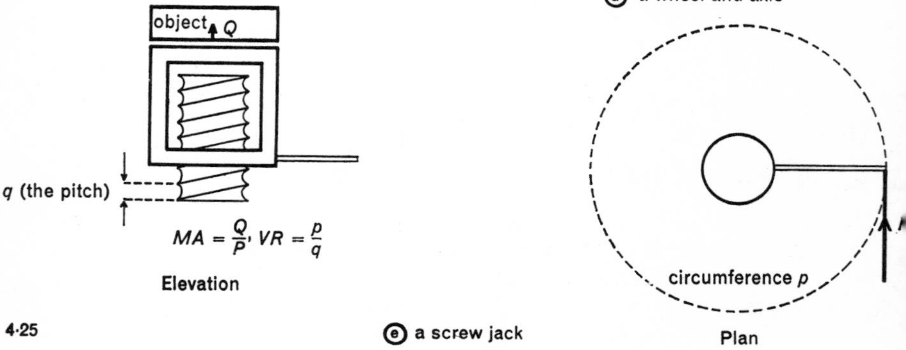

Fig. 4·25

ⓔ a screw jack

The elastic behaviour of bodies

4.20 ELASTICITY

Consider (*a*) a wire being pulled,
(*b*) a gas being compressed,
(*c*) a wire being twisted.

When the force, pressure and couple, respectively, are removed, these bodies regain their original size and shape, and are therefore said to behave **elastically.** Most bodies behave in this way.

For a wire (or a helical spring) being pulled, **Hooke's Law** states that *the change in length is proportional to the force applied,* provided the force is not too great (see p. 38). If the forces are too great, the wire (or spring) may be permanently deformed. The law holds in a similar way for other bodies undergoing other types of deformation.

To test Hooke's Law, for a helical spring:

(*a*) We hang the spring vertically, alongside a vertical ruler. The spring should have a pointer fixed to its lower end.
(*b*) We hang masses of increasing size on its lower end, and record the corresponding extensions.

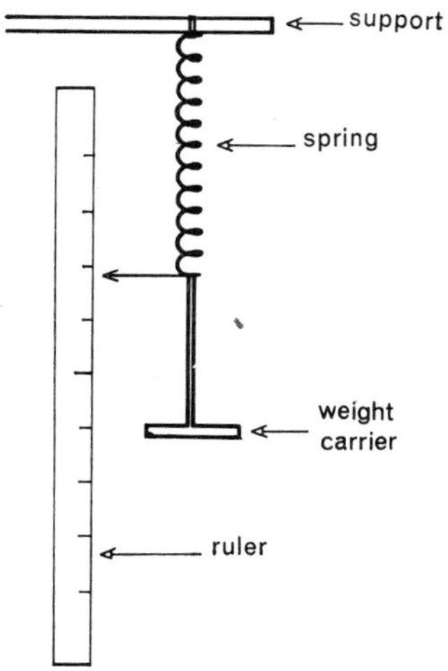

Fig. 4·26

(*c*) We plot the extensions against the load on a graph: in equilibrium, the load is equal to the weight of the masses. If the graph is a straight line through the origin, allowing for experimental error, Hooke's Law has been verified for that particular spring and for that range of forces.

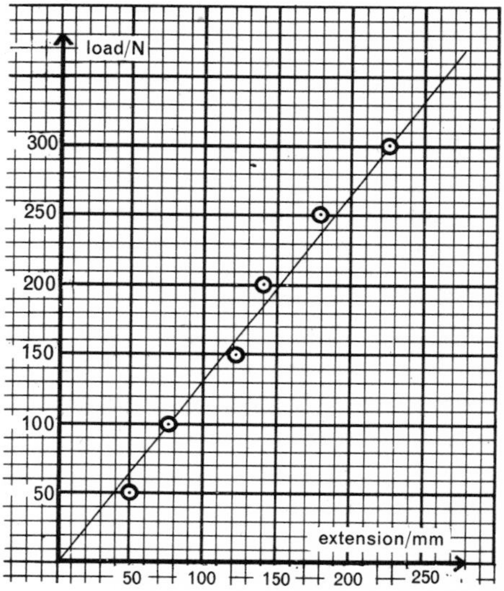

Fig. 4·27

5 Thermal properties of matter

Introduction

5.1 THERMAL PROPERTIES OF MATTER

Heat is that form of energy which is added to a body as a result of a temperature difference, and which may then produce one or more of the following effects:

(1) increase in temperature,
(2) increase in size,
(3) change of physical state,
(4) change of chemical constitution,
(5) change of electrical properties,
(6) change of colour.

We can observe the facts macroscopically (on a scale such that we can see what is happening), and then explain the observations microscopically – meaning in this case in terms of the behaviour of molecules. The subject will be discussed under the following headings:

Temperature – measurement of degree of hotness, which tells us the average kinetic energy of molecules.
Expansion – change of size of bodies as a result of molecules changing speed.
Heat capacity – the amount of heat that has to be supplied to produce required measurable effects.
Gas laws – the consequences of the behaviour of gas molecules.
Change of state – what happens when

(*a*) molecules cease to vibrate about fixed positions, or
(*b*) the attractive forces exerted by one molecule on another become negligible.

Work and internal energy – the relationship between these two forms of energy.

The transfer of internal energy – the methods by which heat moves from one location to another.

Temperature

5.2 PRINCIPLES

Temperature is:

(1) that property of a body that controls the direction of flow of heat when it is put into contact with a second body,
(2) determined by the average kinetic energy of the molecules of which the body is made,
(3) measured by a number that we allot in an arbitrary manner. When we state the number and the scale on which it is allotted, we know how hot the body is.

A **thermometer** is an instrument designed to measure temperature.

A **temperature scale** is a series of numbers selected to show any required temperature, and is defined by the following procedure:

(1) Select a *substance or body* which has some convenient **thermometric property.** (This is any easily measured property whose size varies continuously when heat is added to the body.)
(2) Choose two easily reproduced temperatures (called **fixed points**), and allot to them both numbers and unit.
(3) Define a way of calculating temperature from a measurement of the value of the thermometric property.

Any number and unit subsequently used to denote degree of hotness as a result of measurements with that property of that body, and using the agreed fixed points and method of calculation, is said to be the **temperature** on that temperature scale. For an example see *Calibration of a thermometer* (p. 117).

Temperature scales

The fundamental scale in physics is called the **thermodynamic scale.** The theoretical ideas behind this scale are beyond the scope of this book, but nevertheless the scale we use is based on the thermodynamic scale. The scale is sometimes called the Kelvin scale, and its unit is the **kelvin** (K).

Experiment gives us the following results:

(*a*) The temperature of pure melting ice at standard atmospheric pressure is 273·15 K.

(*b*) The temperature of the steam from pure boiling water at standard atmospheric pressure is 373·15 K.

Because these temperatures are obtained so easily (are **reproducible**), they are taken as calibration points for many thermometers.

The **Celsius scale** of temperature is defined so that

(1) if we write θ[°C] for a temperature **value** on the Celsius scale, and T[K] for one on the thermodynamic scale, then

$$T = \theta + 273{\cdot}15\ \mathrm{K}$$

(2) the **interval** 1 *degree Celsius* (°C) equals the interval 1 *kelvin*.

A Celsius temperature is sometimes called a **common temperature.** Experiment has shown that the calibration points are 0 °C and 100 °C respectively. The Celsius scale is convenient for elementary work, since many temperature values lie between 0 °C and 100 °C.

In this book

(*i*) all temperature *intervals* are expressed in *kelvins*,
(*ii*) many temperature *values* which a student is likely to record himself are quoted in °C,
(*iii*) gas temperatures are often expressed in kelvins (as sometimes they *must* be).

5.3 PRACTICE

Common **thermometric properties** are:

(*a*) the volume of a liquid, which may be made to expand into a narrow tube,
(*b*) the e.m.f. of a thermocouple,

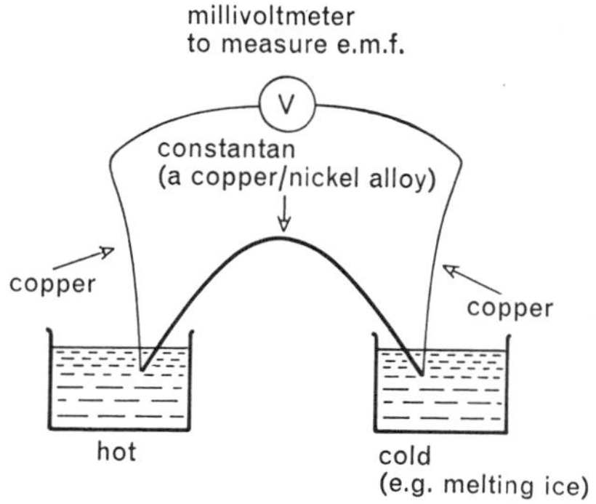

Fig. 5·1 A thermocouple

(*c*) the volume of a fixed mass of a gas kept at constant pressure,
(*d*) the pressure of a fixed mass of a gas kept at constant volume,
(*e*) the electrical resistance of a platinum coil.

Apart from (*c*), each of these has advantages for particular situations.

Liquid-in-glass thermometers

Advantages

(*a*) direct reading,
(*b*) simple and quick to use,
(*c*) can be modified for specific purposes.

Disadvantages

(*a*) unsuitable for very high and very low temperatures,
(*b*) the reading depends on the length of the exposed column,
(*c*) the liquid is inclined to creep as a result of changes in the properties of the glass bulb.

They can be made

(*a*) *more sensitive* by
  (*i*) a larger bulb,
  (*ii*) a narrower capillary tube;
(*b*) *quicker reading* by
  (*i*) a smaller bulb,
  (*ii*) thinner glass for the bulb,
  (*iii*) a bulb of large surface area,
  (*iv*) a liquid of low specific heat capacity,
  (*v*) a liquid of high thermal conductivity.

Special types

(*a*) The photographic thermometer has a small convenient range, and uses coloured alcohol.
(*b*) The clinical thermometer has a very small range, is very sensitive, and retains the reading until shaken.

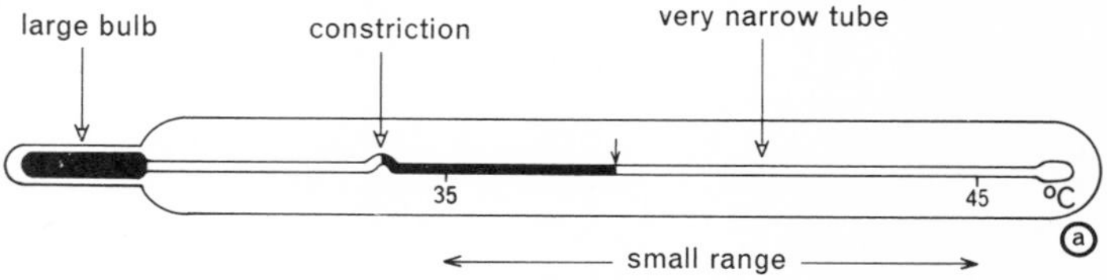

Fig. 5·2 Thermometers   Clinical thermometer

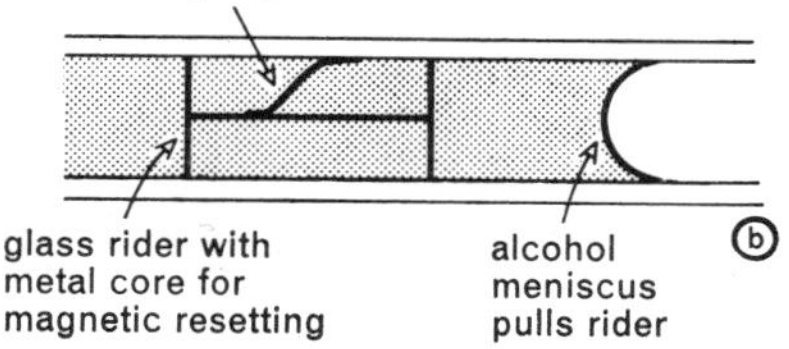

Minimum thermometer

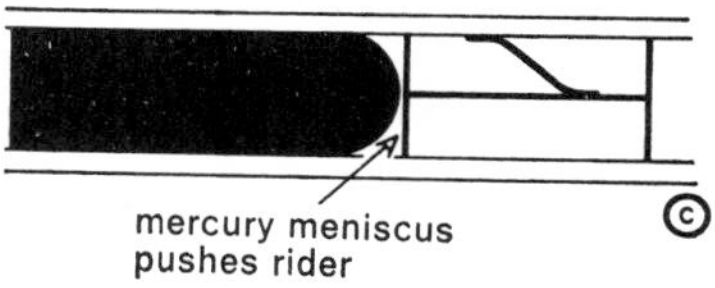

Maximum thermometer

Fig. 5·2 cont. Thermometers

Choice of liquid for thermometers

In addition to the properties mentioned, one must consider:

(*a*) *Range*. Mercury freezes at $-39\,^{\circ}C$, and boils at $357\,^{\circ}C$. Alcohol freezes at $-112\,^{\circ}C$, but boils at $78\,^{\circ}C$, and so cannot be calibrated by steam.
(*b*) *Agreement with other thermometers*. Mercury gives readings such that the numbers correspond fairly closely with the perfect gas scale. This is convenient. Alcohol does not expand uniformly with respect to gases.

Calibration of a thermometer

For a mercury thermometer:

(1) Suspend the bulb in steam from pure boiling water at standard atmospheric pressure. Mark the point to which the mercury rises $100\,^{\circ}C$.
(2) Place the bulb in an equilibrium mixture of ice and water. Mark this point $0\,^{\circ}C$.
(3) The distance between these two points on the stem is called the **fundamental interval.** Divide it into 100 equal divisions.

This thermometer will now read the temperature in degrees Celsius.

Important note

A number that represents temperature only has real meaning when we are told the scale on which it was measured, i.e.

(*a*) using which property of which substance,
(*b*) using which fixed points, and what numbers were allotted to them.

Different scales will only give the same numbers for a given degree of hotness by necessity at the calibration points: there they will do so, because the temperatures will, by definition, be represented by the same numbers.

Expansion

5.4 GENERAL

For a molecular explanation of the reason for expansion, see p. 39.

Examples of expansion

(*a*) The bimetallic strip shows the difference in the expansion of two metals.

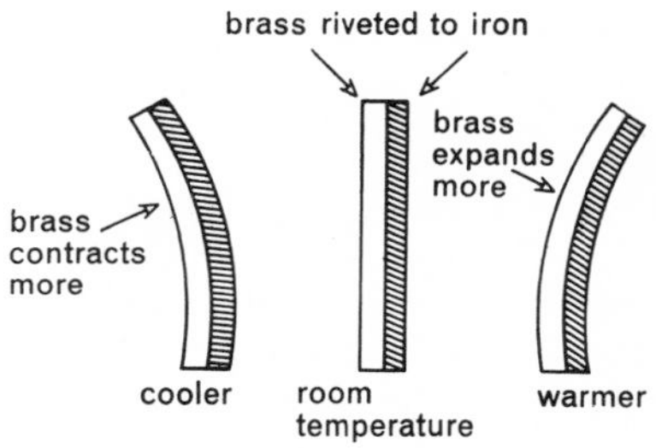

Fig. 5·3 The bimetallic strip

(*b*) Telephone wires sag more in summer than in winter.
(*c*) The ball and ring experiment.
(*d*) The cast iron frame used to break small bars. This shows that the forces exerted by one molecule on another can become very large when the molecules are pulled apart.
(*e*) A metal measuring tape expands when heated, and then records too small a value for a given length.

Expansion in practice

(*a*) *Overcoming the difficulties caused by expansion*

(*i*) Gaps are left between individual railway lines to prevent too big a stress building up. Bolt holes are oval.
(*ii*) Gaps are left between concrete road blocks, and these are filled with pitch.
(*iii*) Pipes through which steam is passing are arranged so as to be flexible.
(*iv*) Large structures such as bridges are on rollers, so that they can move rather than be distorted when they expand.
(*v*) The balance wheels of watches are compensated to take into account changes of size and elasticity.

(*b*) *Utilizing expansion*

(*i*) Linings for the cylinder blocks of internal combustion engines are dipped into liquid oxygen to make them contract before fitting.

(*ii*) Fire alarms (bimetallic strip).

(*iii*) Rivets – the contraction of a cooling rivet binds plates together.

(*iv*) Thermometry – the volume or length of a body is used as a thermometric property.

5.5 QUANTITATIVE WORK ON EXPANSION

The linear expansivity α is defined by

$$\alpha = \frac{\text{increase in length of a body}}{\text{original length} \times \text{temp. rise}}$$

$$\alpha \left[\frac{1}{\text{K}}\right] = \frac{(l_2 - l_1)\ [\text{m}]}{l_1\ [\text{m}] \times (\theta_2 - \theta_1)\ [\text{K}]}.$$

$$\boxed{\alpha = \frac{(l_2 - l_1)}{l_1 \cdot (\theta_2 - \theta_1)}}$$

α is numerically equal to the increase in length of unit length when the temperature is increased by one unit.

From the defining equation

$$l_2 = l_1 \{1 + \alpha(\theta_2 - \theta_1)\}$$

Measurement of α

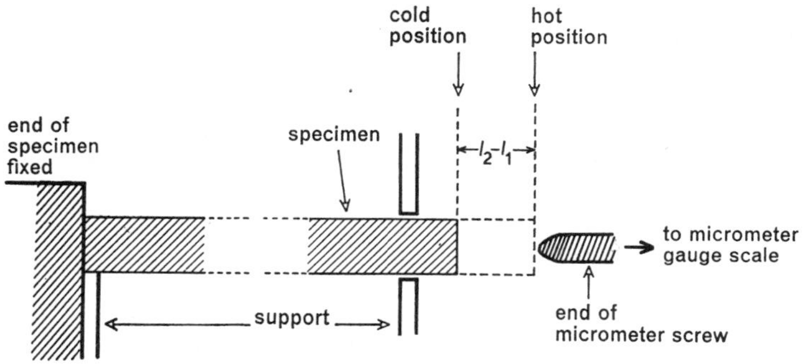

Fig. 5·4 Principle of the measurement of α

(1) Measure the initial length of a specimen rod of the material.
(2) Measure the increase in length on being heated through $(\theta_2 - \theta_1)$.
(3) Apply the defining equation for α (above).

The accuracy of the result is controlled by the accuracy of the reading of $(l_2 - l_1)$, which is therefore read directly by a type of micrometer screw gauge; this, being sensitive, is likely to give a more accurate result.

Changes of area and volume

These can be calculated from the change in the linear dimensions of a body. As a guide, if the fractional change in linear dimensions is x per cent, then the fractional change in area will be $2x$ per cent, and in volume $3x$ per cent. A body made of the same material throughout will not be distorted by expansion. For example

(*a*) an annular ring becomes a larger ring; both inner and outer radii increase;
(*b*) an empty relative density bottle *increases* its *internal* as well as its external volume, and so its fluid capacity is increased.

5.6 EXPANSION OF LIQUIDS

Since a liquid has no fixed shape, linear expansion has no meaning. The observed volume change for a liquid is influenced by the expansion of the vessel which must be used to hold it. Care must be taken to distinguish the *real* expansion of the liquid from its *apparent* expansion, as indicated by its level within the containing vessel.

The peculiar (anomalous) expansion of water

Measurements of volume and temperature for a fixed mass of water enable us to draw this graph:

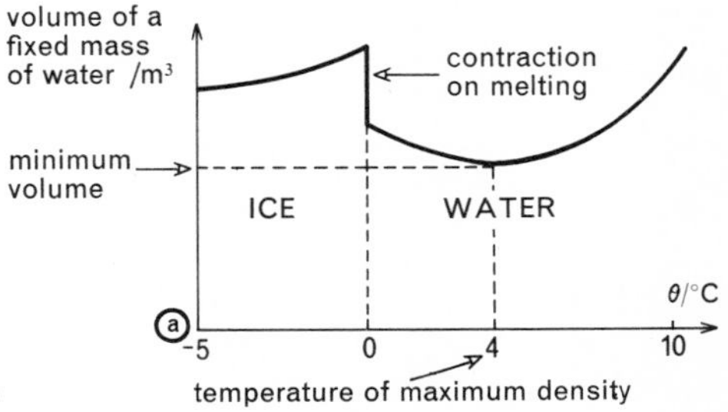

Fig. 5·5

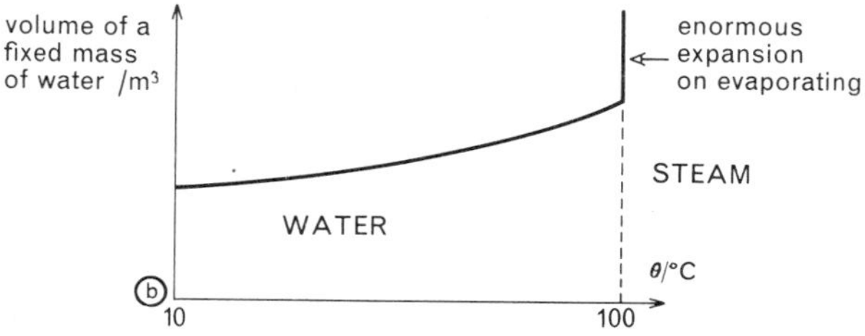

Fig. 5·5 cont. Change of volume of water with temperature (not to scale)

Most substances contract on cooling. Water is unusual in that its volume increases (and so its density decreases) when the temperature drops from 4 °C to 0 °C. This is explained by the fact that water molecules exist in groups, which rearrange so as to occupy a bigger volume when the temperature falls through this range. As a result water

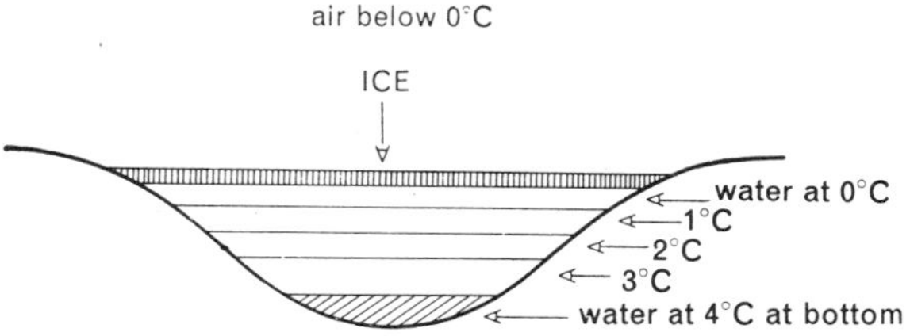

Fig. 5·6 Water temperatures in a pond

at 0 °C will be found at the surface of a pond rather than at the bottom. This means that ice will form from the top downwards, and enable pond-life to continue at the bottom.

Density and temperature

Consider a fixed mass m of fluid.

$$m = V_1\rho_1 = V_2\rho_2,$$

so

$$\frac{\rho_1}{\rho_2} = \frac{V_2}{V_1}$$

In nearly every case an increase in temperature leads to a smaller density – this is important for the movement of heat by convection (see p. 141).

Heat capacity

5.7 SPECIFIC HEAT CAPACITY

We define *energy* as ability to do *work,* which we measure in joules (J). Since *heat* is energy which is in transit (being moved from one point to another), it too is *measured in joules.*

Heat capacity C

The heat capacity of a *body* is defined by the equation

$$\textbf{heat capacity of body} = \frac{\text{heat added to a body}}{\text{increase of temperature produced}}$$

$$C\left[\frac{\text{J}}{\text{K}}\right] = \frac{Q\ [\text{J}]}{(\theta_2 - \theta_1)\ [\text{K}]}$$

$$\boxed{C = \frac{Q}{\theta_2 - \theta_1}}$$

C is numerically equal to the heat required to raise the temperature of a body by one kelvin. Its exact value will depend on the temperature range over which it is measured.

Specific heat capacity c

The word **specific** means 'per unit mass', and so in the SI system it means *per kilogramme.* The specific heat capacity c is the heat capacity of unit mass of a body, and is therefore a property of the *substance* of which the body is made.

$$\textbf{specific heat capacity} = \frac{\text{heat capacity of body}}{\text{mass of body}}$$

$$c\left[\frac{\text{J}}{\text{kg K}}\right] = \frac{C\left[\frac{\text{J}}{\text{K}}\right]}{m\ [\text{kg}]} = \frac{Q\ [\text{J}]}{m\ [\text{kg}].(\theta_2 - \theta_1)\ [\text{K}]}$$

$$\boxed{c = \frac{Q}{m\ (\theta_2 - \theta_1)}}$$

Specific heat capacity is numerically equal to the heat required to raise the temperature of unit mass of a substance by one kelvin. Its value depends on the temperature range over which it is measured.

Notes

(*a*) An increase in temperature indicates an increase in the average molecular kinetic energy (p. 32). This can be achieved by adding heat.

(*b*) We often want to calculate Q rather than c. Re-arranging the defining equation, we have

$$\boxed{Q = mc\,(\theta_2 - \theta_1)}$$

an equation which is useful for problems. In this equation

(*i*) $(\theta_2 - \theta_1)$ is always a temperature *interval* (not a temperature value),

(*ii*) Q is always the heat added to or taken from a body (*never* its energy content).

(*c*) *Typical values:*

Substance	$c / \frac{\text{J}}{\text{kg K}}$
lead	130
copper	380
paraffin	2200
water	4200

Note that the specific heat capacity of water is larger than that of most other substances, in particular than that of the materials of the Earth's crust. This is one reason why water plays such a large role in determining climate.

5.8 PRINCIPLE OF THE METHOD OF MIXTURES

Since heat is one form of the energy which may be added to, or taken away from, a body, the principle of the conservation of energy will apply to heat. If no other body gains or loses heat when two bodies at different temperatures are allowed to reach the same temperature, then

$$\begin{pmatrix}\text{heat given out by one body}\\ \text{in being cooled}\end{pmatrix} = \begin{pmatrix}\text{heat taken in by the}\\ \text{other in being warmed}\\ \text{to the same temperature}\end{pmatrix}$$

i.e.

$$m_1 c_1 \times (\text{decrease in temperature}) = m_2 c_2 \times (\text{increase in temperature}).$$

Nearly always heat will be given to the surroundings, but such losses are usually sufficiently small to be ignored in normal practical work.

5.9 METHODS OF MEASURING SPECIFIC HEAT CAPACITY

(a) Method of mixtures (obsolescent)

Use the method implied in paragraph 5.8. In the equation there must be only one unknown, c_1 or c_2.

(b) Constant rate of supply of heat method

Principle: If energy is supplied to a body at a known rate for a known time, the total energy supplied can be found.

Method: Find the rate at which heat is being supplied, *either*

(*i*) by using an electrical heater, and measuring V and I (see p. 252), *or*

(*ii*) by using the supply to raise the temperature of a known mass of substance of known specific heat capacity (such as water), over a known time.

Now repeat procedure (*ii*) using the substance of unknown specific heat capacity, and apply the relation

$$Q = mc\,(\theta_2 - \theta_1).$$

Heat losses are usually sufficiently small to be ignored.

5.10 SPECIFIC CALORIFIC VALUE

When fuel is burned, or food eaten, the chemical energy contained by the material is evolved directly as heat or useful mechanical energy.

The **specific calorific value** of a substance = $\dfrac{\text{energy liberated when a mass of the substance undergoes complete combustion (i.e. is completely oxidized)}}{\text{the mass}}$

$$\text{Specific calorific value}\left[\frac{\text{J}}{\text{kg}}\right] = \frac{Q\,[\text{J}]}{m\,[\text{kg}]}$$

Examples

Substance	*Specific calorific value/J/kg*
paraffin	46×10^6
coke	29×10^6
fat	38×10^6
cheese	21×10^6
milk	$2{\cdot}9 \times 10^6$

For a gas it is frequently more convenient to consider a volume of one m^3 rather than a mass of one kilogramme. The energy liberated by the complete oxidation of 1 m^3 of coal gas is 16×10^6 J.

The gas laws

[*Note:* in this section 'temperature' means 'temperature as recorded by a mercury-in-glass thermometer'. Extrapolations are made as though this thermometer could record temperatures down to absolute zero. In more advanced work the gas laws are a logical deduction from the *definition* of temperature on the perfect gas scale.]

5.11 INTRODUCTION

A gas can be described fully when four changeable quantities have been specified – these are its mass, pressure, volume and temperature. For solids and liquids the volume is not altered significantly by a change of pressure.

To investigate their interdependence, we use this procedure:

(1) Select a fixed mass of gas.
(2) Fix any one of p, V, and θ.
(3) Vary one of the two that have not been fixed, and see what effect it has on the other.

5.12 EXPERIMENTS TO DISCOVER THE GAS LAWS

(a) Keeping θ constant: Boyle's Law

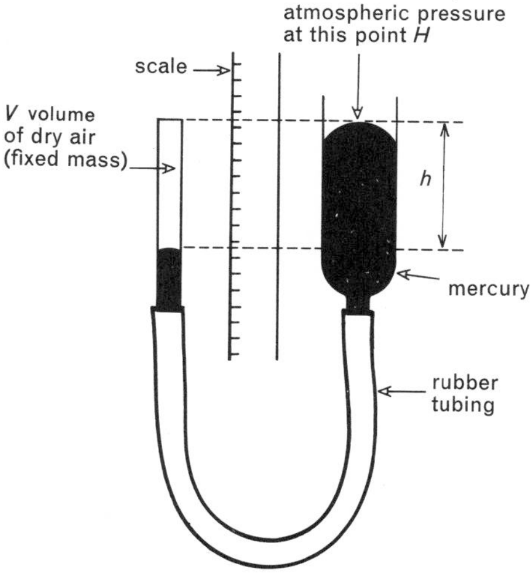

Fig. 5·7 Boyle's Law

Vary the height of the mercury reservoir so as to change the pressure on (and exerted by) the gas. Measure

(*i*) the volume of the gas, V,
(*ii*) the pressure p, made up by (h+atmospheric pressure H). Note that p will be less than H if h is negative.

Draw up a table to show the values:

$p/mmHg$	V/m^3	$p \times V$

The table will show that for all values of the pressure, the product pV is the same. If pV is a constant, we can represent the results of the experiment on the two graphs:

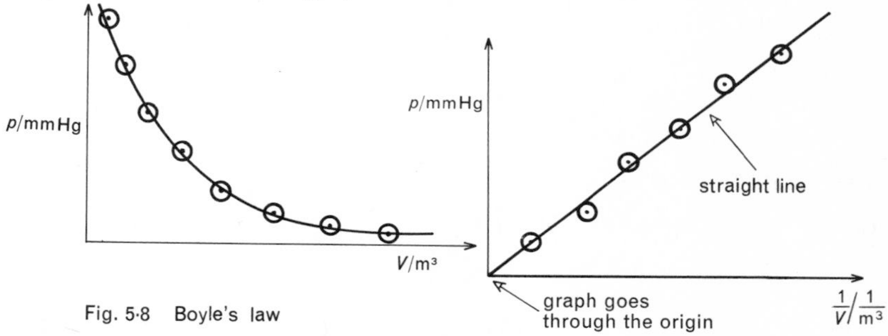

Fig. 5·8 Boyle's law

The straight line shows more clearly that

$$p \propto \frac{1}{V}.$$

See p. 129 for a statement of the law.

(b) Keeping *p* constant: Charles's Law

In Fig. 5.9 allow the gas to reach the temperature of the water. Measure the volume of the trapped air, and the corresponding temperature.

The pressure on (and of) the gas is made up of the pressure due to the index plus that due to the atmosphere, and so is constant. Plot a graph of volume against Celsius temperature for as wide a range as possible. (See Fig. 5.10.) We conclude that volume will be proportional to temperature, provided we choose the zero of our scale correctly, i.e. we will arrange for the line to pass through a new origin.

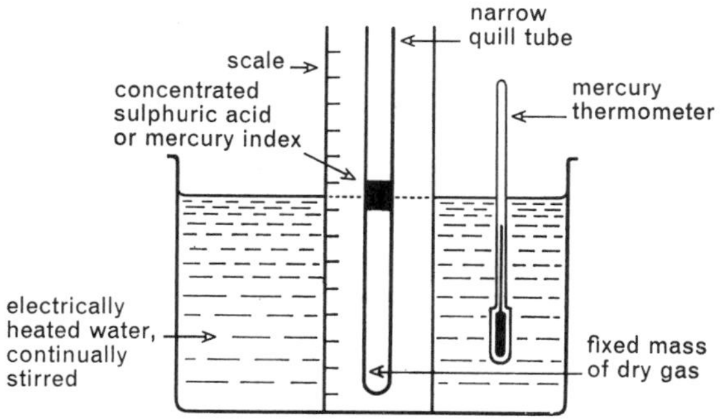

Fig. 5·9 Charles's Law

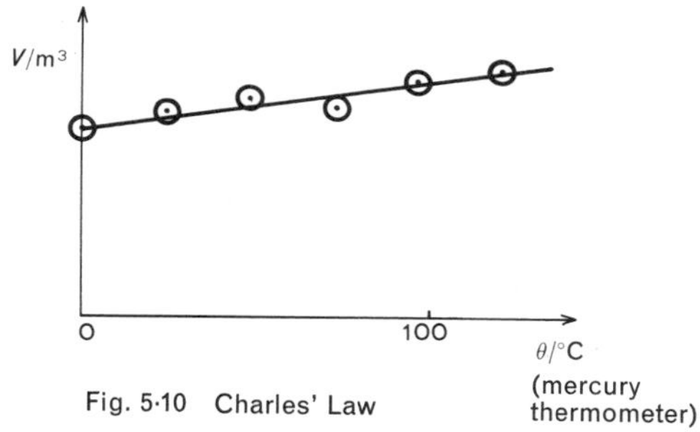

Fig. 5·10 Charles' Law

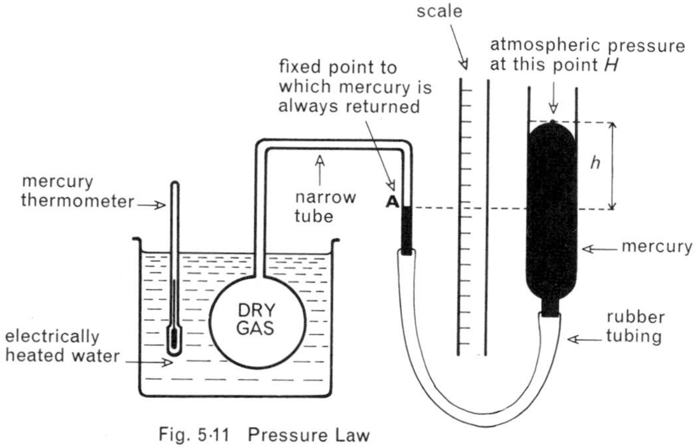

Fig. 5·11 Pressure Law

(c) Keeping V constant: the Pressure Law

Allow the gas to reach the temperature of the water. Measure the temperature, and bring the mercury to point A (Fig. 5.11) so that the volume of the trapped air is fixed, and read h. Calculate $p = (h+H)$. Plot a graph of pressure against Celsius temperature for as wide a range as possible.

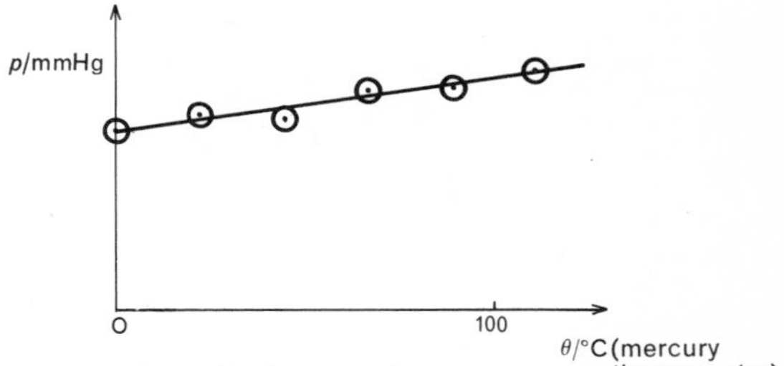

Fig. 5·12 Pressure Law

We conclude that the pressure will be proportional to the temperature, provided we choose the zero of our scale correctly, i.e. we will arrange for the line to pass through a new origin.

5.13 DISCUSSION OF THE GAS LAWS

Graphical representation

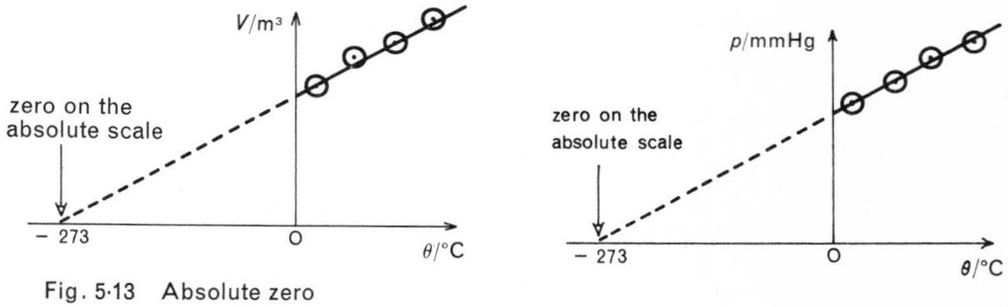

Fig. 5·13 Absolute zero

Both these graphs, when plotted for a fixed mass of nearly any gas, can be extrapolated, and it will be found that they cut the axis at $-273\,°C$. This suggests that at a temperature of $-273\,°C$, any mass of an **ideal gas** would

(*a*) occupy zero volume,
(*b*) exert zero pressure.

This temperature is therefore called the **absolute zero,** because we cannot imagine a gas having a negative volume. **Real gases** are always liquefied before they reach this temperature.

The absolute scale of temperature

So that the gas laws can be represented more conveniently, and used more easily, we adopt a new scale of temperature, such that

(*a*) in temperature interval, 1 kelvin = 1 °C,
(*b*) in temperature values, $T = \theta + 273$ K.

From now on in this section, a capital T will be used to represent temperatures measured on this scale, which is in effect identical to the thermodynamic scale mentioned on p. 114.

Statements of the gas laws

(*a*) **Boyle's Law:** Provided the temperature of a fixed mass of gas does not change, then the product pV remains constant, i.e.

$$p_1V_1 = p_2V_2.$$

(*b*) **Charles's Law:** Provided the pressure of a fixed mass of gas is kept constant, then the volume is directly proportional to the absolute temperature, i.e.

$$V \propto T, \quad \text{or} \quad \frac{V_1}{T_1} = \frac{V_2}{T_2}.$$

(*c*) **The Pressure Law:** Provided the volume of a fixed mass of gas is kept constant, then the pressure is directly proportional to the absolute temperature, i.e.

$$p \propto T, \quad \text{or} \quad \frac{p_1}{T_1} = \frac{p_2}{T_2}.$$

Laws (*b*) and (*c*) are illustrated by Fig. 5.14.

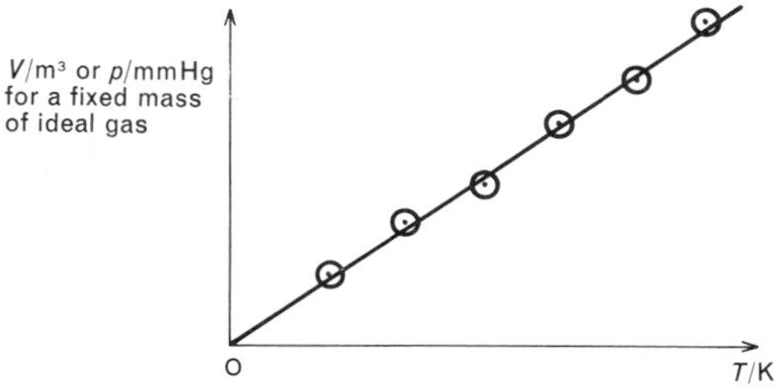

Fig. 5·14 The absolute scale

Gas expansion

The experiment to determine Charles's Law tells us that any ideal gas (and most gases in practice) expands by 1/273 of its volume at 273 K (0 °C) when heated through a temperature range of 1 K.

5.14 THE GAS EQUATION

The equation pV/T = constant for a *fixed mass* of gas can be used for situations in which each of p, V and T is allowed to change. In the form

$$\frac{p_1V_1}{T_1} = \frac{p_2V_2}{T_2}$$

it is useful for calculating the new volume of a gas when conditions have changed.

Note: (*a*) All temperatures must be on the *absolute* scale.
(*b*) Any units can be used for p or V, provided the same units are used on both sides of the equation.
(*c*) To convert to s.t.p. remember that
(*i*) standard pressure is 760 mmHg, and
(*ii*) standard temperature is 0 °C = 273 K.

5.15 THE CONSTANT VOLUME GAS THERMOMETER

See Fig. 5.11. If the volume of a fixed mass of gas is kept constant, we can use its pressure as a thermometric property, i.e. we can calculate the temperature by measuring its pressure.

Advantages: (*a*) Easily reproduced – one thermometer gives the same number for a fixed degree of hotness as another, and so this principle is used as the basis for the standard thermometer.
(*b*) Sensitive, and yet it can be made to cover a very large range (from about 100 K up to 1750 K). Nitrogen is frequently used as the gas.

Disadvantages: Large, cumbersome, and difficult to use.

5.16 GAS MOLECULES AND THE GAS LAWS

A **molecular explanation** for the gas laws is given in Section 2. At **absolute zero** the molecules of an ideal gas may be imagined to have stopped moving, so that they do not collide with the walls of the container, and the pressure is zero. More advanced theory shows that it is not possible for molecules to stop altogether.

The **gas equation** can be derived by applying the laws of dynamics to gas molecules. The fact that theory and experiment agree so well is good support for the theory of the molecular nature of gases.

Change of state

5.17 SPECIFIC LATENT HEAT

The states of matter are explained in Section 2. To summarize:

(*a*) In *solids* the molecules are tightly packed and arranged in distinct patterns.
(*b*) In *liquids* the molecules are nearly as tightly packed, but, except for small groups, are not in fixed patterns.
(*c*) In *gases* the molecules are well separated, and free to move entirely at random.

Examples of change of state

(a) Solidification of naphthalene. Plot a cooling curve for naphthalene that has been heated until it has become liquid. As solidification is taking place there is no fall in temperature. The surroundings absorb

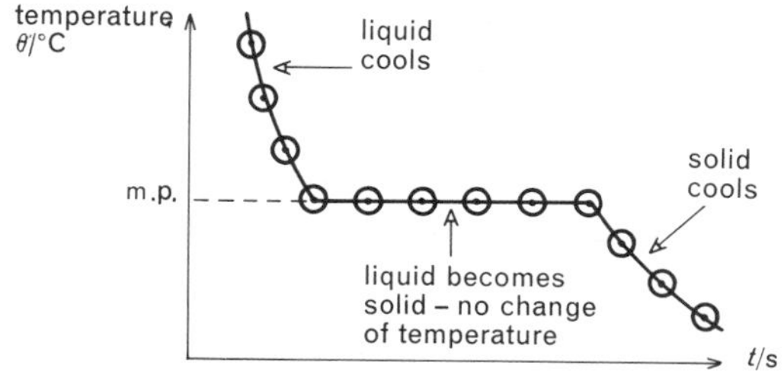

Fig. 5·15 Naphthalene: cooling curve

the latent heat of solidification which is being given out as the molecules settle into their fixed pattern. The horizontal part of the graph enables us to measure the *melting point*.

(b) Boiling of water. Plot a graph of temperature against time for a quantity of water being heated by an immersion heater. The steady increase in temperature is not maintained when the boiling point is reached because the energy supplied is no longer being used to increase the average kinetic energy of the molecules. (A more detailed explanation is given on page 32.)

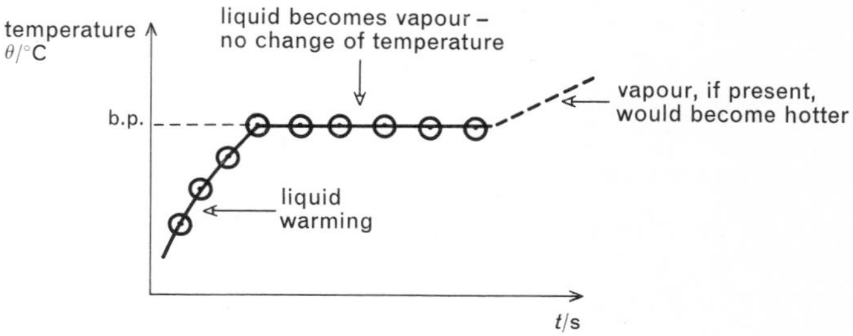

Fig. 5·16 Water: heating curve

Definition of specific latent heat (*l*)

Specific latent heat *l* is defined by the equation

$$\text{specific latent heat of} \begin{cases} \text{fusion} \\ \text{or} \\ \text{vaporization} \end{cases} = \frac{\text{heat required to change the state of a mass of the substance}}{\text{mass of substance}}$$

$$l\left[\frac{\text{J}}{\text{kg}}\right] = \frac{Q\,[\text{J}]}{m\,[\text{kg}]}.$$

$$\boxed{l = \frac{Q}{m}}$$

It is important to note that the change of state occurs without a change of temperature, i.e. at the melting or boiling point.

l is numerically equal to the heat taken in or given out when unit mass of a substance changes state.

Measurement of the specific latent heat of water

(*a*) *Method of mixtures* (obsolescent)

Mix a known mass of dried ice or dry steam with a known mass of water, and observe the subsequent temperature changes. Equate heat given out by hotter bodies to heat taken in by cooler bodies in reaching the same temperature. From the definition of *l*,

$$\text{heat} \begin{cases} \text{taken in by ice} \\ \text{given out by steam} \end{cases} = ml$$

where m is the mass that has changed state.

(*b*) *Constant rate of supply of heat method*
Preliminary: Measure in watts the rate P at which an immersion heat supplies energy. (See p. 124.)
(*i*) *Fusion:* Pack dried ice at 0 °C round the immersion heater in a large can, and measure the time taken to melt all the ice, stirring continuously.
(*ii*) *Vaporization:* Use the immersion heater to boil away a known mass of water, the water starting at 100 °C. Measure the time taken.

In each case apply the principle

$$\text{energy supplied} = \text{energy absorbed},$$

i.e.

$$Pt = ml,$$

where each side of the equation will be in joules.

5.18 EVAPORATION AND BOILING

A molecular explanation of boiling and evaporation is given on page 36.

Evaporation can be defined as the escape of liquid molecules from the surface of a liquid: this will occur at all temperatures at a rate controlled by the surroundings.

Boiling is defined as the escape of faster-than-average liquid molecules from throughout the body of the liquid, and occurs at a fixed temperature for a given pressure. The rate is controlled by the power of the heating source, i.e. the heat supplied in each second.

Cooling on evaporation

Since it is faster molecules which escape, the average kinetic energy of the molecules which are left will be lowered: evaporation will therefore be accompanied by cooling unless some external source supplies heat. This can be shown by

(*a*) sprinkling ether on the hand (it soon evaporates, and cools the hand), or
(*b*) bubbling air through a beaker of ether.

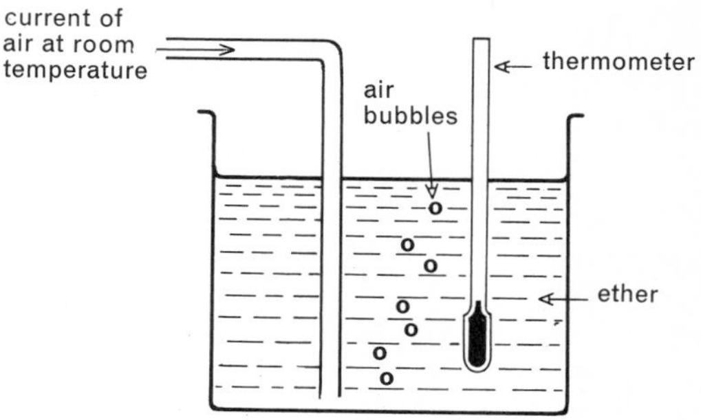

Fig. 5·17 Cooling accompanies evaporation

In either case, the heat required to evaporate the liquid is taken from the liquid itself, and the ether therefore cools.

Applications: (*a*) perspiration,
(*b*) refrigeration,
(*c*) milk coolers,
(*d*) hygrometers (*i*) wet and dry bulb (p. 137),
(*ii*) dew point (p. 137).

5.19 VAPOUR PRESSURE

An explanation of why a liquid exerts a pressure above its surface is given on page 37.

Saturated and unsaturated vapours

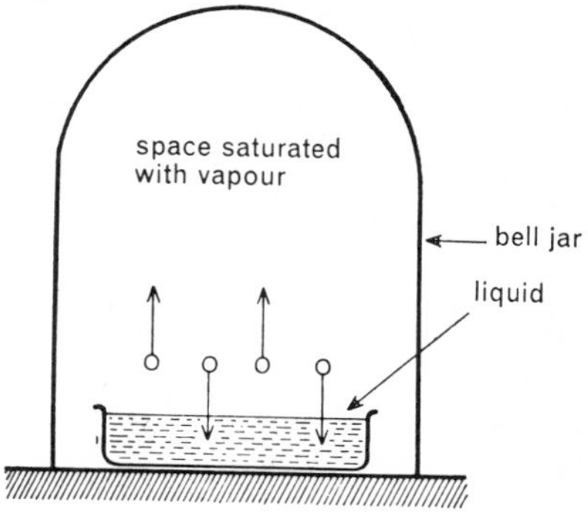

Fig. 5·18 To illustrate saturation

Consider liquid inside an air-tight bell jar. Molecules will leave the liquid surface at a greater rate than they enter it until a **dynamic**

equilibrium has been set up. Then the two rates are equal. A space *saturated* with vapour contains as many molecules from the liquid as it can hold at that temperature. An *unsaturated vapour* contains fewer liquid molecules in a given volume than a saturated vapour at the same temperature – it is capable of absorbing more.

The **saturation vapour pressure** (s.v.p.) is the pressure exerted by a saturated vapour for a particular temperature.

Unit: $\frac{N}{m^2}$, or more conveniently mmHg.

Measurement of s.v.p.

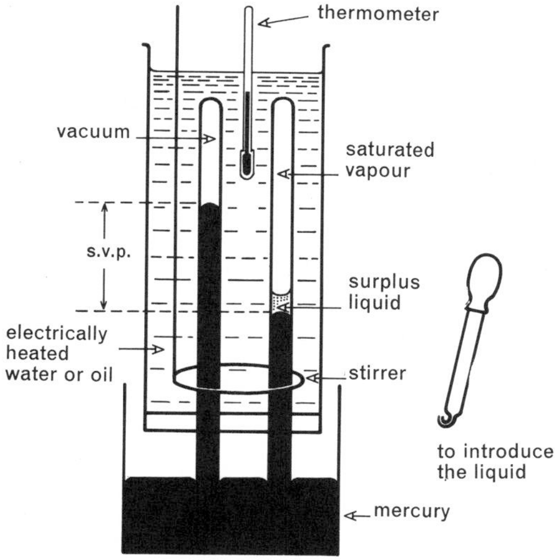

Fig. 5·19 To measure s.v.p.

Introduce an excess of liquid (to ensure saturation) into the vacuum above the mercury in a barometer. Measure the pressure exerted by comparison with another barometer tube alongside. Repeat for a range of temperatures.

Results: The s.v.p. increases very rapidly with temperature, but its value does *not* depend on the external pressure.

Boiling point is defined as the temperature at which a liquid exerts an s.v.p. equal to the pressure acting on the surface of the liquid. Hence Fig. 5.20 also plots boiling point against external pressure. Boiling point increases with pressure, and this fact is used in the pressure cooker. The boiling point is also raised (and the freezing point lowered) by the presence of impurities in the liquid. Thus it is only true that *pure* water at *normal* atmospheric pressure boils at 100 °C.

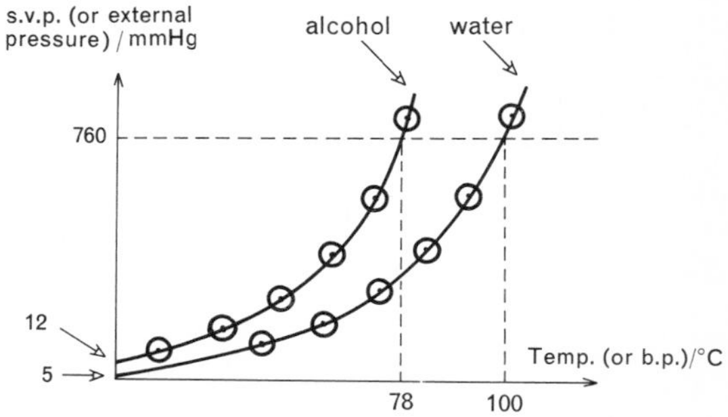

Fig. 5·20 Variation of s.v.p. and temp. (or pressure and b.p.)

Normal boiling point is that temperature at which a liquid exerts an s.v.p. equal to standard pressure, 760 mmHg.

5.20 MISCELLANEOUS TOPICS

Dry steam is uncondensed and therefore invisible. It is present in the region between the spout of a boiling kettle, and the region in which visible condensed 'steam' can be seen. **Scalding** is most severe when inflicted by dry steam, which gives out its latent heat as it condenses before it starts to cool.

Changes of volume: The fact that molecules are arranged in distinct patterns in solids means that a solid will usually occupy a smaller volume than the same mass of liquid. This is shown by the contraction in volume when wax solidifies. This means that very high pressures may raise the melting point of a substance, and so enable it to remain solid, even though it is above its normal melting point. This happens to some of the rocks inside the Earth.

Regelation: Water is exceptional in that the liquid occupies a smaller volume than the same mass of solid. An increase of pressure will lower the melting point, and so encourage ice to turn to water. When the extra pressure is removed, the water will again freeze – this is **regelation.** Examples: ice block and copper wire, snowballs, and (to a small extent) skating.

5.21 MOISTURE IN THE AIR

Humidity is a term used to describe the mass of water vapour present in a given volume of air.

Relative humidity (r.h.) is defined by

$$\text{r.h.} = \frac{\text{mass of water present in a given volume of air}}{\text{mass needed to saturate the same volume at the same temperature}}$$

It has no unit.

If we define **dew point** as the temperature to which a given sample of air must be cooled so as to become saturated with water vapour, then it can be proved that

$$\text{r.h.} = \frac{\text{s.v.p. at the dew point}}{\text{s.v.p. at air temperature}}.$$

Relative humidity is measured by a **hygrometer:** hygrometers are designed using different principles, for example:

(*a*) *The wet and dry bulb.* Evaporation from damp muslin surrounding a thermometer bulb results in cooling, and so it gives a reading different from that of a dry bulb. These two readings enable the r.h. to be found from tables.
(*b*) *Regnault's hygrometer,* which measures the dew point.

Related topics

Air conditioning and humidity control.
Clouds – small droplets of condensed vapour fall very slowly.
Rain – combined droplets ('raindrops') that are big enough fall faster.
Mist, fog and smog – droplets form on dust particles near the Earth's surface.
Hail – frozen rain drops.
Snow – frozen water vapour.

Work and internal energy

5.22 INTRODUCTION

An increase of temperature can be caused not only by supplying heat, but also by doing work. For example

(*a*) When a moving car is brought to rest by applying the brakes, the mass of the car loses its kinetic energy, but the brake drums become hot (and this may lead to brake fading).

(*b*) When wood is rubbed with sandpaper, both become hot.
(*c*) When air is compressed in a bicycle pump, the barrel becomes hot. We deduce that it is the performance of work that has increased the internal energy.

The waterfall

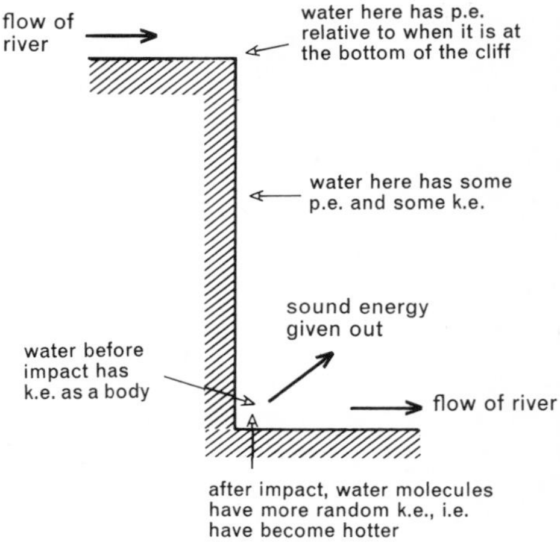

Fig. 5·21 The waterfall

The diagram illustrates the conversion of energy from one form to another. The total energy, taking all forms into account, remains constant.

5.23 THE SHOT TUBE EXPERIMENT

A large number of experiments, particularly those carried out by Joule, have shown that whenever a given quantity of mechanical energy is *totally* converted into internal energy, the same quantity of internal energy is always produced.

It can be illustrated in the laboratory by a mechanical measurement of the specific heat capacity of lead shot. The significant fact about the result is that *it always has the same value* when we make allowance for experimental uncertainty.

The shot tube experiment

The shot tube, Fig. 5.22, is inverted a large number of times (n) so that

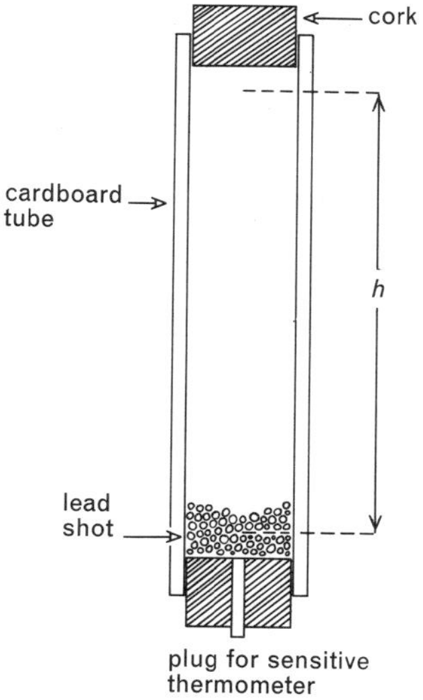

Fig. 5·22 The shot tube

each time the lead experiences the same sequence of events as the water in Fig. 5.21.

We measure

(*i*) the initial and final shot temperatures (θ_1 and θ_2)
(*ii*) h, the average distance through which the shot falls, and we assume a value for g, the acceleration due to gravity.

The work W done by the pull mg of the Earth on the shot

$$= n.mg.h$$
$$= nmgh.$$

If this is totally converted to internal energy Q, then

$$W = Q$$
$$= mc(\theta_2 - \theta_1).$$

The specific heat capacity c of lead can be calculated from

$$nmgh = mc\,(\theta_2 - \theta_1).$$

Variations in the result for c are caused by

(*i*) heat losses,
(*ii*) the difficulty of measuring $(\theta_2 - \theta_1)$ accurately,
(*iii*) uncertainty in the value of h.

The experiment is very unreliable.

Transfer of internal energy

5.24 METHODS AVAILABLE

(a) Conduction – molecules are made to move faster
(*i*) by the transfer of fast electrons, or
(*ii*) by mutual interaction.

(b) Convection – fast molecules are made to move from one place to another.

(c) Radiation – molecules are made to move faster when electromagnetic waves fall on them.

5.25 CONDUCTION

Conduction is defined as the transfer of internal energy through a body which is not at uniform temperature, from places at high temperature to places at low temperature, without effective movement of parts of the body.

Examples of conductors: if we quote the *conductivity* of air as 1, the relative conductivities of other materials are as follows:

1	air
2	glass wool and cork
25	water
35	glass
about 5000	alloys
10 000 to 20 000	pure metals

The different orders of magnitude for the conductivities of metals and non-metals suggest that there are two different mechanisms by which conduction takes place. An account of these is given on page 42. Most substances that are liquid at normal temperatures are non-metals, and are therefore bad conductors.

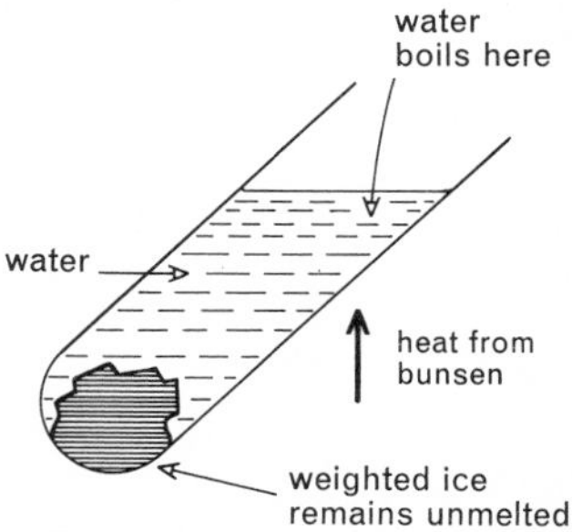

Fig. 5·23

This experiment shows that water is a poor conductor.

The feel of conductors

The better a conductor, the more will it make its temperature felt.

Examples

(*a*) A bare floor feels colder than a carpet (when both are at the same low temperature) because it conducts heat away from warm feet more quickly.
(*b*) A gun barrel heated by the sun in the desert feels much hotter than the wooden butt, because it conducts heat to a cooler hand more quickly.

Applications of high and low conductivity

(*a*) *Low conductivity*

(*i*) double-glazed windows,
(*ii*) Eskimo fur coats, string vests and cellular blankets,
(*iii*) straw on plants in frosty weather, roof thatch,
(*iv*) igloos,
(*v*) wooden saucepan handles.

(*b*) *High conductivity*

(*i*) aluminium and copper saucepans,
(*ii*) cooling fins on petrol engines, which rapidly distribute unwanted energy over a large area so as to disperse it,
(*iii*) the Davy lamp – metal gauze distributes the energy so quickly that no single point is hot enough to cause gas in the mine to ignite.

5.26 CONVECTION

Natural convection is defined as the transfer of internal energy by the circulation of a fluid as a result of temperature differences within it.

Explanation: An increase in temperature usually causes an increase in volume. A given mass of warm fluid will therefore experience an upthrust (from cooler fluid that surrounds it) greater than its own weight. The cold denser fluid thus provides a force that causes the warm fluid to rise. The general *drift* of a mass of fluid is superimposed on the random motions of the individual molecules.

Note: (*a*) Convection cannot occur in solids because the molecules have fixed relative positions.
(*b*) Convection is more effective in gases than in liquids.

Demonstrations of convection

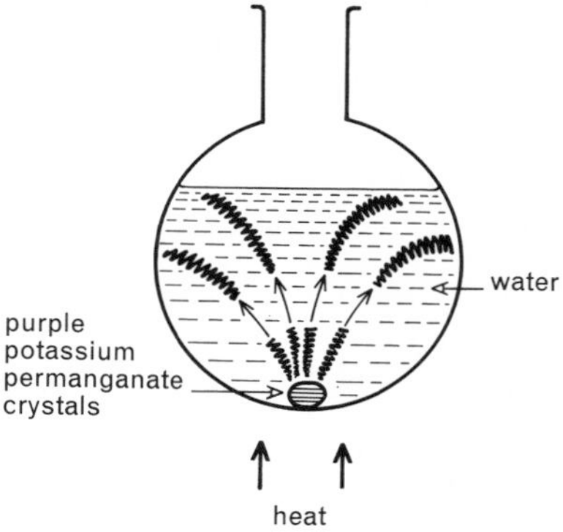

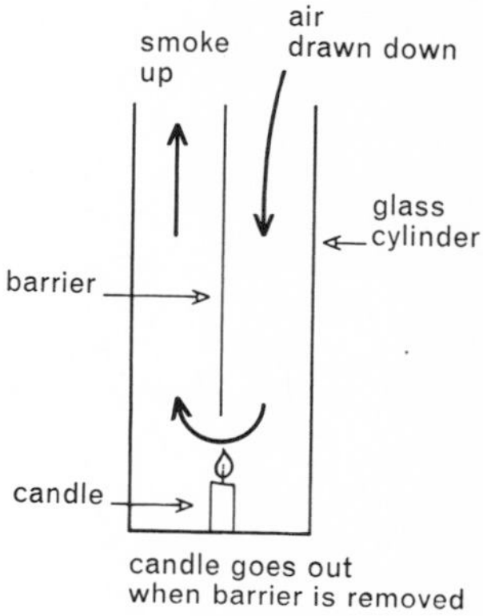

Fig. 5·24 Demonstrations of convection

Examples of convection

(*a*) Cloud formation – warm moist air rises before condensing.
(*b*) Winds.
(*c*) The art of gliding is to trace and use hot air currents (as is done by seagulls).
(*d*) The domestic hot water supply.
(*e*) Sea and land breezes are set up by earth–sea temperature differences (see also p. 123).

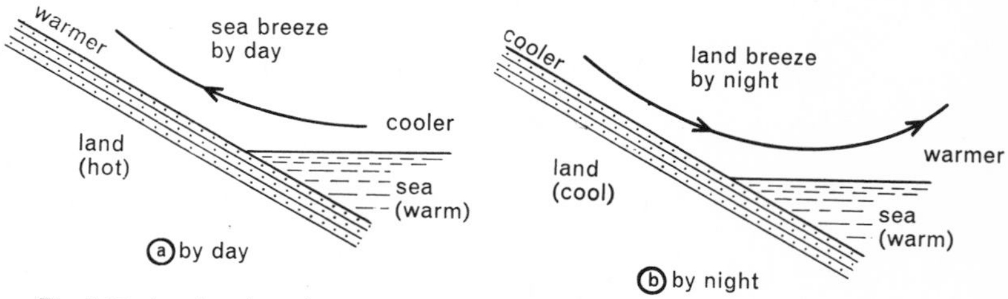

Fig. 5·25 Land and sea breezes

5.27 RADIATION

Electromagnetic radiation is that type of wave motion given out by accelerated electric charges, and it results in the transfer of energy from one place to another. In particular the *infra-red waves* have frequencies such that they are easily absorbed by the particles of which matter is made, and are therefore effective at warming matter. A good analogy is the setting of a swing into vibrations of large amplitude by correctly timed pushes.

In this context we define **radiation** to be the transfer of energy from one place to another by means of electromagnetic waves, during which any intervening medium absorbs little or no energy, and so does not become hot.

Properties: Infra-red waves have the usual properties of electromagnetic waves (see p. 174). In particular they can travel through a *vacuum,* as is shown by the warmth which reaches us from the Sun. They can be detected by a **thermopile.** This is a device which converts the energy of the radiation into an electrical signal, by exposing one junction of a series of thermocouples, which thereby becomes hotter (see p. 115).

Emission and absorption of heat waves

Experiments show that good emitters of radiation are also good absorbers. In particular,

(*a*) black surfaces are good absorbers (i.e. bad reflectors) and good radiators,

(*b*) shiny surfaces are poor absorbers (i.e. good reflectors) and poor radiators.

5.28 THE VACUUM FLASK

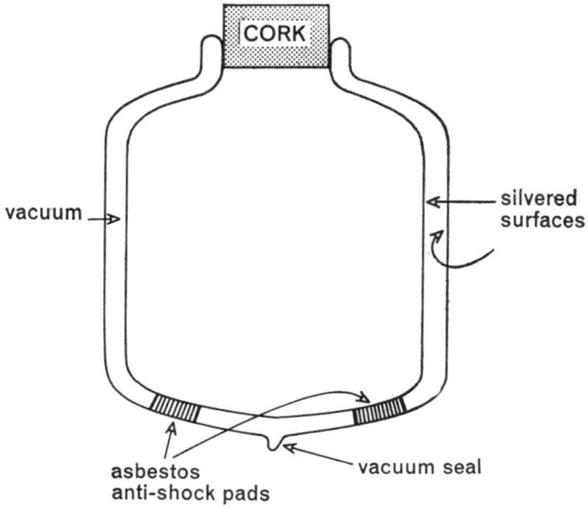

Fig. 5·26 Vacuum flask

This is a device to maintain bodies at a constant temperature, either higher or lower than that of their surroundings.

(*a*) *Conduction* is prevented by the vacuum, and reduced by using the cork, and having a small area of contact between the inner container and the outer. Conduction through the glass to the top of the container is a slow process.
(*b*) *Convection* is prevented by the vacuum.
(*c*) *Radiation* is reduced by the two silvered surfaces.
(*d*) *Evaporation* (which would be accompanied by cooling) is prevented by the cork. The cork may not be used if the contents are likely to build up a high pressure.

6 Wave motion

Vibrations and waves

6.1 MECHANICAL AND ELECTROMAGNETIC WAVES

Definition of **progressive wave motion:** a progressive or travelling wave is the movement of a disturbance from a source. The result of such a movement is the transfer of *energy* from the source to places around it.

There are two basic types of waves, **mechanical** and **electromagnetic** waves. These may be subdivided as follows:

Mechanical waves

(*a*) water waves
(*b*) sound waves
(*c*) waves on springs
(*d*) waves on stretched strings
(*e*) earthquake waves, primary and secondary

Electromagnetic waves

(*a*) radio waves
(*b*) radar waves
(*c*) infra-red waves
(*d*) light waves
(*e*) ultra-violet waves
(*f*) X-ray waves
(*g*) γ-ray waves

Characteristics of waves

Mechanical waves:

(*i*) are caused by a disturbance in a material medium,
(*ii*) require a material medium for the waves to travel,
(*iii*) result in no movement of the medium as a whole, but only in a relative movement of different parts of the medium.

Examples of sources which can produce and media which can carry mechanical waves:

(*a*) a stone dropped on the surface of a pond,
(*b*) a vibrating gong in air,
(*c*) a sudden blow on one end of a coiled spring.

Electromagnetic waves (see also p. 177):

(*i*) are caused by a disturbance in an electromagnetic field,
(*ii*) can travel in a vacuum and in some material media,
(*iii*) leave no evidence of their passage in the electric or magnetic fields in the space through which they travel.

Examples of sources which can produce electromagnetic waves:

(*a*) an electron oscillating up and down an aerial,
(*b*) electrons jumping within atoms,
(*c*) sudden changes in the charged constituents of a nucleus.

6.2 WAVES AND WAVEFRONTS

Pulses and periodic waves

A source can produce a single disturbance or a continuous series of disturbances. The resulting waves are respectively described as **wave pulses** or **wavetrains.**

One method of describing a mechanical wave pulse or wavetrain is to draw a diagram representing the position of each point of the medium carrying the wave *at one instant in time:* such a diagram will be called a *photograph.*

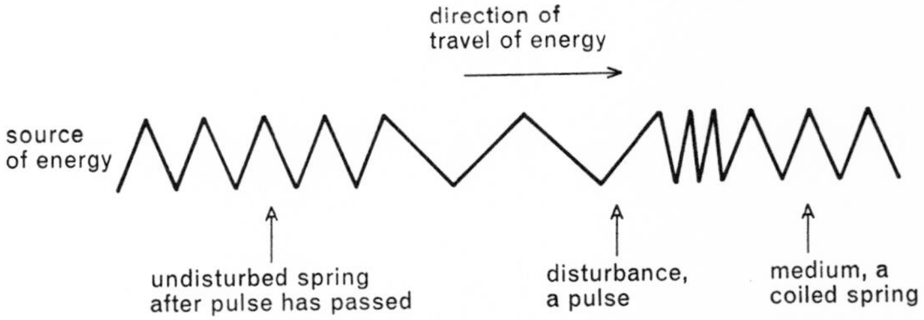

Fig. 6·1 'Photograph' of a wave pulse moving along a spring

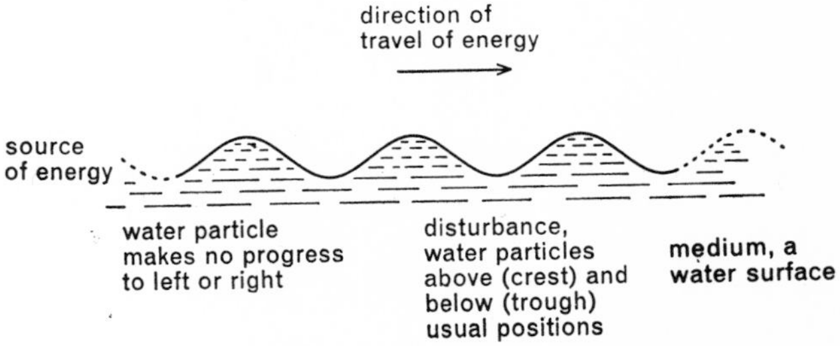

Fig. 6·2 'Photograph' of a wavetrain on a water surface

Wavefronts

If a source produces a wave pulse then the position of this pulse at any later moment is called a **wavefront.** The wavefront can be in one, two or three dimensions, and when one or more sources produce a pulse at the same time, the shape of the wavefront can be:

(*a*) in three dimensions: a sphere, a plane or a cylinder,
(*b*) in two dimensions: a circle or a line,
(*c*) any complicated shape between these simple cases.

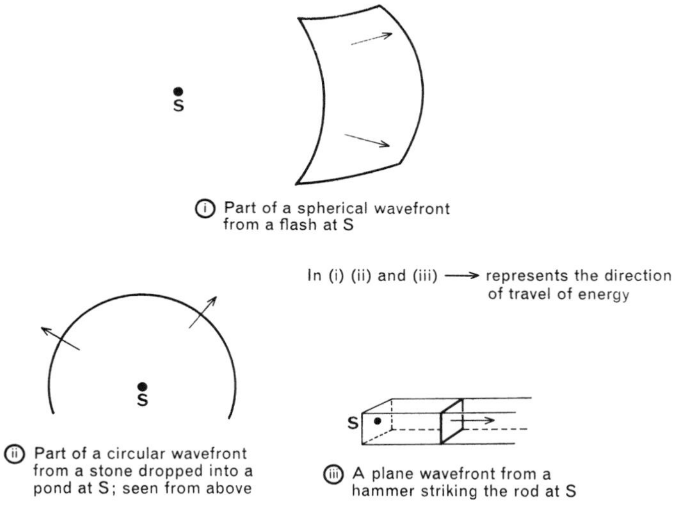

(i) Part of a spherical wavefront from a flash at S

In (i) (ii) and (iii) ⟶ represents the direction of travel of energy

(ii) Part of a circular wavefront from a stone dropped into a pond at S; seen from above

(iii) A plane wavefront from a hammer striking the rod at S

Fig. 6·3

A **periodic source** will produce a regular series of wavefronts each the same shape as its predecessor.

6.3 TRANSVERSE AND LONGITUDINAL WAVES

Consider a coiled spring. The initial disturbance of the source can be

(*a*) *perpendicular* to the direction in which the wave (i.e. the energy) travels. Such a wave is called a **transverse** wave.
(*b*) *parallel* to the direction in which the wave (i.e. the energy) travels. Such a wave is called a **longitudinal** wave.

The result of a wave pulse of type (*a*) or (*b*) sent out by a source can be seen by taking actual photographs of the spring at later times.

Waves of type (*a*) include:

water waves (approximately),
all electromagnetic waves,
waves on a spring (as shown in Fig. 6.4*a*),
waves on stretched strings.

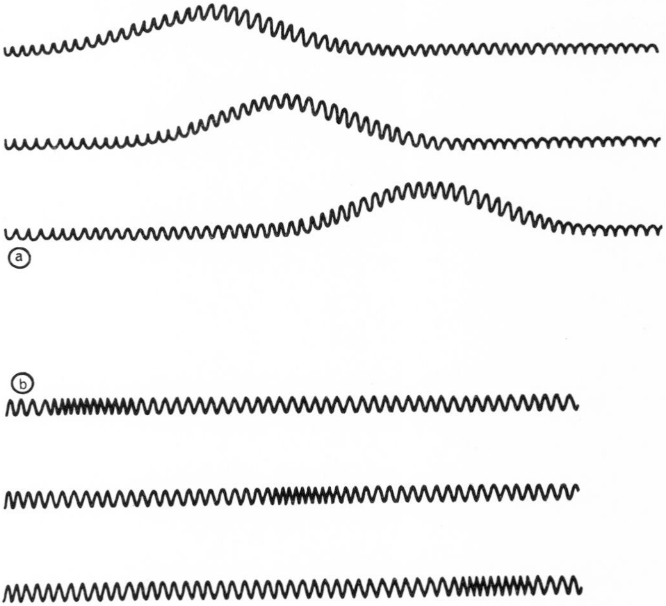

Fig. 6·4

Waves of type (*b*) include:

sound waves,
waves on a spring (as shown in Fig. 6.4*b*).

When representing longitudinal waves it is often easier to draw a diagram of the displacement of points on the wave *as if* the medium were moving across the direction of travel of the wave; i.e. for (*a*)

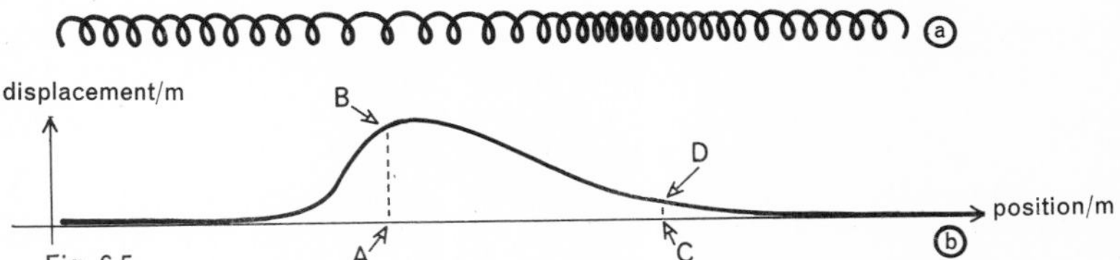

Fig. 6·5

draw (*b*), where *AB* and *CD* represent sideways displacements to the right. The reason for this is that (*b*) is much easier to draw than (*a*), and the sizes of the displacements are easier to see.

Amplitude. The *maximum* displacement produced by a wave pulse or periodic wave is called the **amplitude** of the wave (see Fig. 6.6).

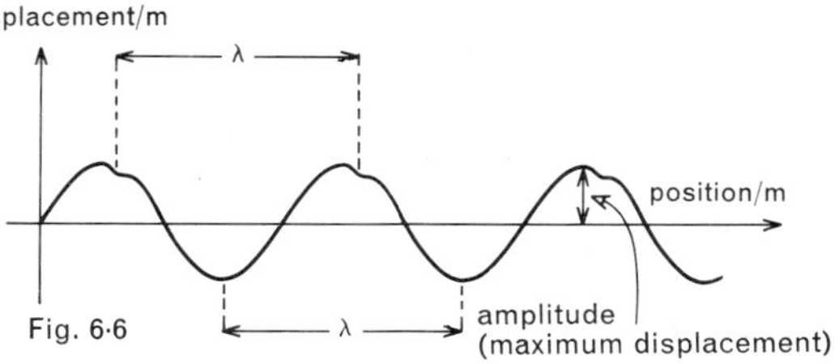

Fig. 6·6

6.4 SPEED, FREQUENCY AND WAVELENGTH

For a progressive periodic wave (the shape being unimportant provided that it is repeated),

> the **wavelength** λ is the distance between successive crests or corresponding points on the wavetrain.

The **frequency** is defined by

$$\text{frequency} = \frac{\text{number of complete waves passing observer}}{\text{time elapsed}}$$

$$f\,[\text{hertz}] = \frac{N}{t\,[\text{s}]}$$

$$f = \frac{N}{t}$$

1 **hertz** (Hz) is the frequency of a periodic phenomenon which is repeated once per second.

Thus in one second f parts of the wavetrain each of length λ travel away from the source. Therefore the total length of the wavetrain after one second is $f\lambda$. So if we define c, the **speed of the wave,** as the speed with which an observer must move so as to see the wavetrain apparently stationary in space, then

$$c\left[\frac{\text{m}}{\text{s}}\right] = f\,[\text{Hz}]\,.\,\lambda\,[\text{m}]$$

$$\boxed{c = f\lambda}$$

6.5 THE PRINCIPLE OF SUPERPOSITION

Two wave pulses pass through each other without either being altered. Two billiard balls, on the other hand, do not behave in this manner. If two pulses are disturbing *the same point,* then the displacement at the point is found by adding the displacements belonging to each pulse at the point. This is called the **Principle of Superposition.** It works for all wave pulses and also for wavetrains. The result of the superposition is sometimes described as **interference.**

If a series of *photographs* are drawn of two pulses moving in opposite senses along a stretched string, the principle leads to Fig. 6.7(*i*) and (*ii*).

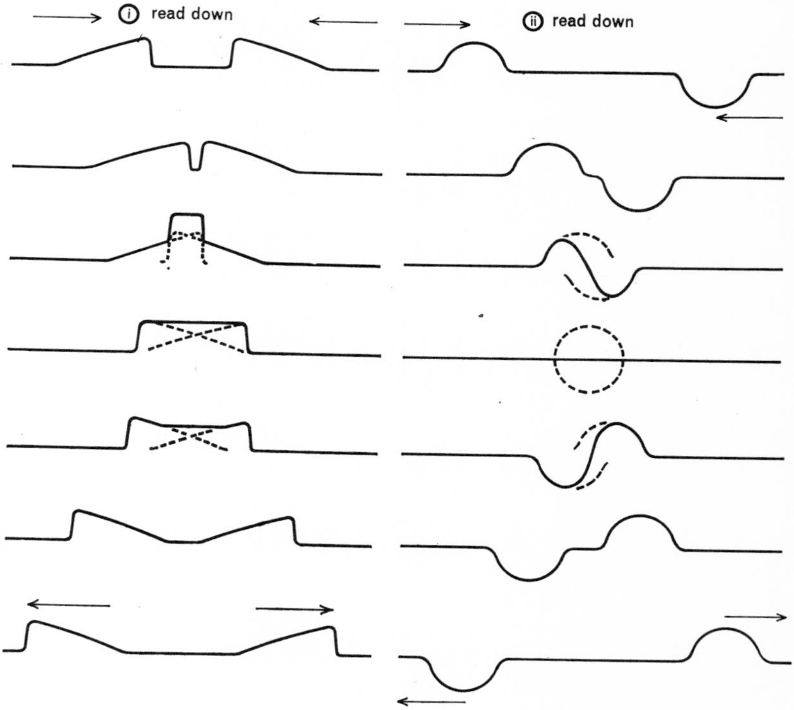

Fig. 6·7

Photographs of two wave pulses on a stretched string at successive instants in time

Alternatively, if a single point on the string is watched (this can be done in practice by attaching a small bit of white tissue paper to the point), a **displacement–time curve** for the point can be drawn. In (*c*)

and (*d*) wavetrains are used and the superposition of two wavetrains of equal f and λ is shown.

In (*c*), C undergoes a violent displacement and is in general called an **antinode:** and two waves are said to be **in phase** at C.

In (*d*), D remains undisturbed and is in general called a **node:** the two waves are said to be fully **out of phase** at D.

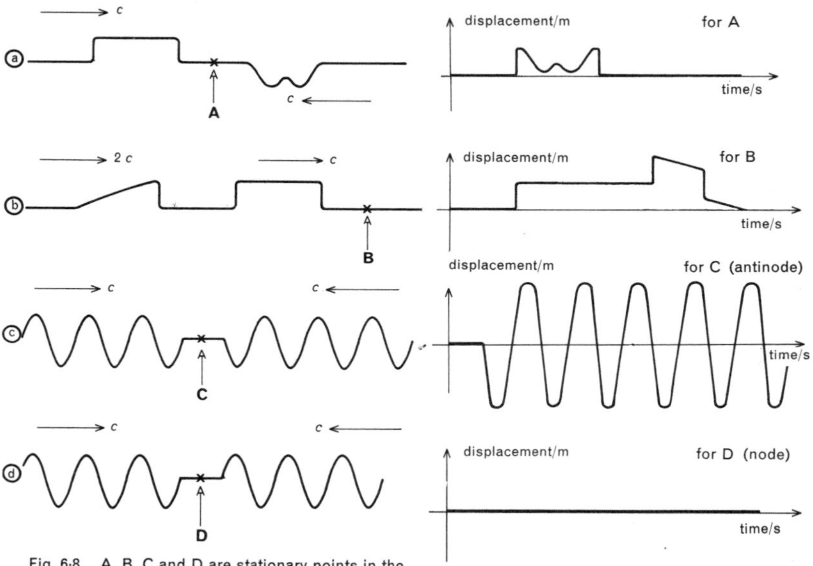

Fig. 6·8 A, B, C and D are stationary points in the path of two wave pulses or wavetrains

Superpositions of the types described above can be drawn for all wave motions, and great care must be taken to distinguish between

(*a*) *photographs of the wave* at an instant in time,
(*b*) *displacement–time graphs* for a point in the path of the wave.

The reader should try some further examples of the nature of those given in Figs. 6.7 and 6.8. Remember that these are examples only, and should not be memorized.

We use the Principle of Superposition to explain:

(*a*) interference patterns,
(*b*) stationary waves,
(*c*) diffraction grating effects.

The behaviour of waves

6.6 WAVE DEMONSTRATIONS

Five types of wave will be used to outline the properties of waves:

(*a*) surface waves on water,
(*b*) sound waves,
(*c*) waves on springs and strings,
(*d*) light waves,
(*e*) radar (30 mm) waves.

(a) Water waves

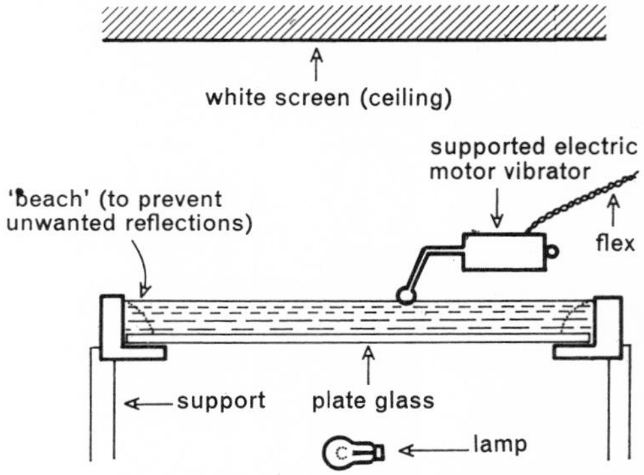

Fig. 6·9 (the lamp may be above the water surface and the screen below)

The disturbances on the water surface, which are projected up or down by the lamp on to a flat white surface, are produced by either

(*i*) a vibrating prong (this gives circular wavefronts), or
(*ii*) a vibrating bar (this gives plane wavefronts).

If the source is periodic, the wavefronts can be 'frozen' by means of a **stroboscopic device** (see p. 166). When taking measurements with this arrangement one must allow for the scale of the projection.

(b) Sound waves in air

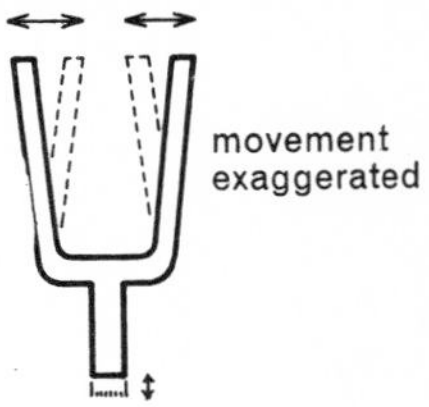

Fig. 6·10 A tuning fork in vibration
↔ and ↕ represent displacements

Sources of sound waves can be:

(*i*) a vibrating tuning fork,
(*ii*) an audio-frequency oscillator and loudspeaker.

In (*i*) and (*ii*) the disturbances are detected by the ear or a microphone.

Two sets of wavefronts are produced by (*i*), each set consisting of two halves occupying opposite quarters of a sphere around the fork, and one approximately hemispherical wavefront by (*ii*).

(c) Springs and strings

Springs (such as those shown in Fig. 6.4 to describe transverse and longitudinal waves), and stretched strings will be used.

(d) Light waves

Examples of light sources:

(*i*) incandescent objects such as the tungsten filament in an electric light bulb or some hot sodium vapour in a street light,
(*ii*) the Sun,
(*iii*) fluorescent and phosphorescent objects.

The wavefronts from (*i*) are approximately spherical, while those from (*ii*) are effectively plane over a small area on the Earth's surface.

(e) Radar waves

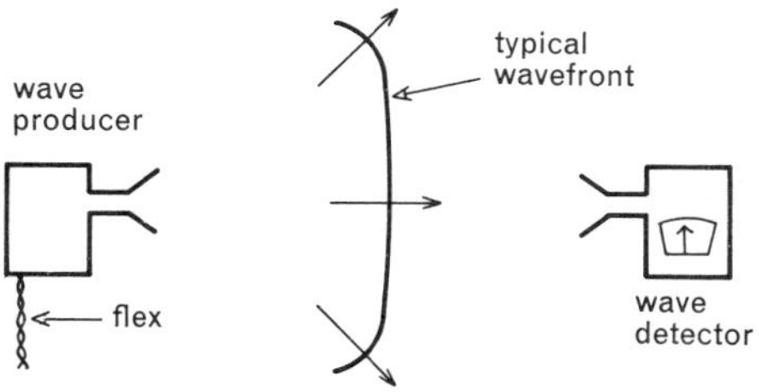

Fig. 6·11 Radar (30 mm) waves

The effect of these electromagnetic waves is shown by the pointer on the detector. The effects can also be made to stimulate a loudspeaker.

The wavefronts are of no simple shape. They are approximately plane directly in front of the wave producer, but act as approximately spherical waves for wide angles.

Summary of numerical values for f, λ and c:

	Water waves	*Sound waves in air*	*Waves on springs and strings*	*Light waves in air*	*Radar waves*
f/Hz	about 6	20 to 20 000	about 2	about 10^{15}	usually 10^{10}
λ/m	about 0·02	15 to 0·015	about 0·5	4×10^{-7} to 7×10^{-7}	usually 0·03
$c\Big/\frac{\text{m}}{\text{s}}$	about 0·12	about 3×10^2	about 1	3×10^8	3×10^8

6.7 REFLECTION

When a wave is regularly reflected, the direction in which the *energy* of the wave is travelling is altered, but the wave remains in the same medium as it was initially (see p. 184). The speed of the wave remains constant.

(a) Reflection at plane reflecting surfaces

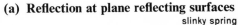

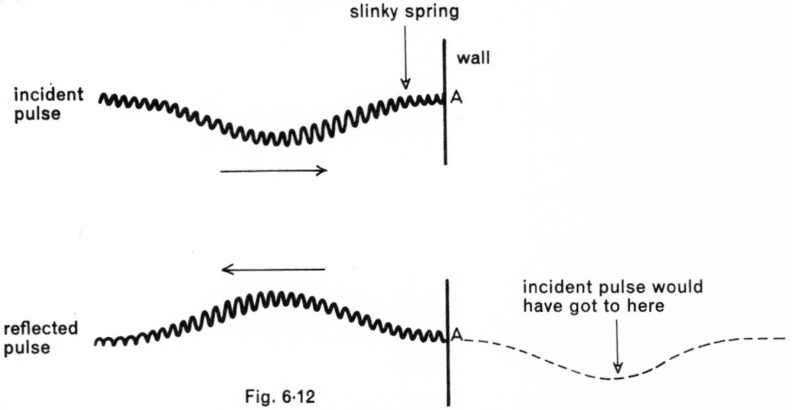

Fig. 6·12

A, the end of the spring fixed to the wall, can never move – it is a node. Notice that the reflected pulse is inverted.

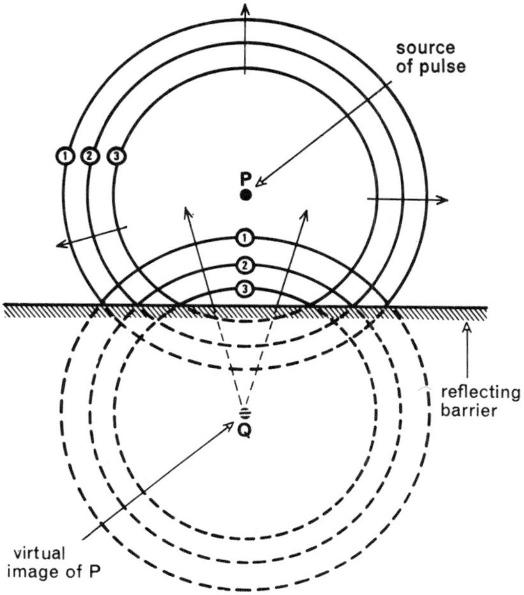

Fig. 6·13

The **image** of the point source P is that point from which the wavefronts seem to come after reflection (see p. 185). The full lines represent

(*i*) wavefronts from P, circles centre P, before reflection,
(*ii*) wavefronts after reflection, circles centre Q, i.e. wavefronts *seeming* to come from Q.

Distance from P to barrier = distance from Q to barrier.

Total internal reflection (see p. 193). Radio waves are totally reflected by layers in the ionosphere, high in the Earth's atmosphere, and this enables radio waves to be transmitted to places beyond the visible horizon.

(b) Reflection at spherical reflecting surfaces

Two diagrams are best drawn to represent the position of the wavefronts before reflection and after reflection. For convenience, only a part of a circular wavefront is sometimes drawn. In Fig. 6.14 the source is at the centre of the circle of which the barrier forms a part. The reflected waves pass through the same point, forming there a **real image.**

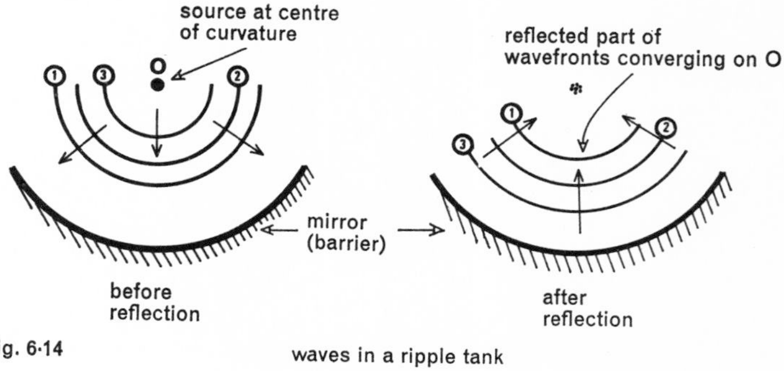

Fig. 6·14

In Fig. 6.15 the waves are focused at F, forming there an image of a distant source. As a considerable amount of energy is thus concentrated on F, a detector at F could record the arrival of very weak wavefronts. This idea is used, for example, when radar waves are used to detect aeroplanes.

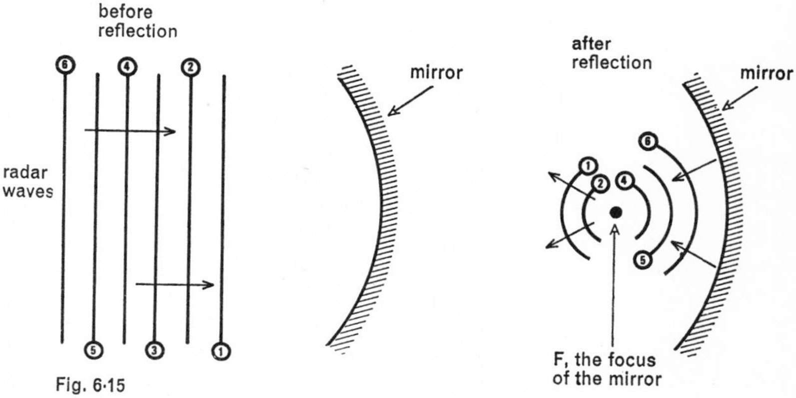

Fig. 6·15

If a source is placed at F the reflected wavefront is approximately plane, and thus the energy of the wave travels in one direction and does not spread out. This idea is used with light waves in such devices as searchlights.

6.8 REFRACTION

When a wave is refracted at the boundary between two media, the speed of the wave alters as it enters the second medium (see p. 189).

(a) At plane refracting boundaries

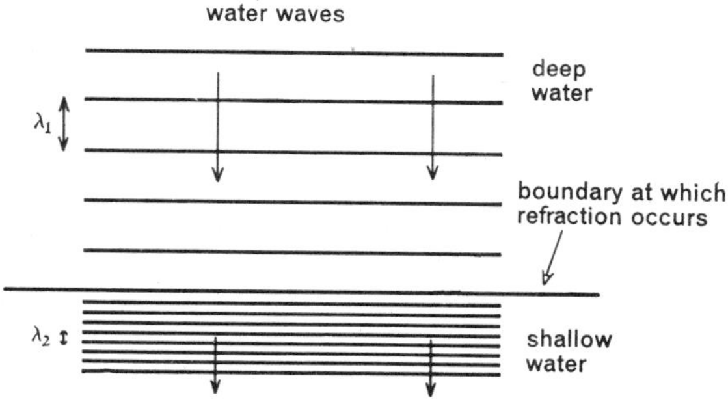

Fig. 6·16

Snell's Law:

The wavefronts are closer together in the shallow water than in the deep water. Therefore

$$\lambda_2 \text{ in shallow water} < \lambda_1 \text{ in deep water;}$$

But
$$c = f\lambda,$$

$\therefore$
$$c_2 \text{ in shallow water} < c_1 \text{ in deep water.}$$

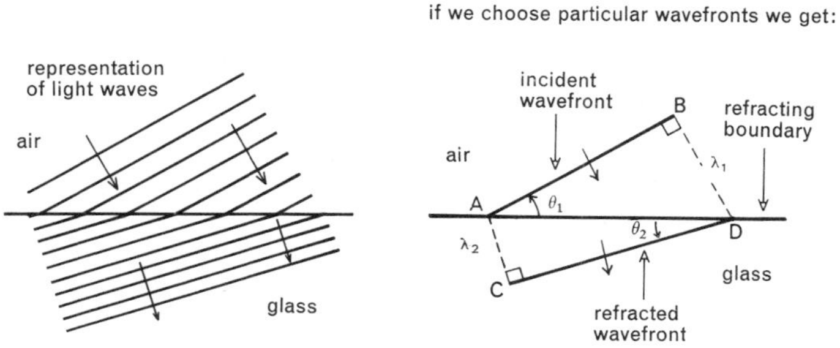

Fig. 6·17 Proof of Snell's Law of refraction

In Fig. 6.17 a wave in air is bent when it passes into glass, and, as for the ripple tank, c_1 and c_2 are the velocities of the waves before and after the refraction.

Consider a time interval $\frac{1}{f}$, so that

$$BD = \lambda_1,$$
$$AC = \lambda_2.$$

In the right-angled triangles ABD and ACD,

$$\sin \theta_1 = \frac{\lambda_1}{AD}, \quad \sin \theta_2 = \frac{\lambda_2}{AD},$$

$$\frac{\sin \theta_1}{\sin \theta_2} = \frac{\lambda_1}{AD} \times \frac{AD}{\lambda_2} = \frac{\lambda_1}{\lambda_2}.$$

$$\frac{\sin \theta_1}{\sin \theta_2} = \frac{\lambda_1}{\lambda_2} = \text{a constant for two given media.}$$

This is **Snell's Law.**

In a ripple tank, λ_1 and λ_2 can be measured directly and the law can be tested. As $c = f\lambda$, then the ratio λ_1/λ_2 = the ratio c_1/c_2. Direct measurements of c_1 and c_2 for light waves in air and some other medium enable us to test the law.

Real and apparent 'depth' (see p. 191). The wavefronts *seem* to come

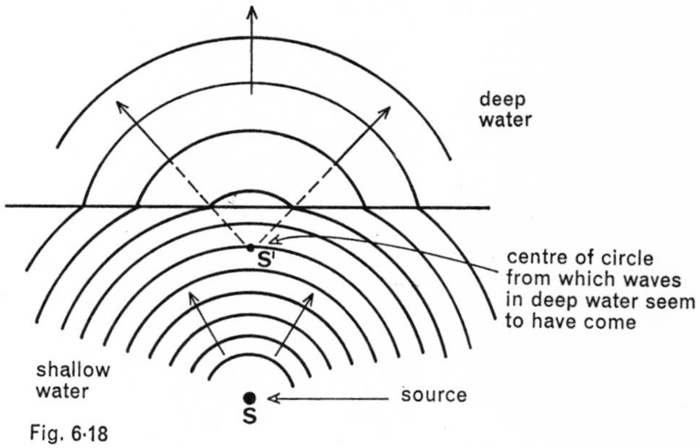

Fig. 6·18

from S′, that is, they are parts of circles centred on S′, which is a *virtual* image of the source S.

(b) At spherical refracting boundaries

Lenses. Lenses can be used with both light waves and sound waves. In the latter case the waves which hit a carbon dioxide lens travel more slowly in carbon dioxide than in air. The sound energy is focused at P after passing through the lens, and P is a real image of the source S. Any refracting device of this shape which can achieve such a focusing is called a *lens*.

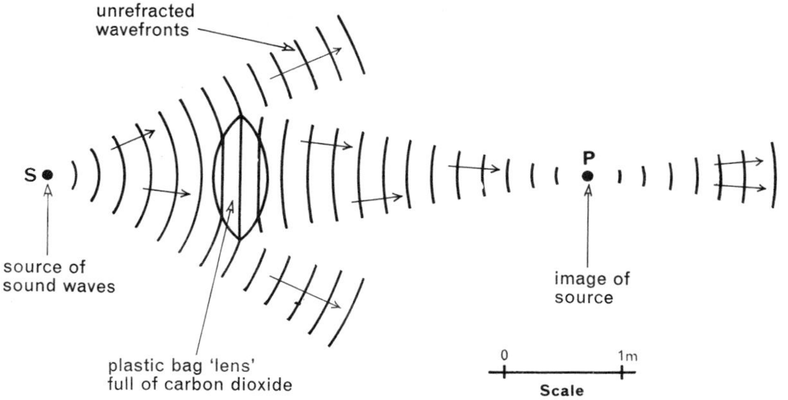

Fig. 6·19

(c) Dispersion of waves (see p. 196)
Dispersion occurs for light waves, but not for audible sound waves.

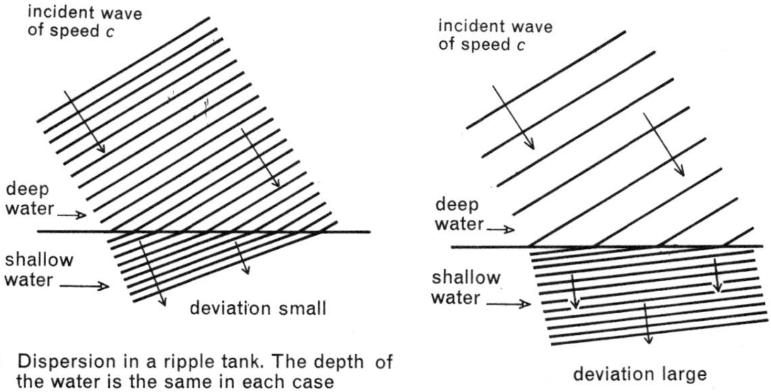

Fig. 6·20 Dispersion in a ripple tank. The depth of the water is the same in each case

6.9 DIFFRACTION

In a ripple tank it can be seen that the amount of diffraction at a gap, that is, the degree to which the waves extend beyond the expected region into the 'shadow', depends upon the *ratio of the size of the gap to the wavelength of the waves*. For sound waves and light waves this dependence enables an estimate of the order of magnitude of the wavelength to be made. See Figs. 6.21 and 6.22.

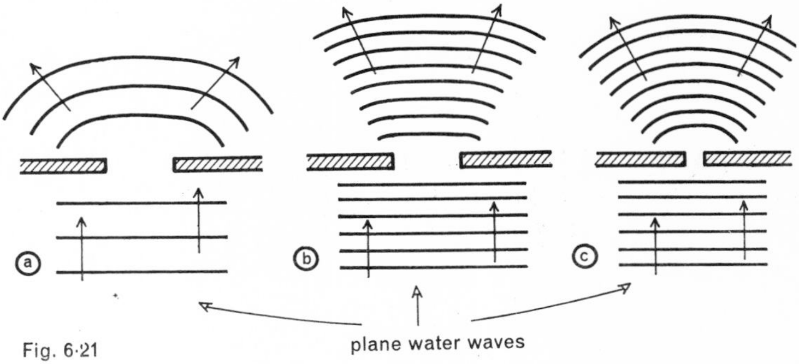
a
b
c
plane water waves

Fig. 6·21

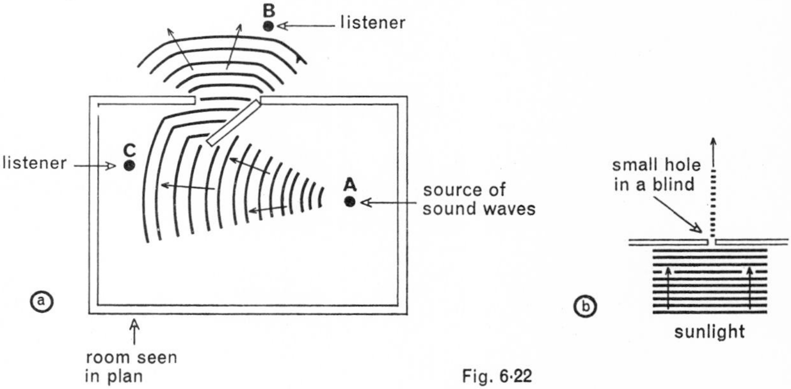
B
listener
C
listener
A
source of
sound waves
a
room seen
in plan
small hole
in a blind
b
sunlight

Fig. 6·22

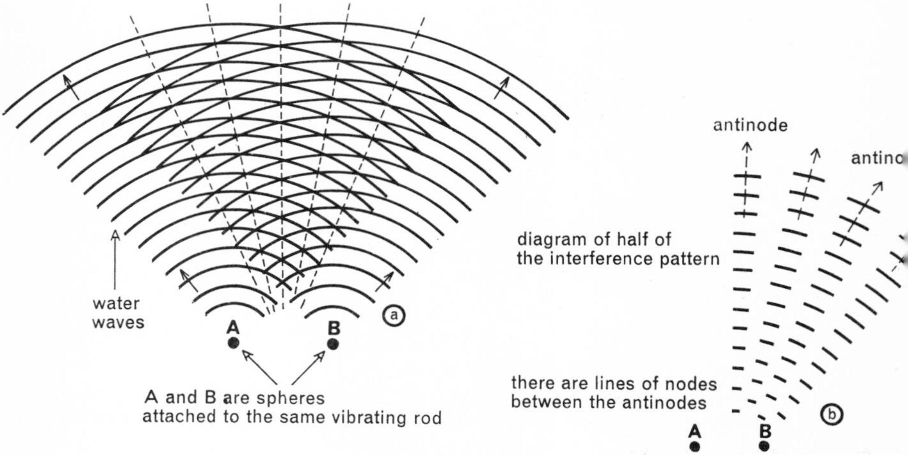
water
waves
A
B
a
A and B are spheres
attached to the same vibrating rod
antinode
diagram of half of
the interference pattern
there are lines of nodes
between the antinodes
A
B
b

Fig. 6·23

In Fig. 6.22(*a*) a person at B can hear a person at A talking, as can the person at C. In (*b*) the noticeable spreading is very slight. We conclude that sound waves have wavelengths very much greater than those of light waves.

6.10 INTERFERENCE PATTERNS

When each of two sources produces periodic waves of the same frequency, the region in which the wavefronts overlap exhibits a pattern of nodes and antinodes. It is called an **interference pattern.** The nodes and antinodes are the result of the *superposition* of the waves from the two sources.

Such a pattern can be produced by:

(*a*) Two prongs in a ripple tank. The pattern can be distinguished without the use of a stroboscope.
(*b*) A tuning fork. The pattern is heard by rotating the tuning fork slowly close to one ear.

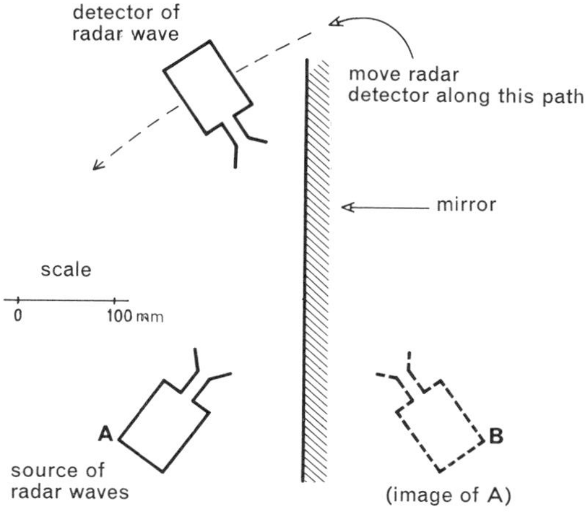

Fig. 6·24

(*c*) A source of radar waves and the waves seeming to come from the image of the source in a plane mirror. Several nodes and antinodes can be detected in the region of the detector.
(*d*) A source of light which produces two sources by diffraction through two very narrow close slits.

In each case the distance between adjacent nodes as one moves across the interference pattern increases further away from the two sources.

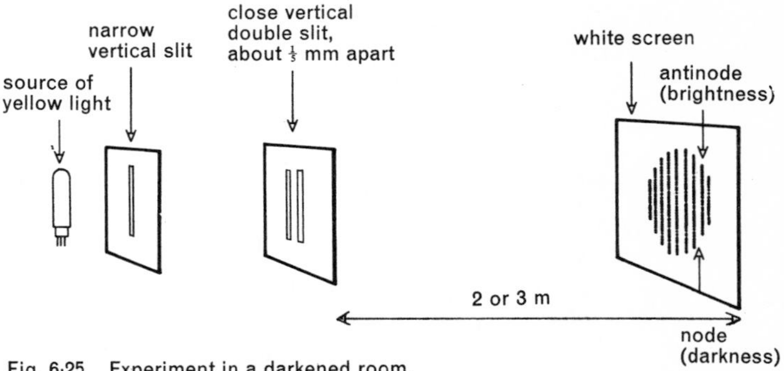

Fig. 6·25 Experiment in a darkened room.
The nodes are separated by a few mm

The experimental arrangements can be interchanged: e.g. the mirror technique could be used for water waves or the two-slit diffraction used for radar waves, etc.

6.11 STATIONARY WAVES (standing waves)

If tuning forks A and B send identical waves towards one another along a string and the distance between A and B is suitably adjusted, a pattern emerges. P is always at rest (a *node*) and Q undergoes a violent displacement (an *antinode*). As the eye retains an image on its retina for about $\frac{1}{20}$ of a second, a person viewing the string will see the nodes and antinodes without the use of a stroboscope.

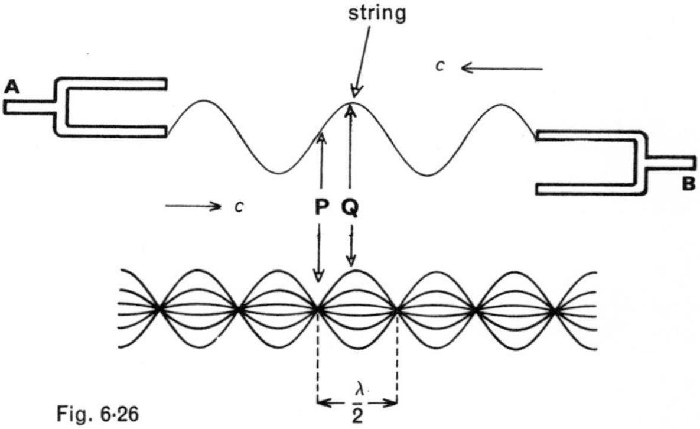

Fig. 6·26

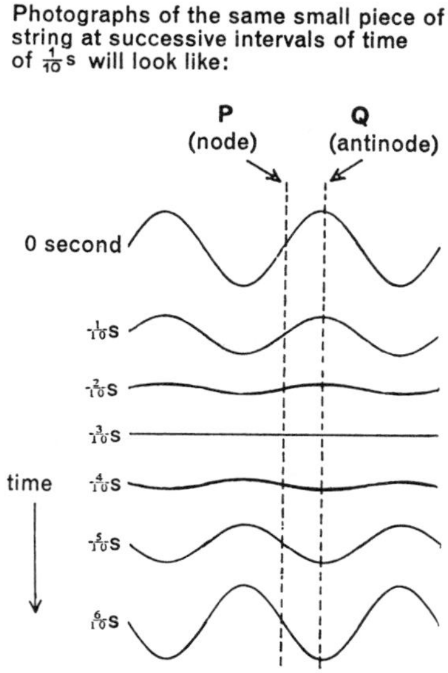

Photographs of the same small piece of string at successive intervals of time of $\frac{1}{10}$ s will look like:

$\frac{1}{10}$s

Fig. 6·27

$$\text{The distance between adjacent nodes} = \tfrac{1}{2}\,(\text{wavelength}) = \frac{\lambda}{2}.$$

In a ripple tank, or using radar waves, stationary wave patterns can be produced by reflecting plane waves at normal incidence. The resulting nodes and antinodes are common features in many wave experiments owing to unwanted stray reflections.

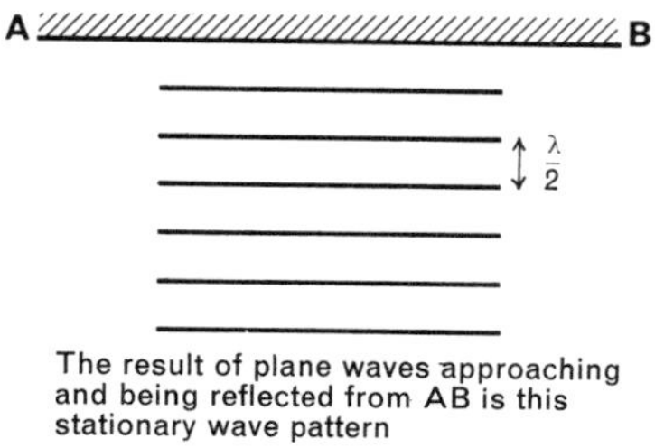

A
B
$\frac{\lambda}{2}$
The result of plane waves approaching and being reflected from AB is this stationary wave pattern

Fig. 6·28 Ripple tank or radar waves

For sound waves, see p. 169.

6.12 THE DIFFRACTION GRATING

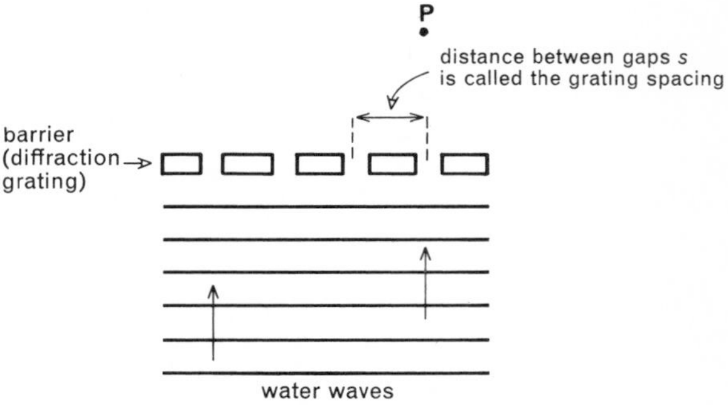

Fig. 6·29 A diffraction grating

When plane water waves reach a diffraction grating, *each* gap will result in a large amount of diffraction. Beyond the barrier, at P for example, wavefronts will be arriving from each gap. At P the *Principle of Superposition* will apply. The result is very complex.

At large distances from the barrier, however, a simple pattern emerges, with plane wavefronts travelling in only a few *directions*. In the other directions the result of superposition is zero.

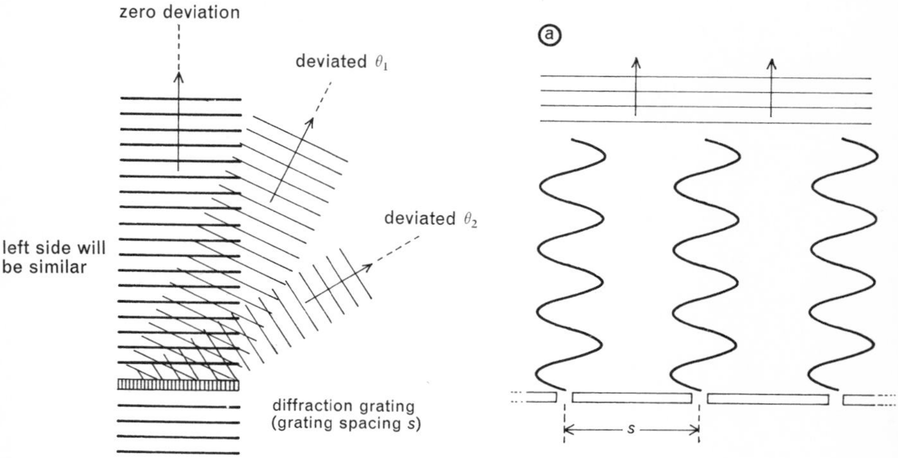

Fig. 6·30

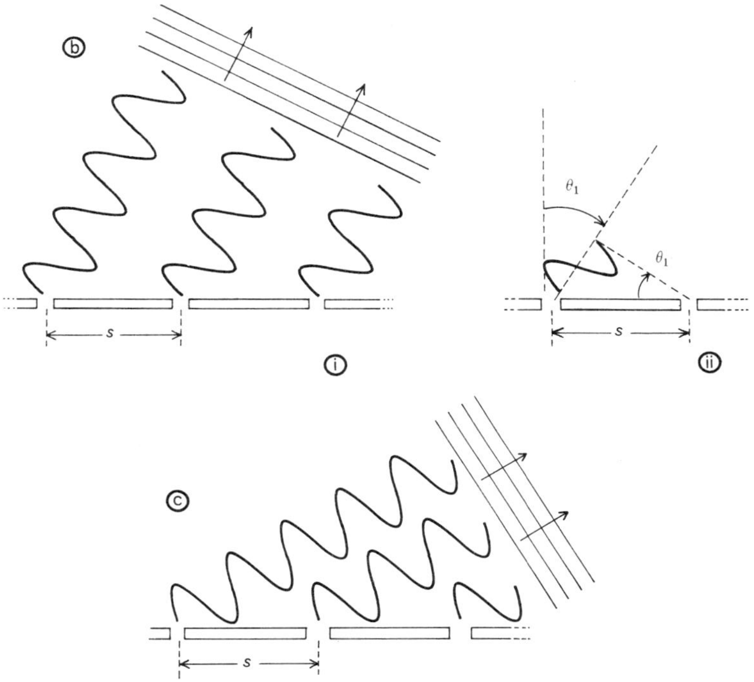

Fig. 6·30 cont.

In Fig. 6.30 the waves from adjacent gaps travel

(*a*) equal distances,
(*b*) distances which differ by λ, their wavelength,
(*c*) distances which differ by 2λ, etc.

Thus the directions of emerging waves are given by

(*a*) zero deviation,

(*b*) $\sin\theta_1 = \dfrac{\lambda}{s}$ (see Fig. 6.30*b*(*ii*)),

(*c*) $\sin\theta_2 = \dfrac{2\lambda}{s}$, etc.

The main deviated wave (θ_1) can be used to measure λ if s is known, since

$$\boxed{\lambda = s \sin\theta_1.}$$

Diffraction gratings can be made for all wave motions, radar, sound, visible light, X-rays, etc. For light the grating spacing must be very small, of the order of 10^{-6} m.

The wave nature of sound

6.13 SOUND WAVES

Sound is a longitudinal mechanical wave motion (see p. 145). The energy of a sound wave comes from the mechanical energy of a vibrating source, such as a gong or violin string, and eventually becomes internal energy.

Sound requires a *material medium* (solid, liquid or gas) for its transmission. To demonstrate that *sound cannot travel through a vacuum,* place an electric bell in an airtight container. Remove the air, and watch the bell. The clapper continues to vibrate, but the sound, as heard by the listener, diminishes. The bell is again heard when the air is returned.

A source of sound *vibrates.* To demonstrate this:

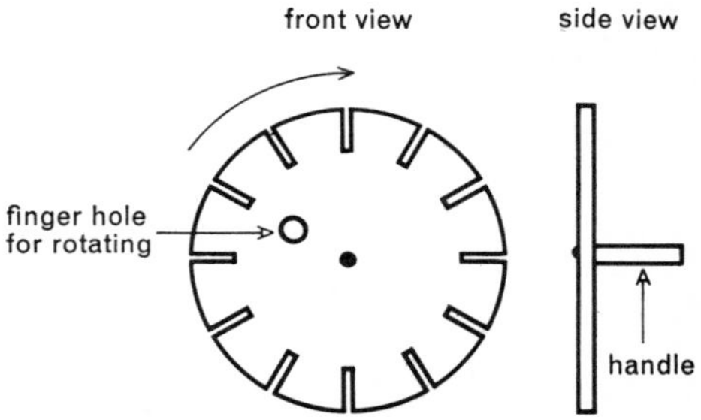

Fig. 6·31 A stroboscope

(*a*) bring a suspended pith ball close to the source and observe its movement,

(*b*) use a **stroboscope.** Hold the stroboscope between the eye and vibrating source, and rotate it. The eye sees the source at successive time intervals, and if it is vibrating it is possible to 'freeze' it by a suitable adjustment of the speed of rotation. The action is helped by the fact that each glimpse remains on the retina of the eye for longer than $\frac{1}{20}$ of a second (see p. 208). A similar freezing can be achieved by using a lamp flashing at the right frequency.

The *reflection, refraction,* and *diffraction* of sound waves, and the *interference pattern from two identical sources,* are outlined in paragraphs 6.7 to 6.10.

The dispersion of sound waves is negligible, i.e. all audible sound waves have the same speed in air – the notes of both high and low frequency from a distant band are heard in time.

6.14 SOUND WAVES IN AIR

Air molecules are in a state of continual random motion (see p. 31). A sound wave superimposed on this produces a series of **rarefactions** and **compressions.** These are sometimes represented as shown in Fig. 6.32*a*. The displacement of the air layers is usually represented as in

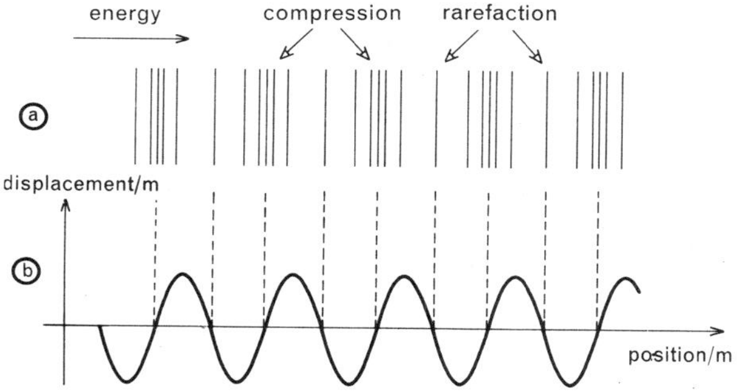

Fig. 6·32 Representation of sound waves in air

Fig. 6.32*b*, by a 'photograph'. Displacement–time curves for a given layer of air are also used (see Fig. 6.35). We detect these displacements with the *ear*. The ear is not sensitive enough to hear the *random motion* of the air molecules: it can, however, be heard if it is amplified, e.g. by a sea shell.

The ear is only sensitive over a limited range of frequencies: the normal limits are

(*a*) lower: 20 Hz, (*b*) upper: 20 000 Hz,

although the upper limit drops with age.

In this **audible range** the ear judges the *ratio* of the loudness of two sounds. The **loudness** of a sound wave is a measure of the power stimulating the ear. It is proportional to

(*i*) $(\text{frequency})^2$, (*ii*) $(\text{amplitude})^2$.

Both these factors are represented on a displacement–time graph for a layer of air.

6.15 $c = f\lambda$: MEASUREMENTS IN SOUND

Speed

(*a*) *Assume* light travels instantaneously. Use the time interval t between the arrival of the flash and the bang produced by a gun at a known distance d from an observer.

$$\text{speed } c = \frac{d}{t}.$$

In order to eliminate the effect of any wind, c should be measured for the sound travelling *each* way, and an average taken.

(*b*) *Echoes.* A sound heard by reflection is called an **echo.** Stand a distance d from a reflecting surface and clap two pieces of wood together N times in a time t so as to make each clap coincide with the echo of the previous clap. This establishes that sound travels a distance $2d$ in a time t/N.

$$\text{speed } c = \frac{2d}{t/N}.$$

$$c = \frac{2dN}{t}.$$

The speed c

(*i*) increases as the *temperature* of the air increases,
(*ii*) does not depend on the *pressure* of the air.

If the speed c is known, then distances can be found by using echo techniques, and applying $c = \dfrac{2dN}{t}$.

Applications

(*i*) depth sounding,
(*ii*) navigation (as used by bats).

The *speed of sound in air* at $0\,^\circ\mathrm{C} = 331$ m/s.

Frequency

(*a*) 'Freeze' the source with a *stroboscopic device.* If a stroboscope with N slits can freeze a source when turning at a rotational frequency n, and yet *cannot* do so when turning at a rotational frequency $2n$, then the frequency of the source, and thus of the periodic wave it produces, is nN.

(*b*) Compare the pitch of a note (see p. 170) with that of a series of standard tuning forks, a siren, an audiofrequency oscillator and loudspeaker, or a sonometer (see p. 173).

Wavelength

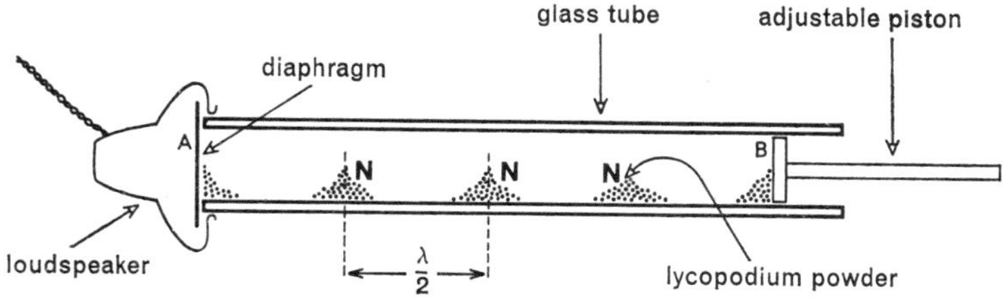

Fig. 6·33 A stationary wave pattern; N are nodes

(*a*) Set up a stationary wave pattern within a glass tube. Measure $\lambda/2$, the distance between successive nodes of the stationary wave pattern (standing wave pattern). The longitudinal wave at A is produced by the vibrating diaphragm of a loudspeaker driven by an oscillator of variable frequency. The wave is reflected at the face of the piston B, whose position can be adjusted. The powder is buffeted *away from* the antinodes of violent displacement when a stationary wave pattern is achieved.

(*b*) Use a resonance tube (see p. 171).

6.16 MUSICAL NOTES

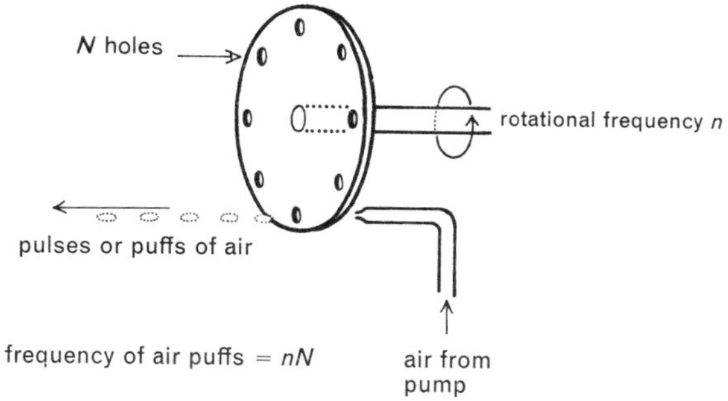

Fig. 6·34 A siren

A **musical note,** henceforth called a **note,** is produced by a siren when the disc is driven at a uniform rate. If the holes are regularly spaced a note of frequency Nn is heard.

A **noise** is heard if the holes are irregularly spaced.

The **pitch** of a note depends on its frequency. If the frequency increases then the pitch rises. If the frequency doubles, then the pitch of the note rises one **octave.**

The **loudness** of a note is explained on p. 167. It also depends on the sensitivity of the ear to the pitch of the particular note.

The **quality** of a note depends upon the number, pitch and loudness of the harmonics or overtones (see p. 172) accompanying the note. The note itself is called the **fundamental tone,** or **first harmonic.** The displacements of all the contributions add according to the principle of superposition: the resulting displacement–time curves are called **waveforms,** and show obvious differences.

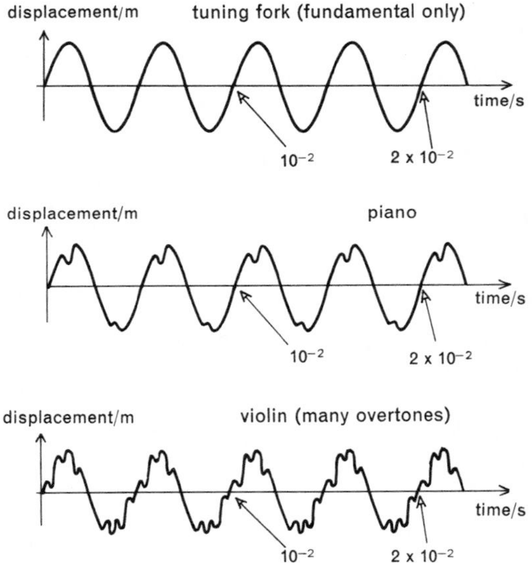

Fig. 6·35 Waveforms for sound waves from three different sources

6.17 RESONANCE AND VIBRATING AIR COLUMNS

If a vibrating source is placed near a system, and the frequency of the source is related in a simple way to the natural frequency of the system, the system is set into sympathetic vibration. The amplitude of this vibration builds up: this phenomenon is called **resonance.** The energy of the resonant system can be useful, but in some cases the amplitude reaches a magnitude which breaks the resonating system.

Examples

(*a*) A vibrating tuning fork and the air in a milk bottle.
(*b*) A diver jumping on a springboard.
(*c*) Radio waves stimulating the charge in an electrical circuit to oscillate.
(*d*) A soprano causing a wine glass to shatter.

Resonance can be *used* in sound to pick out and amplify a note of a certain frequency by having a system whose resonant frequency can be varied. Sometimes a given system can be set into resonant vibration, using a source of variable frequency as in (*d*) above.

If a vibrating source is placed in contact with a system which does not resonate, the source will nevertheless force the system to vibrate. These **forced vibrations** are of the same frequency as that of the source. They can be useful, e.g. in the sounding board of a pianoforte, where they set a larger body of air into vibration than the vibrating string would have done by itself (hence piano*forte*).

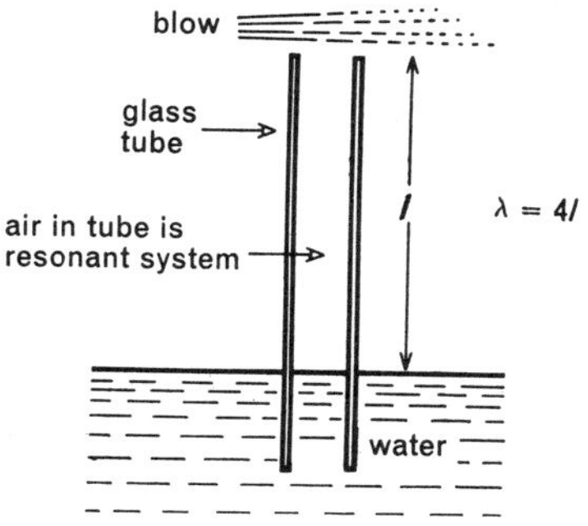

Fig. 6·36 A closed resonance tube

Closed resonance tubes

The length of the tube, and thus of the air it contains, can be altered. The wavelength λ of the fundamental note is $4l$, where l is the length of the air column in the tube.

$$\lambda = 4l$$

Overtones with 3 ×, 5 ×, 7 ×, etc., the fundamental frequency also produce resonance, and they affect the *quality* of the note heard. For *open ended tubes* the frequencies of the overtones are 2 ×, 3 ×, 4 ×, 5 ×, etc., the fundamental frequency. (See Fig. 6.37.)

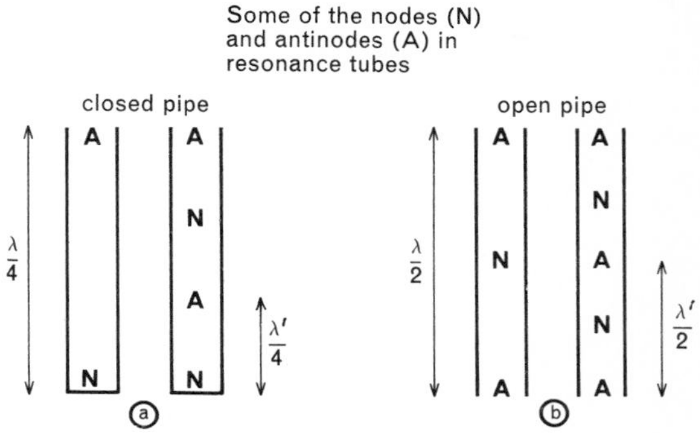

Fig. 6·37 The stationary wave patterns produce nodes separated by ½ (wavelength)

The resonance of air columns is important for the design of all *musical wind instruments:* each instrument is a resonant system with either

(*a*) a fixed set of notes available, as in the flute, *or*
(*b*) a fully variable arrangement, as in the trombone.

The exact design of the instrument, i.e.

(*i*) its shape,
(*ii*) the materials of which it is made,

and the way in which it is used, all help to determine the amplitude of the overtones and thus the characteristic sound that it gives.

6.18 VIBRATING STRINGS

A stationary wave can be produced on a stretched string (see p. 162). For a string fixed at both ends, and stimulated by a bow or by plucking, each end must be a node. The possible modes (ways) of vibration of the string are shown in Fig. 6.38. The *overtones* or *harmonics* are seen to be notes whose frequencies are whole-number multiples of the fundamental frequency $f_\circ$. The frequencies of the notes produced are those of the string. Musically:

$f_\circ$	$2f_\circ$	$3f_\circ$	$4f_\circ$	
doh	doh′	soh′	doh″,	etc.

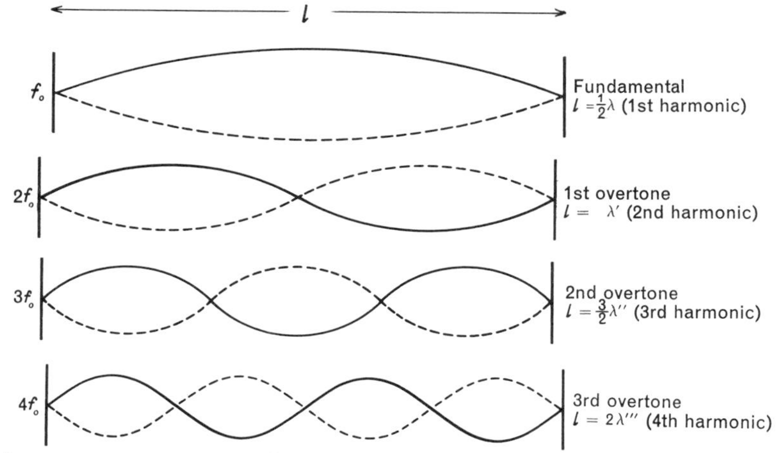

Fig. 6·38

The **sonometer** is an instrument with a stretched string PQ of variable length and controllable tension. If f_o is the fundamental frequency of the string, then

$$f_o . l = \text{constant for a given tension.}$$

A sonometer

Fig. 6·39

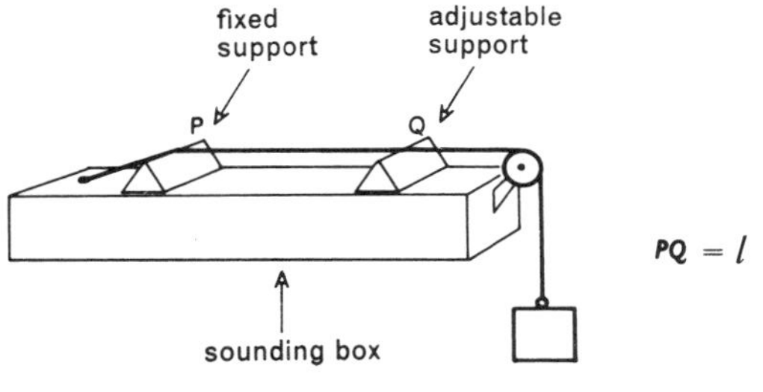

A sonometer can be used to find the frequency of a note, by comparing it with f_o. All *musical stringed instruments* are basically sonometers, the length *PQ* being either

(*a*) set to give a number of fixed notes, as in the guitar, or
(*b*) fully variable, as in the violin.

The exact design of the instrument determines the importance of the various overtones: these in turn determine the *quality* of the note that the instrument produces, and give it its character.

Light waves and the electromagnetic spectrum

6.19 LIGHT WAVES

Light is a transverse electromagnetic wave motion (see p. 145). The energy of the light wave comes from changes in the electrical energy within atoms and molecules.

Light can travel through a vacuum, so we receive light from distant stars.

The *reflection, refraction, dispersion,* and *diffraction* of light waves, and the *interference pattern from two identical sources* are all outlined in paragraphs 6.7 to 6.10.

We detect light waves with the *eye*, although they may also be detected by

(*a*) their heating effect,
(*b*) their ability to cause a chemical reaction, as in photographic devices,
(*c*) their ability to cause photoelectric emission from the surfaces of certain metals (electrons receive enough energy to leave the surface).

The **eye** is sensitive over a limited range of frequencies which correspond to wavelengths in air of

$$4 \times 10^{-7}\,\text{m} \quad \text{(lower limit),}$$
$$7 \times 10^{-7}\,\text{m} \quad \text{(upper limit).}$$

The sensitivity of the eye to the power of a light wave varies over this visible range. It is *most* sensitive at about $5{\cdot}5 \times 10^{-7}$ m (yellow–green).

Light is a part of the electromagnetic spectrum (see p. 177).

6.20 $c = f\lambda$: MEASUREMENTS IN LIGHT

Speed

An *echo* method (see p. 168) can be used, provided that the light can be reflected from a very distant mirror. The small time taken can be measured with the aid of a motor-driven stroboscope.

The *speed of light energy in a vacuum* $= 3{\cdot}00 \times 10^8$ m/s, and is less in water, glass and all other media.

A knowledge of the speed of radar waves in air, which is the same as the speed of light waves in air, enables radar to be used as a ranging technique.

Frequency

Use $c = f\lambda$, when c is known, and λ measured.

Wavelength

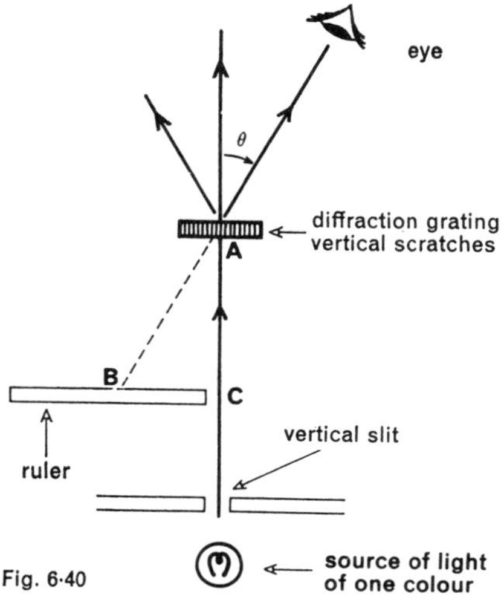

Fig. 6·40

Use a diffraction grating (see p. 164). For light the grating spacing s must be very small, of the order of 10^{-6} m. This would be produced by scratching, say, 500 parallel straight lines within a width of 1 mm; the light passes through the gaps between these lines and is diffracted. The source, a slit, is arranged to be parallel to the scratches on the grating. Measure AB and BC:

$$\sin\theta = \frac{BC}{AB}.$$

Measure s by calibrating the grating with a light of known wavelength (see p. 18), or use the data provided by the manufacturer.

$$\sin\theta = \frac{\lambda}{s},$$

so λ can be calculated. This experiment, by actually measuring λ, convincingly demonstrates the *wave nature of light*.

6.21 COLOUR AND THE ELECTROMAGNETIC SPECTRUM

If **white light** from a filament lamp or the Sun is used with a diffraction grating, a **spectrum** of colours results. We can deduce that every colour of light has a different frequency, since this experiment shows that each colour has a different wavelength in air.

Colour	violet	indigo	blue	green	yellow	orange	red
λ/m	4×10^{-7}	⟶	5×10^{-7}		⟶	6×10^{-7}	7×10^{-7}

If a hole is made in the screen, and the light passing through is allowed to fall on another grating, no new colours are then produced.

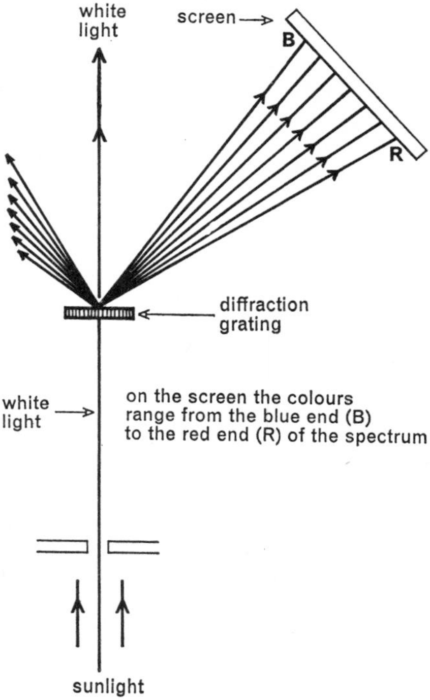

Fig. 6·41 The spectrum of white light

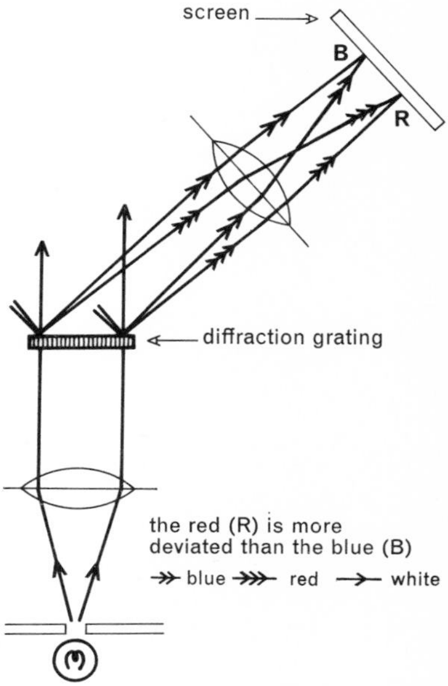

Fig. 6·42 Production of a pure spectrum

A **pure spectrum** can be formed by the additional use of two converging lenses. In Fig. 6.42 the light hitting any part of the screen is of one wavelength only – there is no overlapping.

Spectra

Different substances when gaseous (so that their atoms are far enough apart not to affect each other) produce light of certain wavelengths only. These spectra can be used to *identify* the elements in chemical compounds, or in mixtures, even when they are present in only very small quantities.

All *electromagnetic waves* travel in a vacuum with the same speed as light, and are caused by similar processes (see p. 146). The spectrum of these waves over a wide range of frequencies (and wavelengths in air) is shown opposite:

	high frequency							*low frequency*
	γ-rays	X-rays	ultra-violet waves	LIGHT	infra-red waves	microwaves	radio waves	a.c.
f/Hz	10^{21} 10^{19} 10^{17} 10^{15} 10^{13} 10^{11} 10^{9} 10^{7} 10^{5} 10^{3} 10^{1}							
λ/m	10^{-13} 10^{-11} 10^{-9} 10^{-7} 10^{-5} 10^{-3} 10^{-1} 10^{1} 10^{3} 10^{5} 10^{7}							
produced by	radio-active nuclei	electrons hitting hard targets		see page 174		oscillating electrons		rotating coils
detected by			chemical plates				free electrons in aerials	

The divisions are not exact, any more than are the colours of the visible spectrum – one colour grades into the next imperceptibly.

6.22 ULTRA-VIOLET AND INFRA-RED WAVES

Ultra-violet

Production

Ultra-violet waves are produced by very hot bodies. Any body hotter than white hot (about 6000 K) emits a large proportion of such waves. In the laboratory a mercury vapour lamp is the most common source.

Detection

Ultra-violet waves can be detected by

(*a*) photographic plates,
(*b*) their ability to cause fluorescence in certain substances, such as

diamond and paraffin oil, i.e. to stimulate these substances to emit visible waves when they absorb ultra-violet waves,
(*c*) photocells,
(*d*) thermometers.

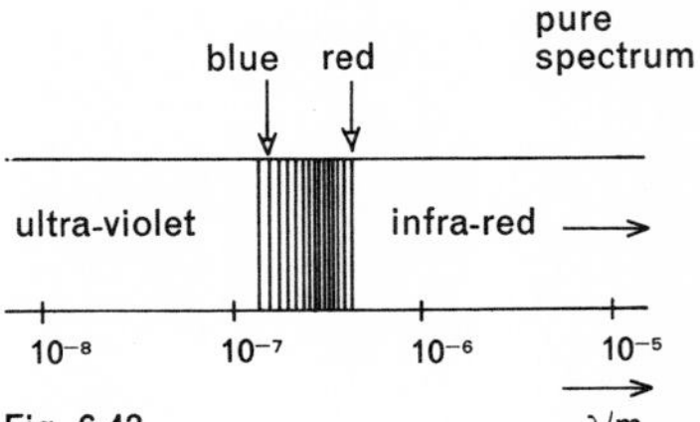

Fig. 6·43

Uses
Ultra-violet waves are

(*a*) used in the coating of fluorescent lamps to increase the percentage of available energy which becomes visible light energy,
(*b*) useful for producing vitamin D in the human body. They also tan the skin, but would be dangerous to us if they were not absorbed strongly by the Earth's atmosphere.

Infra-red

Production
All bodies emit infra-red waves all the time. As the temperature of the body rises (*a*) it emits more radiation and (*b*) it emits waves of shorter wavelength. Below about 800 K the wavelengths are such that the radiation is not visible.

Detection
Infra-red waves can be detected by

(*a*) thermometers,
(*b*) the human skin,
(*c*) photoconductive cells,
(*d*) thermopiles (see p. 143),
(*e*) photographic plates.

Uses
Infra-red waves are used

(*a*) to treat certain muscular disorders,
(*b*) to take photographs through haze or slight fog (since they are less scattered than visible light),

(*c*) to detect hot or relatively hot bodies; e.g.
  (*i*) a missile tracking a jet aircraft by tracing the infra-red waves,
  (*ii*) investigating where a given system has high surface temperatures.

When ultra-violet or infra-red radiation are dispersed, care must be taken to ensure that the prism or diffraction grating and any associated lenses do not absorb the radiation.

It must be stressed that the divisions in the electromagnetic spectrum, as between, for example, ultra-violet – visible light – infra-red, are arbitrary, and do *not* represent any sudden changes in the general properties of the waves.

7 Geometrical optics

The rectilinear propagation of light

7.1 INTRODUCTION

The study of *visible light* is the study of the type of energy that stimulates the retina of the human eye. A body is detected by the sense of sight only if light (energy) leaves the body and then enters the eye.

Self-luminous objects emit their own light.

Non-luminous (but illuminated) objects scatter into the eye the light which falls on them from self-luminous bodies.

Incandescent objects are self-luminous as a result of their being heated to 1100 K or more.

The *propagation* of light means its spreading out or travelling from one point to another.

A *medium* is a material (solid, liquid or gas) through which the light passes, although light can pass through a vacuum. Media can be

(*a*) *translucent* – light can pass through them, as it does through tissue paper,
(*b*) *transparent* – light passes through them so that we can see clearly objects on the other side, as it does through glass,
(*c*) *opaque* – light cannot penetrate. The thickness as well as the nature of the material will determine what fraction of the light can penetrate a specimen.

7.2 WAVES AND RAYS

Light is a wave motion. Fig. 7.1 shows a source of light emitting waves.

A **ray** is defined to be the direction of the path of light energy in travelling from one point to another. According to the **Principle of Reversibility,** rays can travel in either sense along a path known to be possible. An arrow on a ray shows the sense of travel of the energy.

A **beam** or **pencil** is a stream of light energy, which will be shown in a diagram by a number of rays. (Fig. 7.2.)

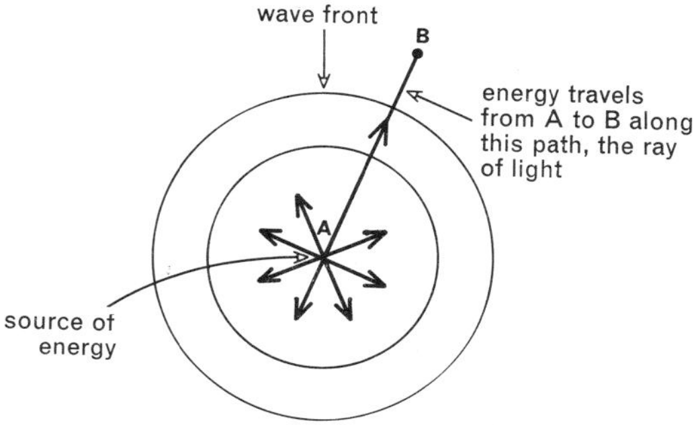

Fig. 7·1 A ray

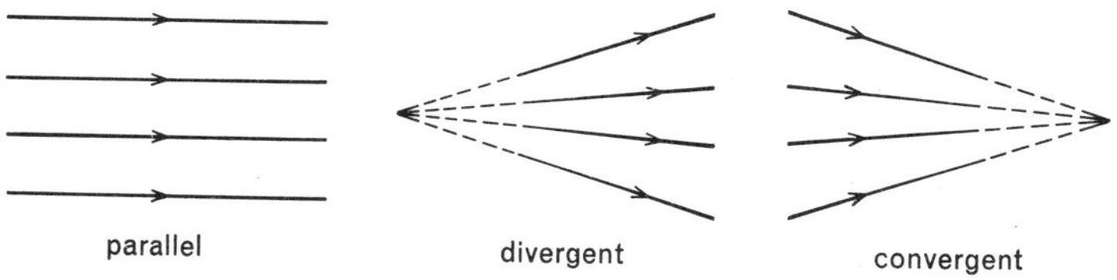

Fig. 7·2 Beams or pencils of light

7.3 RECTILINEAR PROPAGATION

A beam of light passing through dusty air has clearly defined straight edges, e.g. sunbeams. This suggests that light travels in straight lines, and this is confirmed by

(*a*) experiment (see Fig. 7.3),
(*b*) the pinhole camera,
(*c*) the formation of shadows and eclipses,
(*d*) the formation of images whose position and nature have been predicted on the assumption that light travels in straight lines.

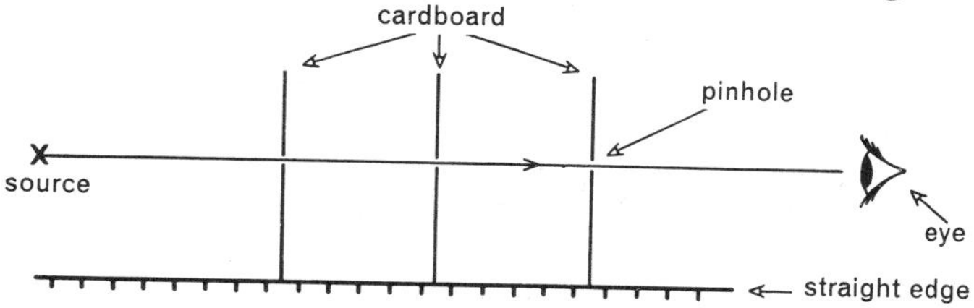

Fig. 7·3 To illustrate rectilinear propagation

Experiment

The source is only visible when the pinholes lie in the same straight line. That this is so can be checked by using a straight edge ruler or a taut string (but not of course by looking through the holes).

Nevertheless, because light is a wave motion, it can be made to show diffraction effects (see p. 159). The effects are not easily seen by the eye, because the wavelength is so small relative to the sizes of common objects, and the distances between objects.

Conclusion

The study of geometrical optics is based on this idea:

> **light travels in a straight line** in a particular medium, if we ignore diffraction effects. Of course its direction changes if it is reflected.

7.4 THE PINHOLE CAMERA

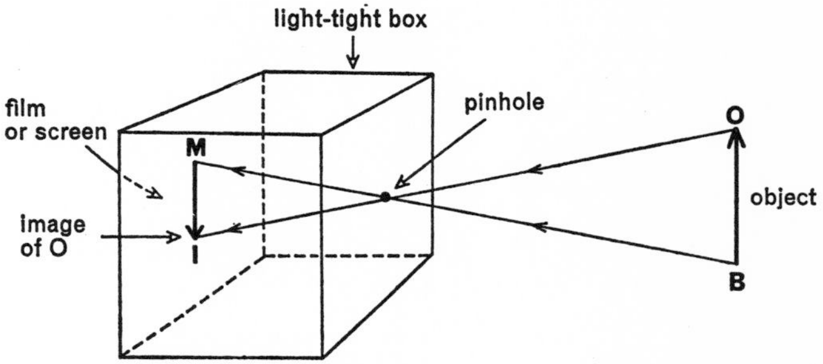

Fig. 7·4 Pinhole camera

This is additional evidence for rectilinear propagation.

Note: (*a*) The image is inverted.
(*b*) The image is always sharp if the hole is small.
(*c*) A small hole would give a clear but dim image if we could ignore diffraction.
(*d*) A bigger hole gives a brighter image, but with overlapping of the point images, and so the total effect is blurred.
(*e*) The shape of the hole is not important provided it is small enough.
(*f*) A longer box gives a larger image, but it is less bright.

7.5 FORMATION OF SHADOWS AND ECLIPSES

Terms

(*a*) The **umbra** is that part of the shadow from which no source of light energy can be seen. It will appear black if there is no stray light falling on it.

(*b*) The **penumbra** is that part of the shadow from which some, but not all, of the source can be seen.

Extended source

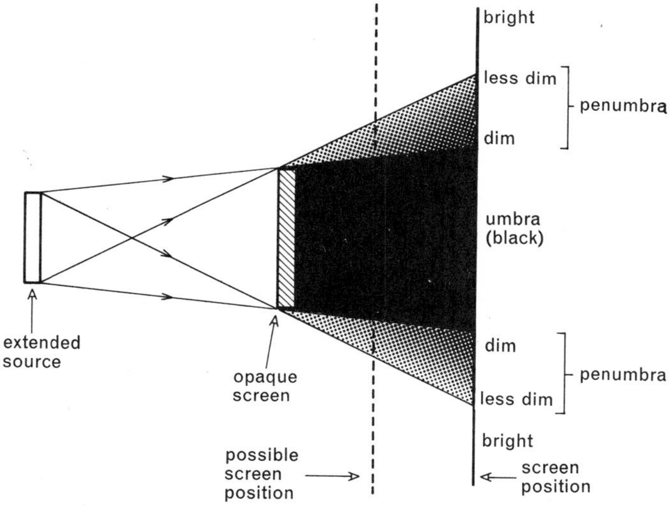

Fig. 7·5 Shadow from an extended source

The penumbra will appear shades of grey, as different parts are exposed to different fractions of the source.

Eclipses

(*a*) *Of the Moon* (Fig. 7.6)
These occur at the full Moon. Draw similar diagrams to show these phases of the Moon: new, first quarter, full, last quarter.

(*b*) *Of the Sun*

(*i*) Total eclipse
(*ii*) Annular eclipse

These occur at the new Moon, when the shadow of the Moon falls on the Earth.

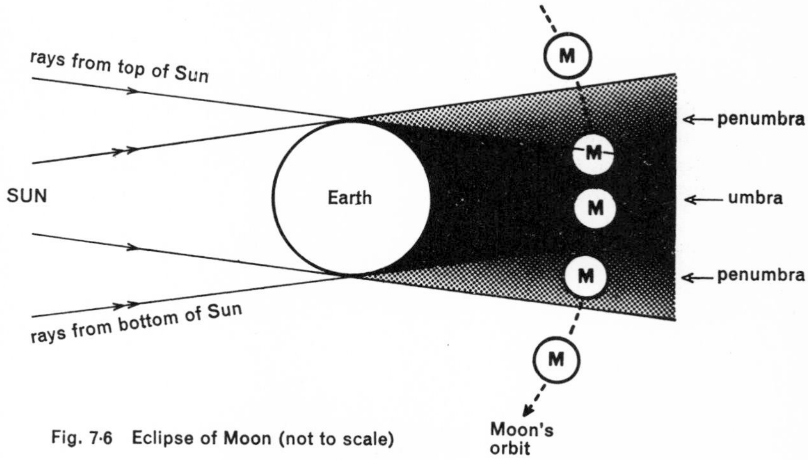

Fig. 7·6 Eclipse of Moon (not to scale)

Reflection at plane surfaces

7.6 LAWS OF REFLECTION

Since light travels in straight lines, once we have established the laws that control its change of direction on reflection and refraction, we shall be able to predict its behaviour under simple circumstances.

Laws of reflection

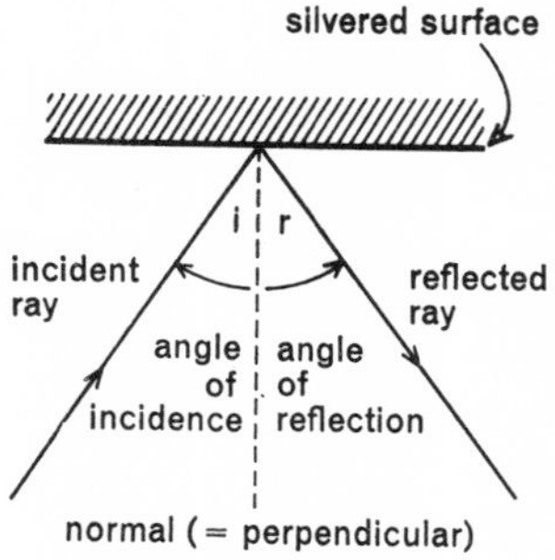

Fig. 7·7 The laws of reflection

> *Law I:* The reflected ray lies in the same plane as the incident ray and the normal at the point of incidence.

(This means that we can draw the ray diagrams on a flat piece of paper.)

Law II. The angle of reflection equals the angle of incidence.

The laws of reflection are obeyed under all circumstances.

Reflection and diffusion

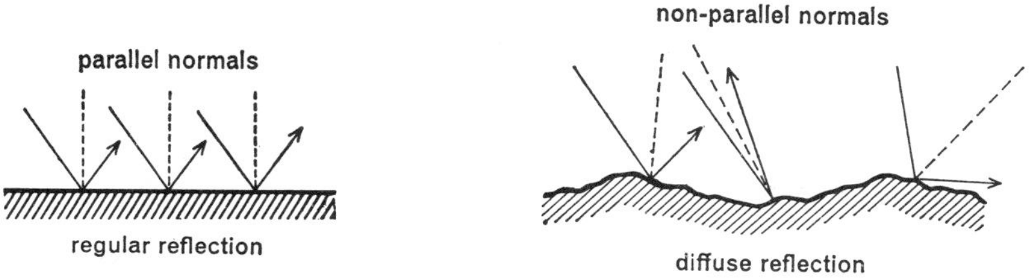

Fig. 7·8 The nature of the reflecting surface

Regular reflection occurs when nearly all the light incident on a surface from one direction is reflected into the same direction. The normals to the surface at all points are parallel.

Diffusion or **diffuse reflection** occurs when light is *scattered* at random in all directions from a comparatively rough surface.

7.7 THE IMAGE FORMED BY A PLANE MIRROR

For a full discussion of images, see page 197. In this case an image is the point from which rays of light that enter the eye seem to have originated.

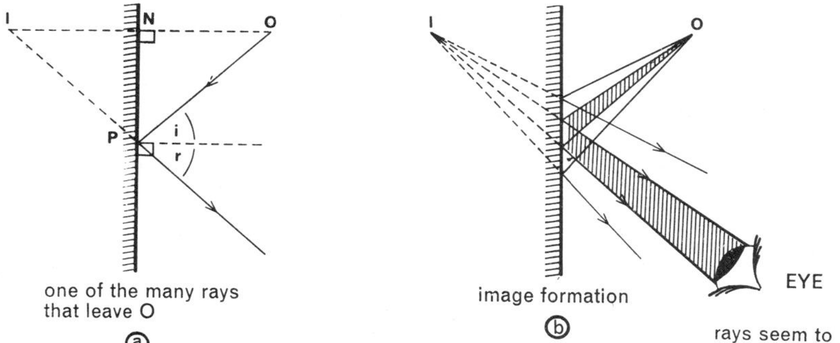

Fig. 7·9

Since $i = r$, triangles INP and ONP are congruent. Hence

$$IN = ON.$$

The diagram shows that I is the image of the point object O, because it is the point from which all the rays of light that enter the eye (after reflection at the mirror) seem to have come.

Note: (*a*) The image is erect relative to the object, and the same size.
(*b*) It is virtual – no light energy reaches the image, and thus it cannot be formed on a screen.
(*c*) It lies on the normal from O to the mirror, and is as far behind the mirror as the object is in front.
(*d*) It is laterally inverted. **Lateral inversion** occurs each time rays from one point on the object cross one another before they enter the eye.

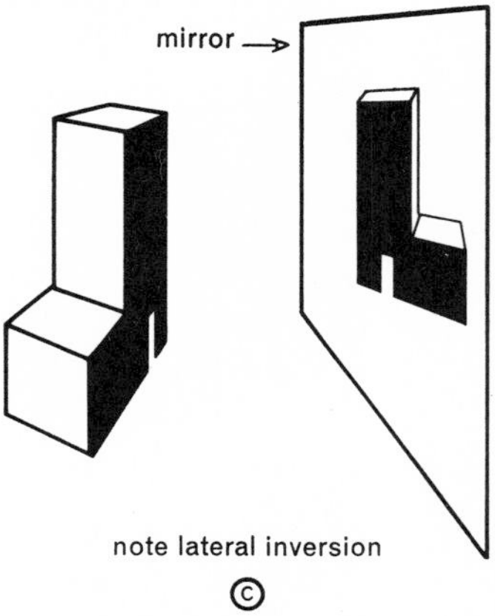

Fig. 7·9 cont. Image formed by a plane mirror

The location of such a virtual image can frequently be found by the **method of no-parallax.** Place an object pin in front of a plane mirror, and view its image which will be seen behind the mirror. Take a search pin, and place it so that it appears to be in line with the image of the object pin. If a slight movement of the head causes one to move relative to the other, then the position of the search pin must be adjusted until they appear to be coincident for all positions of the head: they are then said to be in a **position of no-parallax,** and the position of the search pin is that of the virtual image.

7.8 ROTATION OF A PLANE MIRROR

When a mirror is rotated through an angle θ, the reflected beam is turned through an angle 2θ, if the direction of the incident beam is fixed. This idea is used in (*i*) the mirror galvanometer, (*ii*) the sextant.

7.9 MORE THAN ONE MIRROR

(a) A thick glass mirror

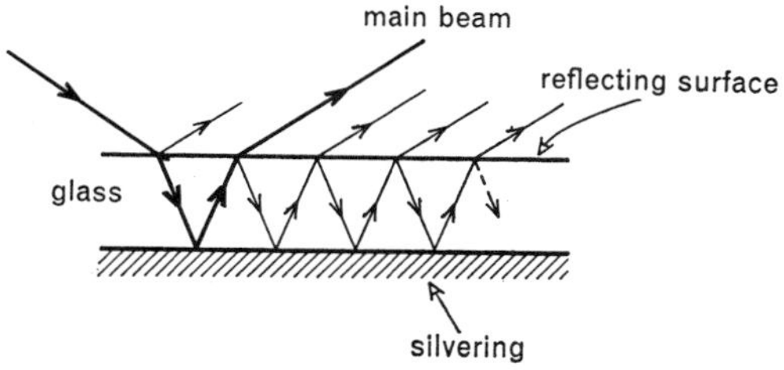

Fig. 7·10 Multiple reflection in a thick glass mirror

This diagram explains the formation of multiple images by a plane mirror which uses a reflecting surface behind thick glass. This type of mirror is avoided in optical instruments.

(b) The periscope

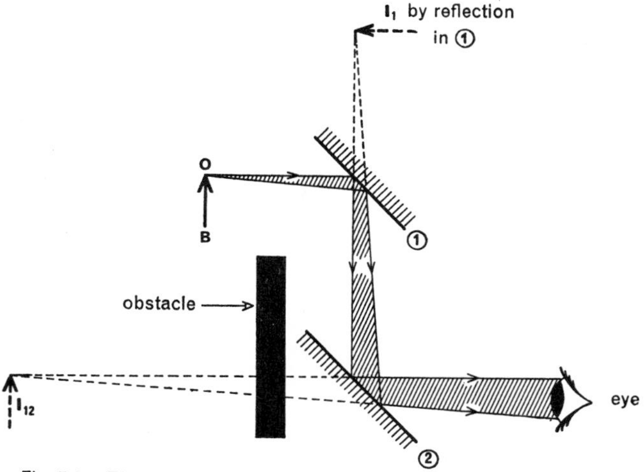

Fig. 7·11 The periscope

Note: (*i*) There are two reflections and so no net lateral inversion.
(*ii*) Prisms can be used instead of mirrors (see page 194).

(c) Inclined mirrors

Three surfaces which are mutually perpendicular (like the walls at the corner of a room) will reflect an incident beam parallel to its original

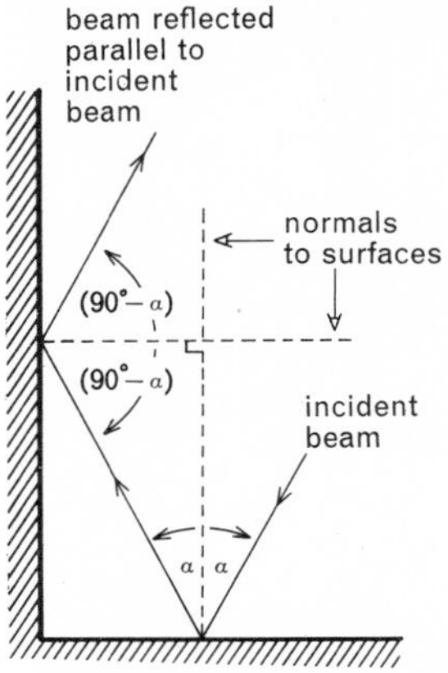

Fig. 7·12 The principle of the corner cube shown in two dimensions

direction. This idea is used in the design of rear reflectors for vehicles. The figure shows the effect in two dimensions.

(d) Several mirrors

A single plane mirror cannot be used to concentrate the light energy from a single source. Parallel rays remain parallel, and diverging rays continue to diverge, making the same angle with one another after reflection. On the other hand, several plane mirrors, correctly orientated, can be used to make different pencils from the same source cross in a small region.

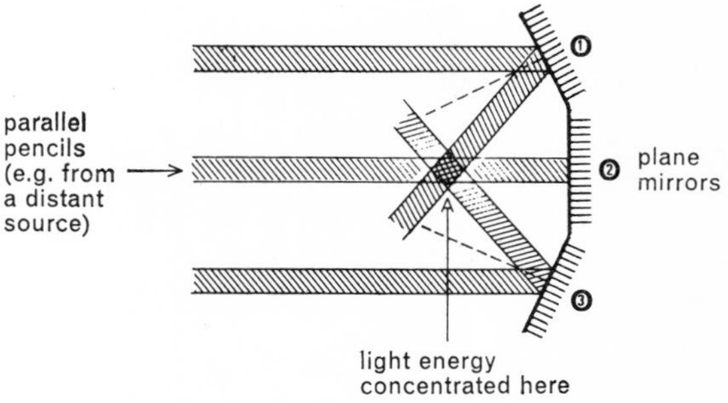

Fig. 7·13 Origin of the concave reflecting surface

As we use more and smaller plane mirrors, the more closely do the mirrors approach a continuously curved surface. This leads to the design of a smooth mirror which can be used to focus parallel light (see p. 201).

Refraction and dispersion

7.10 LAWS OF REFRACTION

Light is a wave motion. Section 6 has shown that if the speed of a wave motion is changed, the wavefront may change direction. We therefore expect a ray of light to be bent if it moves obliquely into a medium in which its speed is different.

Refraction is the change in direction of travel of light energy when it crosses the boundary between two transparent media.

The laws of refraction

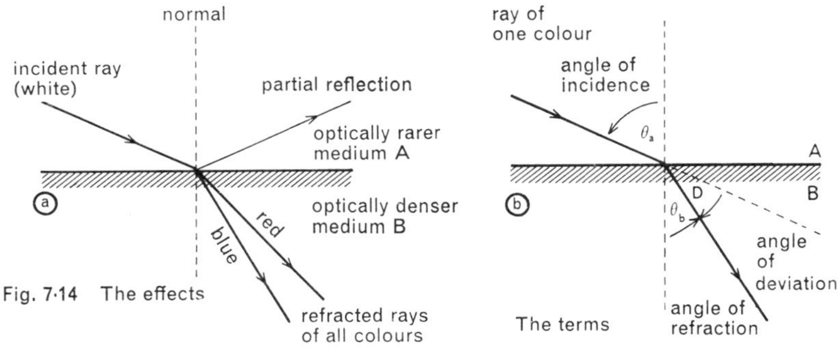

Fig. 7·14 The effects ... The terms

Law I: The refracted ray lies in the same plane as the incident ray and the normal at the point of incidence.

Law II: the ratio $\frac{\sin \theta_a}{\sin \theta_b}$ is a constant for light of a given frequency (and so wavelength) passing from one given medium to another. This is **Snell's Law.**

Note: (*a*) Partial reflection nearly always occurs at the same time as refraction, but will not always be shown in diagrams.

(*b*) There are exceptions to these laws.

7.11 REFRACTIVE INDEX

Refractive index is a term used to describe optical density, the ability of a transparent medium to cause refraction by changing the speed of light.

$$\text{Absolute refractive index} = \frac{\text{speed of light in a vacuum}}{\text{speed of light in a medium}}$$

$$\text{Relative refractive index} = \frac{\text{speed of light in medium A}}{\text{speed of light in medium B}}$$

(for light which goes from A to B).

Absolute refractive index is nearly the same as relative refractive index when medium A is air. For most practical purposes we ignore the difference, and talk about the refractive index of a medium.

It can be shown by using the wave theory that

$$\text{refractive index } n = \frac{\sin \theta_{\text{air}}}{\sin \theta_{\text{medium}}} \qquad \text{(see p. 158)}$$

i.e. that refractive index is the constant of Snell's Law. It has no unit.

Examples

(*a*) For air, $n = 1{\cdot}00$.
(*b*) For water, $n = 1{\cdot}33$.
(*c*) For glass, $n =$ about 1·5, depending on the type of glass.

The exact value of n depends upon the frequency, and so on the wavelength of the light (see *Dispersion,* p. 196).

7.12 EXAMPLES OF REFRACTION

(a) The apparent direction of a star

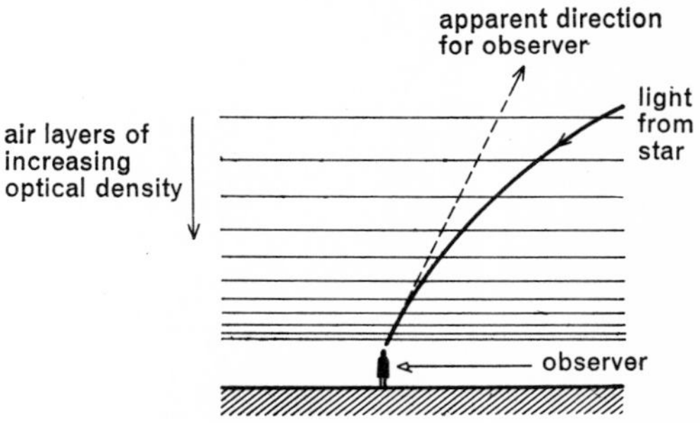

Fig. 7·15 Apparent direction of a star

The observer sees the star apparently along the direction in which light finally enters the eye. It seems to be higher than it really is.

(b) Real and apparent depth

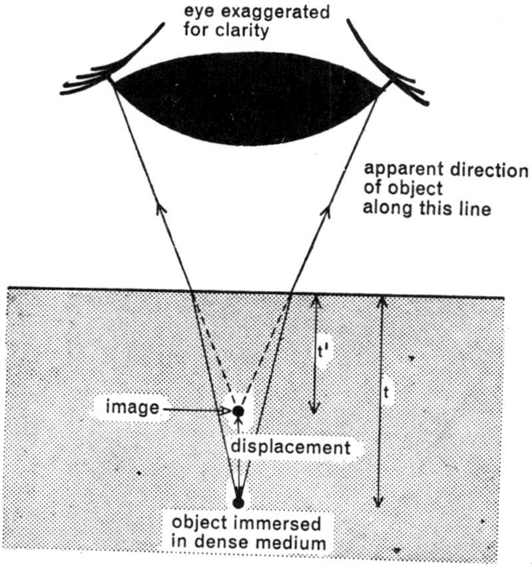

Fig. 7·16 Real and apparent depth

When an object in one medium is viewed by an observer in another medium, its apparent position is displaced as a result of the refraction which occurs at the boundary. When the object is viewed from a point such that the rays are nearly normal to the boundary, as shown, then it can be proved that

$$n = \frac{\text{real depth}}{\text{apparent depth}} = \frac{t}{t'}.$$

This is demonstrated by the bent stick illusion shown in Fig. 7.17.

Note that the light rays are refracted away from the normal *in air*, whereas the stick appears to be bent away from the normal *in water*.

(c) Refraction through a parallel slab (Fig. 7.18)

Note: (*i*) The ray emerges parallel to its original direction – there is no deviation.

(*ii*) The refraction at A is the reverse of that at B (see the Principle of Reversibility, page 180).

(*iii*) There would be no resultant dispersion even if white light were used.

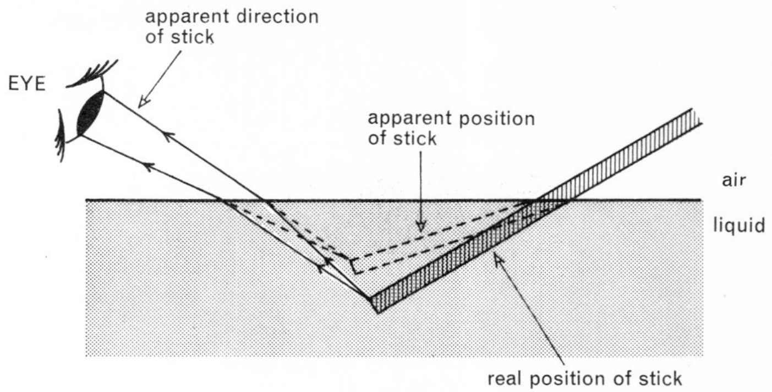

Fig. 7·17 Apparent bending of a stick

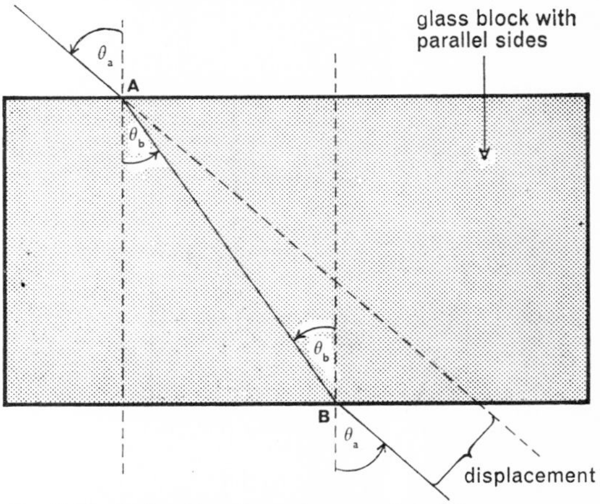

Fig. 7·18 Refraction through a parallel slab

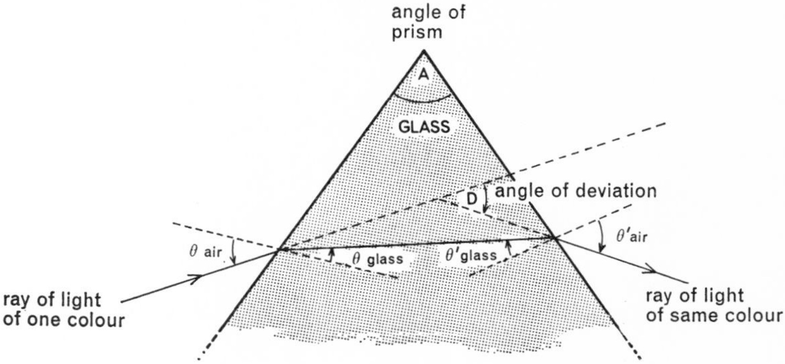

Fig. 7·19 Refraction through a prism

(d) Refraction through prisms (Fig. 7.19)

The diagram shows that light is always deviated when it passes through a prism. White light is found to emerge coloured (see *Dispersion*).

7.13 MEASUREMENT OF REFRACTIVE INDEX

(*a*) Measure the real and apparent depths of a mark on a piece of paper as seen through the medium, using the method of no-parallax. (Two points are in a position of no-parallax when small movements of the eye cause no relative movement between them (see p. 186).)

$$n = \frac{t}{t'}$$

(*b*) Using pins or a ray box, trace the paths of rays of light through a block of material such as a parallel-sided slab or a prism. Measure a series of values for θ_{air} and θ_{medium}.

$$n = \frac{\sin \theta_{\text{air}}}{\sin \theta_{\text{medium}}},$$

and according to Snell's Law should be the same for each ray traced.

7.14 TOTAL INTERNAL REFLECTION

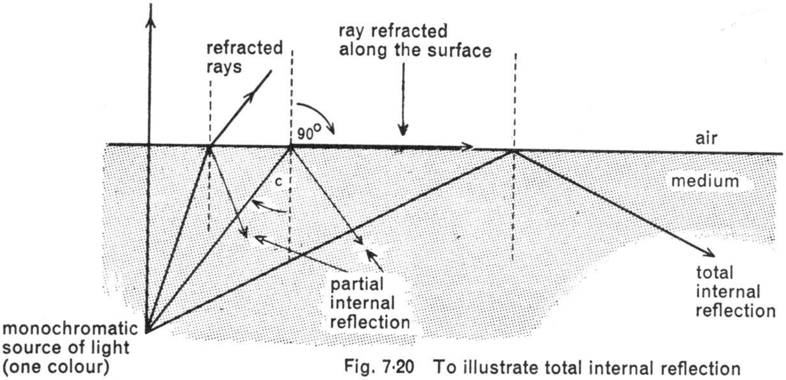

Fig. 7·20 To illustrate total internal reflection

Snell's Law does not give any meaningful result if it predicts the sine of an angle to be greater than one. The diagram illustrates what takes place when it does.

The **critical angle** (*c*) for a medium is the angle in the medium for which the angle in air is 90°.

$$n = \frac{\sin \theta_{\text{air}}}{\sin \theta_{\text{medium}}} = \frac{\sin 90°}{\sin c},$$

so

$$\sin c = \frac{1}{n}.$$

The fact that the value of c for glass is less than 45° is of practical importance.

The *conditions* under which total internal reflection will occur are
(*i*) the light must be trying to pass from the medium into air,
(*ii*) the angle of incidence must exceed the critical angle.

Experimental demonstration

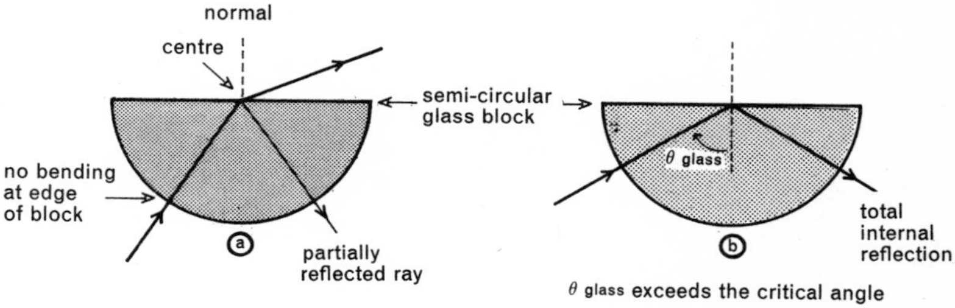

Fig. 7·21 To demonstrate total internal reflection

7.15 EXAMPLES OF TOTAL INTERNAL REFLECTION

(a) Totally reflecting prisms

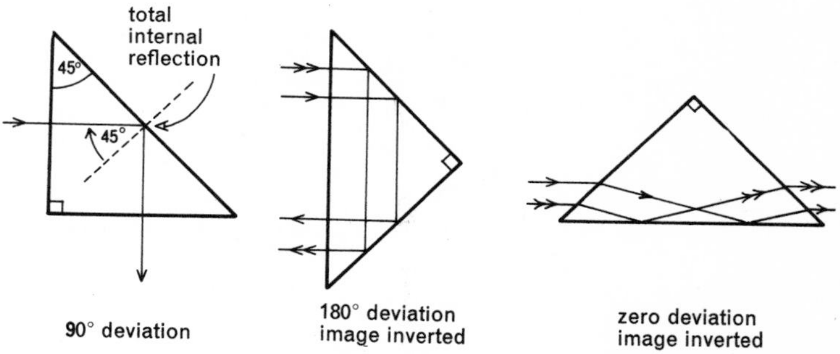

Fig. 7·22 Totally reflecting prisms

Prisms are used in optical instruments in preference to mirrors because they give no ghost images (see p. 187), and do not tarnish. The angle of incidence is arranged to be greater than the critical angle, so that *total* reflection occurs.

(b) The light pipe

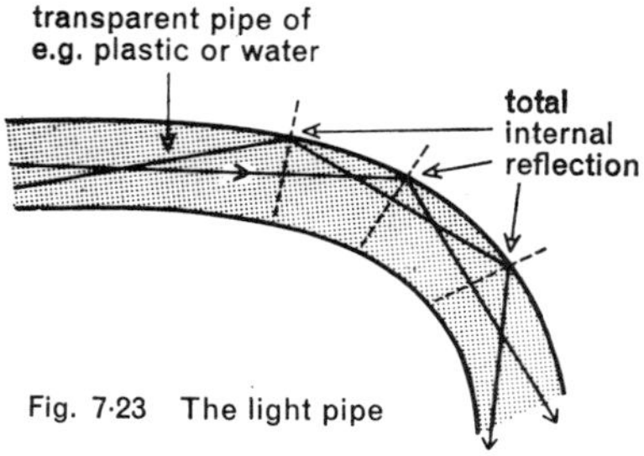

Fig. 7·23 The light pipe

Light is totally reflected inside a bent transparent pipe provided that the curvature is not too great.

Applications

(*i*) The microscope slide illuminator.
(*ii*) A device to see round corners in medical work.
(*iii*) Luminous fountains.

(c) The mirage

When the ground is warmed by the Sun, one sometimes finds an unstable situation in which there are hot layers of air near the ground which are optically rarer than cooler layers just above. For angles of incidence close to 90° this may result in total reflection within the cooler layer. Since the warm air layer then acts as a mirror surface, a small patch of sky will be seen reflected at the boundary between the layers: what one sees is similar to the (partial) reflection of light from the surface of water. It is noticeable on tarmac roads on a hot day.

(d) The fish-eye view (Fig. 7.24)

Light refracted into the fish's eye from objects outside the pond is concentrated into a narrow cone.

(e) Precious stones

Their beauty is based on two factors:

(*i*) their ability to reflect light totally with relatively small angles of incidence (the critical angle for diamond is 27°),
(*ii*) carefully cut plane faces.

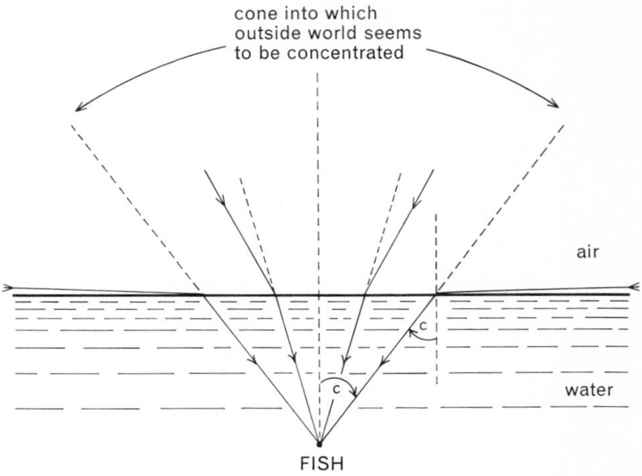

Fig. 7·24 The fish-eye view

7.16 DISPERSION

When different frequencies (and therefore wavelengths) of a wave motion have different speeds in a particular medium, wavefronts of different wavelengths which start together will tend to become separated or **dispersed.**

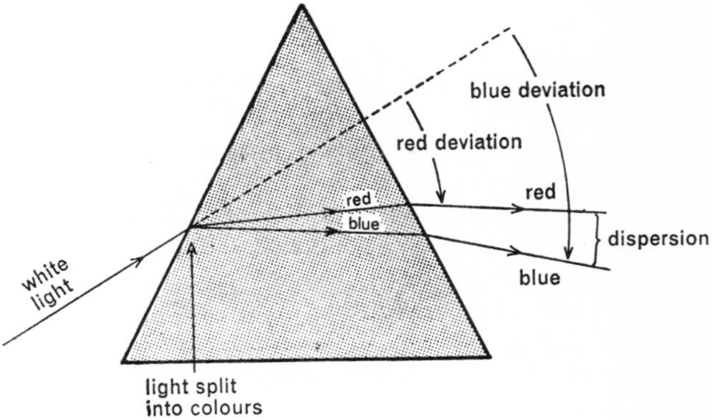

Fig. 7·25 Dispersion (exaggerated)

Since

$$n = \frac{\text{speed in a vacuum}}{\text{speed in a medium}},$$

the refractive indices are different for different wavelengths.

Dispersion in light can be illustrated by different angles of deviation for different colours when white light passes through a prism. For an account of the *spectrum*, see the diffraction grating on page 176.

7.17 CONVERGENCE OF LIGHT BY A SET OF PRISMS

Light cannot be concentrated by a single prism, which only serves to produce a fixed deviation from a fixed incident beam. Nevertheless several prisms, correctly orientated, can be used to make different

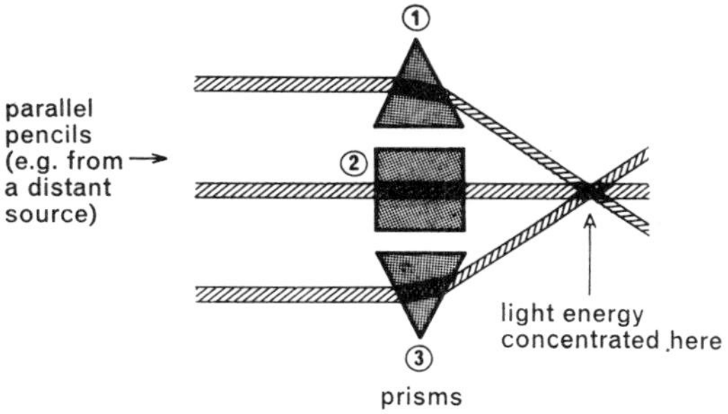

Fig. 7·26 Origin of the lens

pencils of light from the same source cross in a small region. The more prisms used, the more concentrated the light, and the more closely do the prism surfaces approach a continuously curved surface. This leads to the design of a smooth *lens* which can be used to focus parallel light.

Formation of images

7.18 THE NATURE OF AN IMAGE

Meaning of image

Refer to Fig. 7.27. O is a point object. Rays of light leave O, and some are intercepted by the optical system, which may be an arrangement of mirrors or lenses. If after emergence, they *all* pass, or seem to have passed through the single point I, then that point is called the *image* of the object O. An image of an extended object is made up of the point images of points on the object.

A real image of a point object is formed when the rays are made actually to pass through a point. This image can be

(*i*) made into a photographic negative directly,

(*ii*) seen by the eye directly,
(*iii*) formed on a screen.

It affects a photographic film because the optical system concentrates the energy on to the point concerned, and causes a chemical reaction.

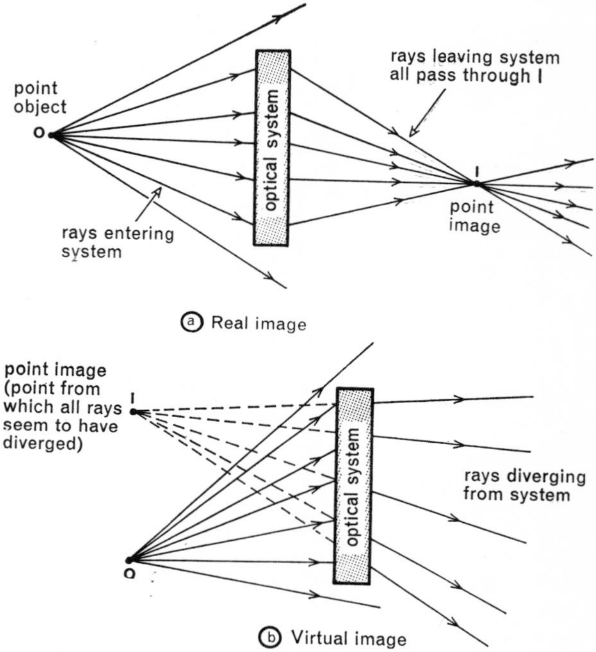

Fig. 7·27 Formation of images

A virtual image of a point object is formed when rays of light only *seem* to have passed through a point. The eye will interpret the position of the object as being the point of apparent convergence of the rays that finally enter the eye. This image

(*i*) can be made into a photographic negative only after the rays have been made to pass through a converging optical system,
(*ii*) can be seen by the eye directly,
(*iii*) cannot be formed on a screen.

No energy is concentrated at a virtual image.

An *aberration* is the phenomenon of a point object not giving rise to a point image. Aberrations are shown by spherical lenses and mirrors, but will be ignored in this book.

7.19 SIMPLE CONVERGING LENSES

A lens can be thought of as made up of a large number of small prisms, as described on page 197. It is found experimentally that a thin lens bounded by spherical surfaces produces a point image of a point object placed near its principal axis.

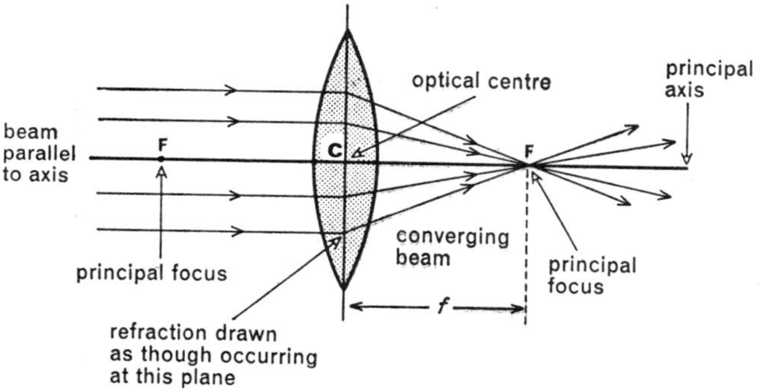

Fig. 7·28 The converging lens

The **principal focus** is the point through which all rays originally parallel to the principal axis pass after refraction. Every lens has two principal foci.

The **optical centre** is the point on the lens through which the light passes so that it emerges parallel to its original direction. For a thin lens the displacement of the beam is small enough to be ignored.

The **focal length** (f) is the distance FC.

Drawing ray diagrams for lenses (the graphical construction of images). Since a point is defined by the crossing of two lines, we need draw only two of the following rays, whose paths we can predict with certainty:

(*i*) A ray of light which starts parallel to the principal axis is refracted so that it passes through a principal focus.
(*ii*) A ray which passes through the optical centre passes undeviated.
(*iii*) A ray which passes through a principal focus is refracted so that it emerges parallel to the principal axis.

A third ray provides confirmation that the previous two have been correctly drawn. Measurements are made more accurate by drawing a fairly tall object: they are made simpler if the construction is done on graph paper.

Procedure

(*a*) Using a convenient horizontal scale, draw the principal axis, and mark in the positions of the lens and the principal foci.
(*b*) Draw a line at right angles to the axis to represent the lens. All rays will be drawn as though the refraction took place at the plane represented by this line.
(*c*) Mark in the top half of the object, using as large a vertical scale as possible, bearing in mind the probable size of the image.
(*d*) Draw any two rays from a point on the object to establish the position of its point image. Complete the image by inspection.

Examples

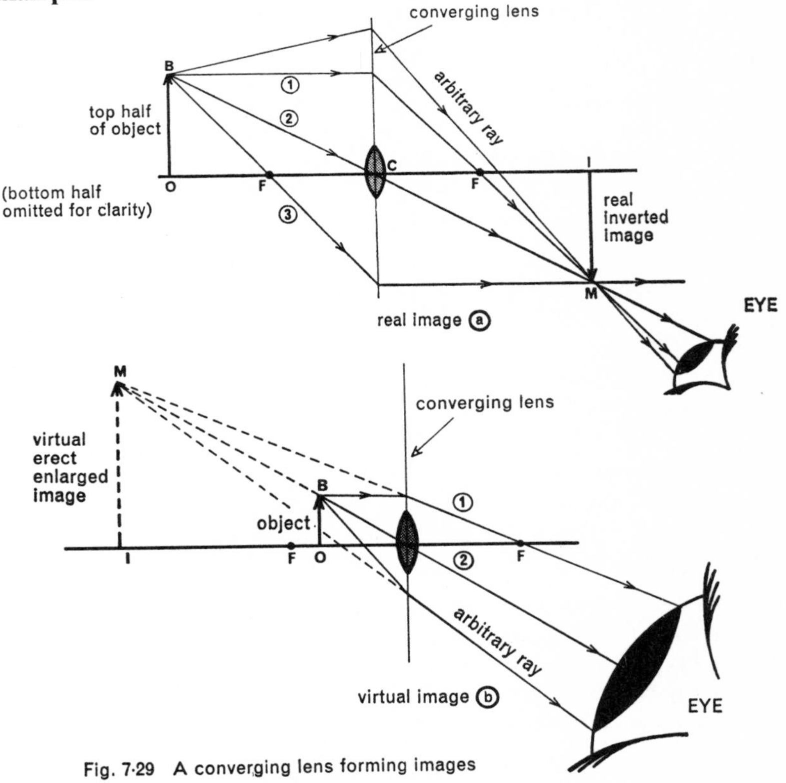

Fig. 7·29 A converging lens forming images

Magnification is defined as $\frac{\text{height of image}}{\text{height of object}} = \frac{IM}{OB}$.

Table of images

Object position	*Image position*	*Nature*	*Size relative to object*
at infinity	at F	real, inverted	very small
between infinity and 2*f*	between F and 2*f*	real, inverted	smaller
at 2*f*	at 2*f*	real, inverted	same size
between 2*f* and F	between 2*f* and infinity	real, inverted	enlarged
at F	at infinity	indeterminate	very big
between F and C	between infinity and C, but on the same side as the object	virtual, erect	enlarged

Do not learn this table. Confirm that you can obtain the results by the graphical method, and visualize the gradual changes that take place when the object is slowly moved.

Measurement of focal length

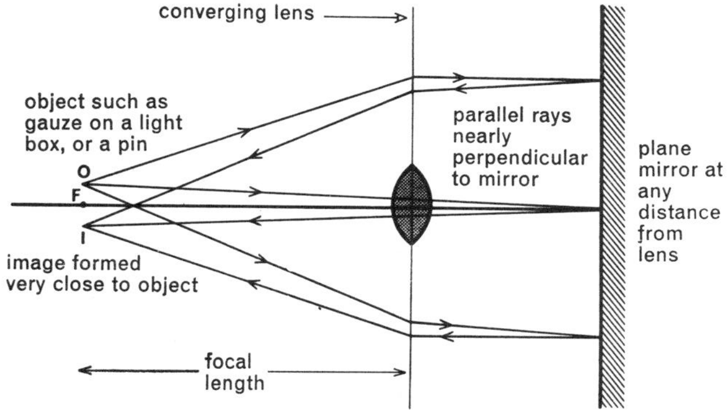

Fig. 7·30 The return image method (construction of image not shown)

Use the **return image** method: object and image coincide when light is reflected so as to travel back along its original path.

7.20 CONCAVE SPHERICAL MIRRORS

A concave spherical mirror is made by silvering the inside of a small part of a sphere (see also p. 188).

Definitions (Fig. 7.31)

The **centre of curvature** C is the centre of the sphere of which the mirror forms part.

The **principal focus, principal axis** and **focal length** are similar to those of the converging lens, and are shown in the diagram.

Drawing mirror diagrams

Follow the same procedure as that detailed for lenses on page 200. Rays whose directions we can predict with certainty are as follows:

(*i*) A ray of light which starts parallel to the principal axis is reflected so that it passes through the principal focus.
(*ii*) A ray which passes through the centre of curvature strikes the mirror normally, and so is reflected back along its original path.
(*iii*) A ray which passes through the principal focus is reflected so that it is parallel to the principal axis.
(*iv*) A ray which strikes the pole: the normal at the pole is the principal axis, and so i can easily be drawn equal to r.

Examples (Fig. 7.32)

Magnification is defined, as for lenses, by

$$m = \frac{IM}{OB}.$$

Table of images

Object position	*Image position*	*Nature*	*Size relative to object*
at infinity	at F	real, inverted	very small
between infinity and C	between F and C	real, inverted	smaller
at C	at C	real, inverted	same size
between C and F	between C and infinity	real, inverted	larger
at F	at infinity	indeterminate	very large
between F and P	between infinity and P but on the opposite side from the object	virtual, erect	larger

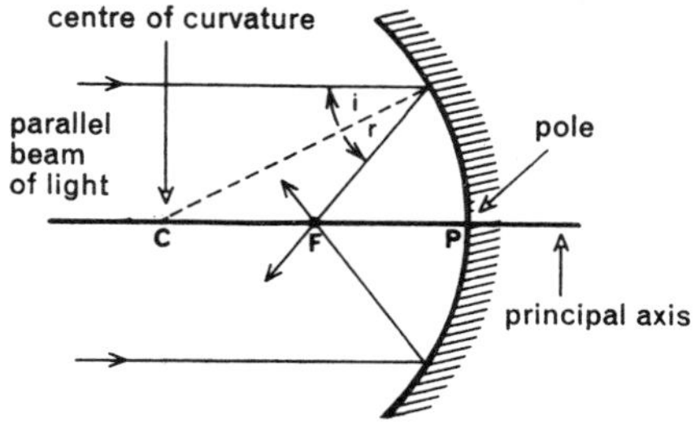

Fig. 7·31 The concave mirror

Fig. 7·32
Image formation by a concave mirror – compare also with fig. 7·29

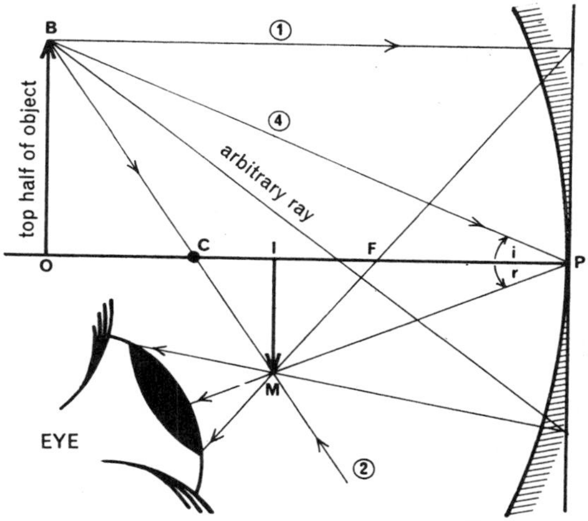

ⓐ Real image

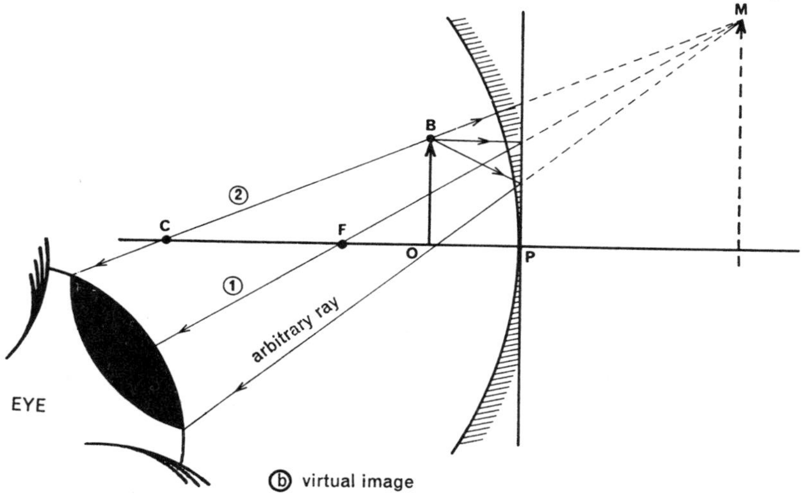

ⓑ virtual image

Measurement of focal length

When object and image coincide, they are both at the centre of curvature

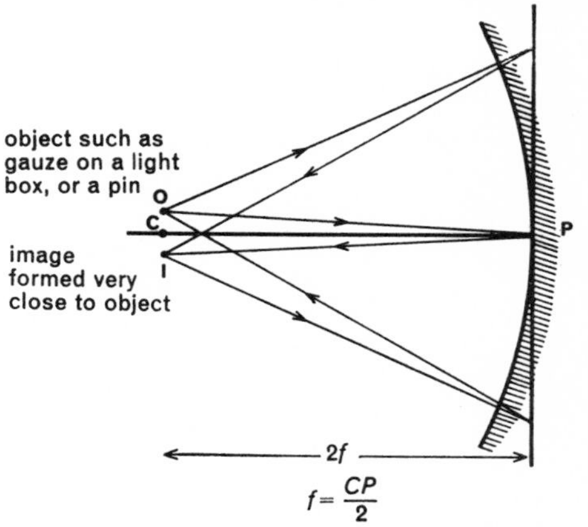

Fig. 7·33 The return image method

– light from O is returning along its original path to I. It can be proved that the focal length is half the radius of curvature.

7.21 SIMPLE DIVERGING LENSES

A spherical lens which is thicker at the edges than at the centre will cause a parallel beam of light which has passed through the lens to become *divergent*.

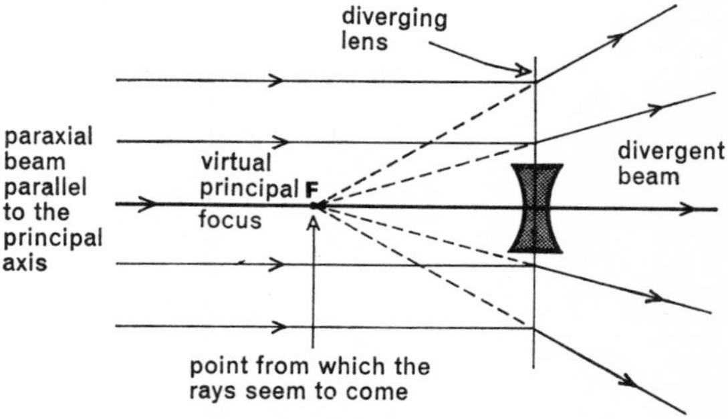

Fig. 7·34 The action of a diverging lens

A construction can be used to find the position of the image formed by a diverging lens. The method is similar to that used for a converging lens, except that the ray which starts parallel to the principal axis is refracted *as though* it had passed through a principal focus.

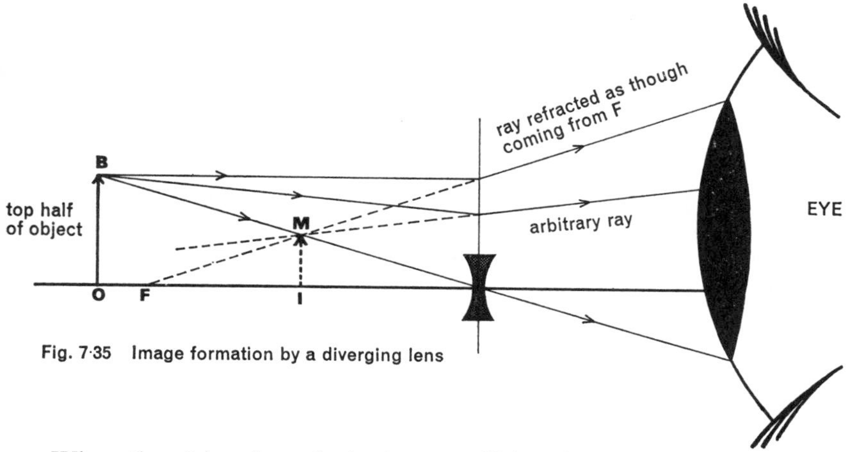

Fig. 7·35 Image formation by a diverging lens

When the object is real, the image will be virtual, and will always lie between the lens and a principal focus. It will be upright and smaller than the object.

7.22 CONVEX SPHERICAL MIRRORS

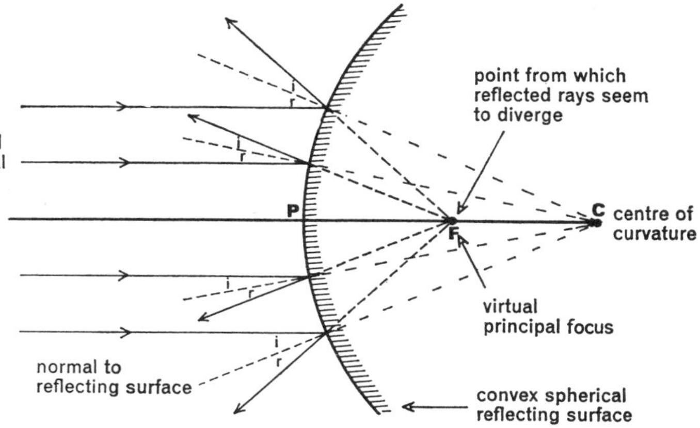

Fig. 7·36 The action of a convex spherical mirror

A parallel paraxial beam of light which strikes a convex mirror is reflected *as though* coming from a single point behind the mirror.

The diagram shows how a typical image may be constructed graphically:

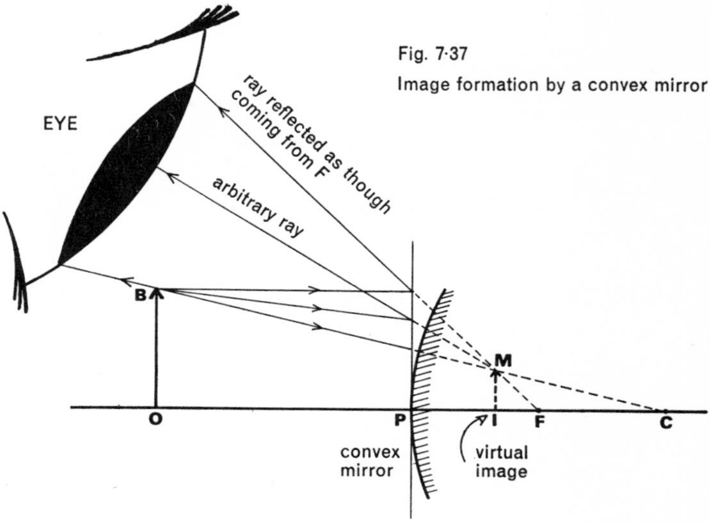

Fig. 7·37
Image formation by a convex mirror

When the object is real, the image will always be virtual, and will lie between the mirror and its principal focus. It will be upright, and smaller than the object.

A convex mirror is frequently used in a car as the driving mirror. The **field of view** (the region whose image is visible to the driver) is larger than that given by a plane mirror of the same size.

Optical instruments

7.23 THE PURPOSE OF AN OPTICAL INSTRUMENT

For an object to be clearly visible, a sufficiently large and bright image must be focused on the retina at the back of the eye. The purpose of an optical instrument is to help the eye to see a particular occurrence more easily. For instance it may

(*a*) make a permanent record of a brief occurrence,
(*b*) increase the apparent size of an object, either because it is otherwise too small or too far away,
(*c*) increase the apparent brightness of an object by collecting light from it over a period of time,
(*d*) project a large image of a small object so that many people can see it at the same time,
(*e*) be a specialized application, such as in a rangefinder or a spectrometer (a device for examining spectra).

We will discuss

(1) the camera,
(2) the human eye,
(3) the simple magnifying glass,
(4) the telescope,
(5) the compound microscope,
(6) the projector.

7.24 THE CAMERA

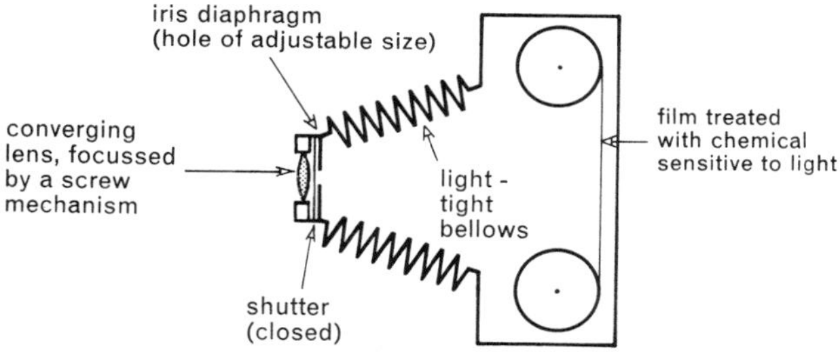

Fig. 7·38 The simple bellows camera

Note: (*a*) The purpose is to produce a focused real image of objects of different brightness and distance on a light-sensitive film.
(*b*) Focusing is achieved by moving the lens relative to the film.
(*c*) Brightness control is achieved by changing the size of the hole (the *iris diaphragm*) through which the light passes.
(*d*) The shutter controls the time for which light falls on the film.

7.25 THE HUMAN EYE

Fig. 7.39 shows the main features of the eye. The optical mechanism is very similar to that of the camera. The *cornea* makes the light converge, and the *crystalline lens* then focuses it accurately on the *retina*. The *iris* controls the intensity of the light reaching the retina. The retina can change its sensitivity according to the rate at which energy reaches it; this is the main method by which the eye becomes dark-adapted.

Accommodation is the ability of the eye to alter the focal length of the crystalline lens so that objects at different distances can be seen clearly.

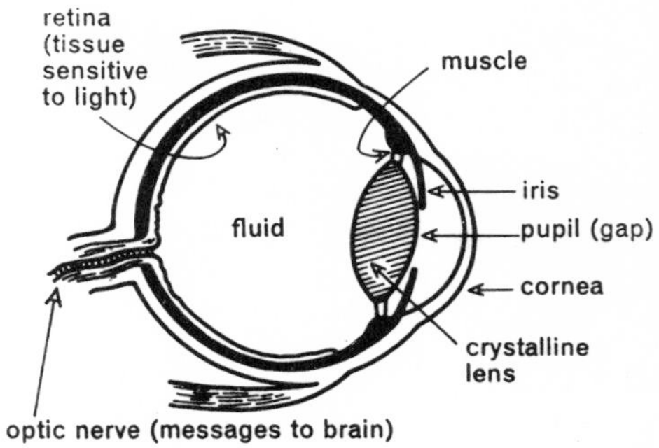

Fig. 7·39 The human eye

The **near point** is the position of the nearest object that can be seen both clearly and without strain by the unaided eye (i.e. without the use of lenses).

The **far point** is the position of the farthest object that can be seen by the unaided eye.

For the **normal eye** the far point is at infinity, and the near point is taken to be a point 250 mm from the eye. This distance is called the **least distance of distant vision.**

Persistence of vision. The retina remains stimulated by light energy for at least $\frac{1}{20}$ second after its arrival. This is why a discontinuous jerky movement, such as the succession of images on a cinema screen, can appear smooth.

Binocular vision. Each eye has a slightly different view of a given situation. Experience teaches us to judge distances using the two images.

Defects

(*a*) short sight **(myopia),**

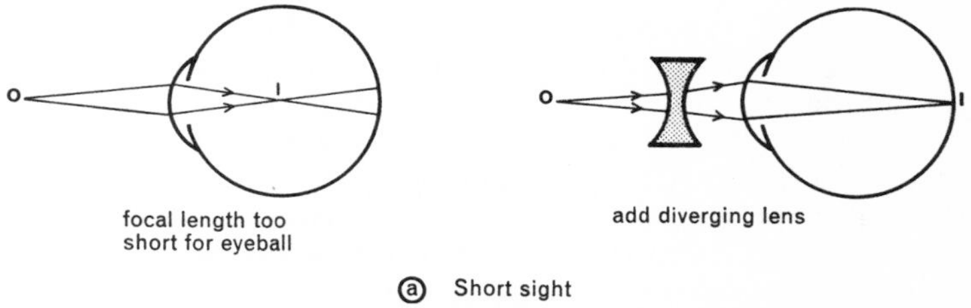

Fig. 7·40 Defects of the eye and their correction (not to scale)

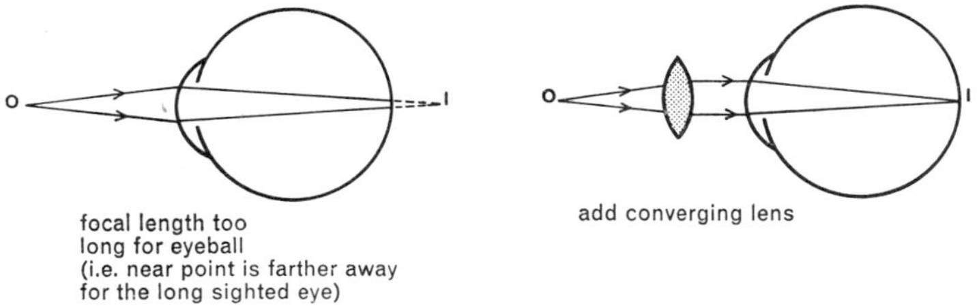

Fig. 7·40 cont. (b) Long sight

(*b*) long sight **(hypermetropia),**

(*c*) **presbyopia** – this is the loss of the power to accommodate, and often accompanies old age. It is corrected by using a convex lens for close work.

7.26 THE SIMPLE MAGNIFYING GLASS

When an object is placed between a converging lens and its principal focus, an enlarged virtual image is seen. The eye can focus this so as to give a bigger image on the retina than could be given by the unaided eye with the object placed at the near point. The brain can therefore distinguish more detail. The same effect can be achieved using a concave mirror (see Fig. 7.29*b*, and 7.32*b*).

7.27 THE TELESCOPE

Fig. 7.41 brings out the following points:

(*a*) Rays from *any one point* on a distant object are effectively parallel where they enter the objective lens of the telescope.

(*b*) Rays from the top of an extended object are *not* parallel to rays from the bottom of the object.

(*c*) The objective lens forms a real *diminished* image in its focal plane (the plane drawn through the principal focus perpendicular to the principal axis).

(*d*) This real image is viewed through the eye lens, which is used as a magnifying glass. The rays drawn in the diagram show how to find the point image of a point on the top of the object. This virtual image is at infinity. The images of other points on the object can be found by the same method.

The object appears bigger to the observer because the image *on the*

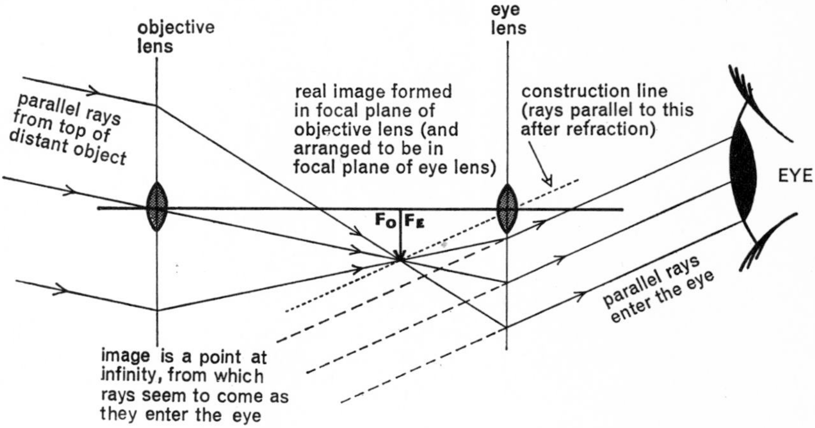

Fig. 7·41 The telescope

retina is larger than that formed by the unaided eye. This apparent size can be increased

(*i*) by increasing the focal length of the objective lens, and/or
(*ii*) by decreasing the focal length of the eye lens.

7.28 THE COMPOUND MICROSCOPE

The purpose of the microscope is to produce an enlarged virtual image of a very small but accessible object.

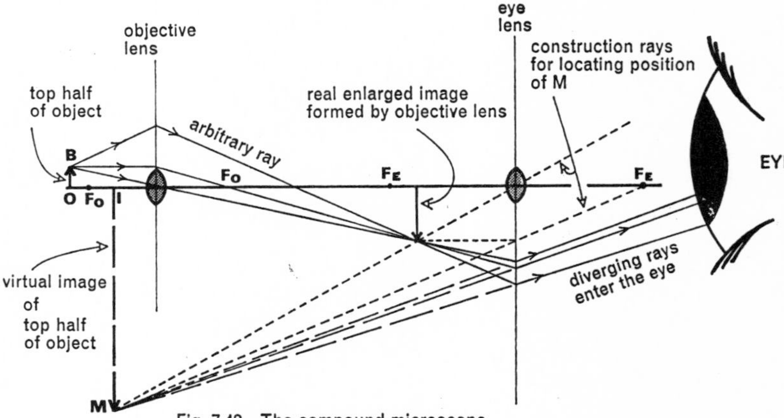

Fig. 7·42 The compound microscope

The diagram brings out the following points:

(*a*) The objective lens produces an *enlarged* real image of the object.
(*b*) The eye uses the eye lens as a simple magnifying glass to view this real image which is used as an object. The enlarged virtual image is usually formed at the near point which is 250 mm from the normal eye.

For clarity the diagram has been drawn for the top half only of the object.

7.29 THE PROJECTOR

The diagram shows two distinct operations:

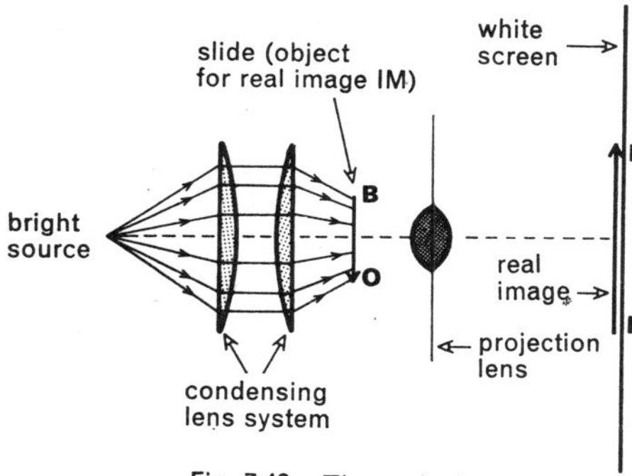

Fig. 7·43 The projector

(*i*) The **condensing lens system** concentrates light from a bright source on to the transparent slide.
(*ii*) The **projection lens** then focuses a real image of the illuminated slide on the screen. The rays for this are not shown – confirm that you can complete the diagram.

Note that the slide is inserted upside-down.

In the **diascope** light shines through the specimen: in the **episcope** light is shone on to the specimen, and diffusely scattered light then passes through the projection lens so as to form the final image.

8 Magnetism and electrostatics

Permanent magnetism

8.1 EXPERIMENTAL FACTS ABOUT PERMANENT MAGNETISM

(*a*) A permanent magnet will only attract **ferromagnetic** materials, such as iron, cobalt, nickel and some alloys. (If these are already magnetized, they may be repelled.)

(*b*) Iron filings will only stick near the ends or *poles* of a bar magnet, where its magnetic effect seems to be concentrated. These poles always *occur in pairs,* which are of equal strength.

(*c*) A magnet pivoted so that it can swing freely is used as a **compass.** One pole, the **North-seeking pole** (N), always points roughly towards Geographic North (see Fig. 8.6*g*, and Fig. 8.7).

(*d*) Using a compass and a permanent magnet, it can be shown that an N-pole of the permanent magnet exerts a push F on the N-pole of the compass: at the same time, the N-pole of the compass exerts a push on the N-pole of the magnet which is equal to F in magnitude and direction, but of opposite sense. Newton's Law III requires this to be so. Summarizing such experiments, we can say that

(*i*) like poles [(**S–S**) or (**N–N**)] repel,
(*ii*) unlike poles attract.

This is the (qualitative) **law of force** between poles. Because of (*a*) above, *repulsion* is the only valid test that a ferromagnetic material is a permanent (as opposed to induced) magnet.

(*e*) Only ferromagnetic materials can *shield* an object from the influence of a magnet: e.g. watches sometimes have a soft iron case.

(*f*) When a magnet is *broken* into two, the two pieces also act as magnets (see Fig. 8.1*c*).

(*g*) If a magnet is *heated* to near red heat, then its magnetic effect is destroyed, though it can be remagnetized.

(*h*) A magnet cannot indefinitely increase its ability to produce magnetic effects (its strength reaches a maximum): it is said to become **saturated.**

8.2 THEORY OF MAGNETISM

A satisfactory theory of magnetism must be able to explain facts (*a*) to (*h*) above.

Molecular theory

Suppose that each *molecule* of a ferromagnetic substance is an **elementary magnet.** When the substance is not magnetized, the elementary magnets form closed chains: there are no free poles, and so there is no

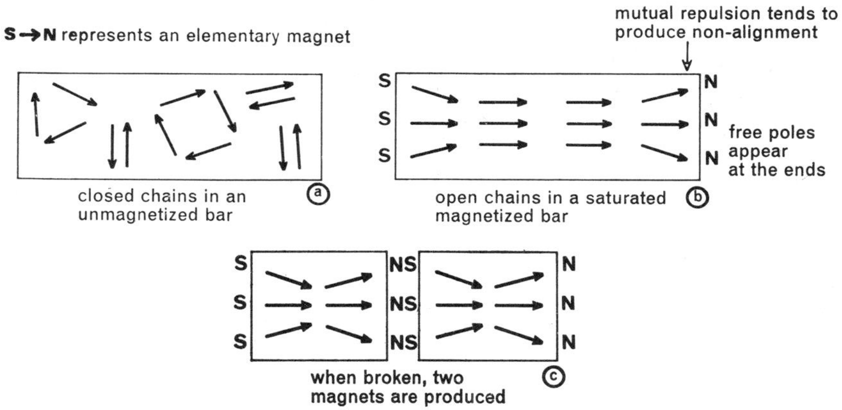

Fig. 8·1 Elementary magnets

external magnetic field. The act of magnetizing causes the closed chains to open, and rejoin as open-ended chains: there are now free poles at the ends, and so there is an external field.

The theory does explain:

why the poles are at or near the ends,
why heating destroys magnetism,
why hammering destroys magnetism,
why saturation occurs.

It does not explain:

why some molecules should be magnetic and others not,
why some alloys are magnetic, even though their constituents are not,
why some alloys which contain magnetic constituents are not themselves magnetic.

Because of these difficulties, the molecular theory has been superseded by:

The domain theory

This theory supposes that the elementary magnets are made up of small regions called **magnetic domains,** each containing about 10^{15} molecules. The molecules within a domain all combine to produce a magnetic field in the same direction. Pure non-ferromagnetic materials do not have the ability to form domains. There is direct experimental evidence for the existence of domains.

Magnetic induction

When a permanent magnet is brought close to a bar of unmagnetized soft iron, that bar acquires the property of attracting other ferromagnetic material. The soft iron has become an **induced magnet** by the temporary lining-up of some of its domains. The effect explains why a previously unmagnetized bar can be attracted by a magnet: it may disappear when the permanent magnet is removed.

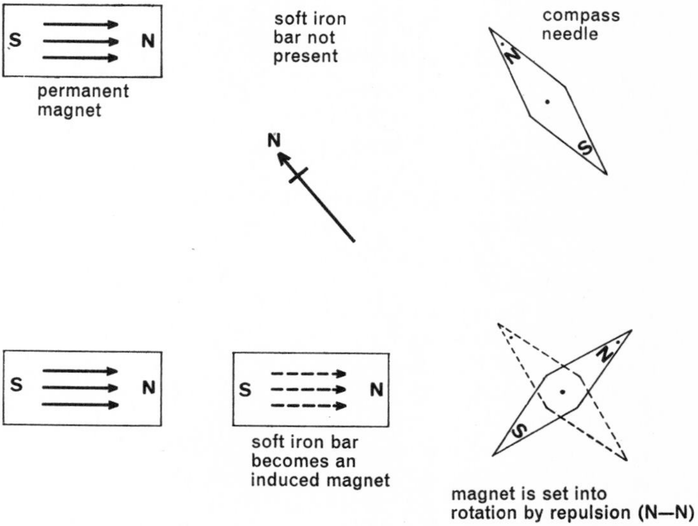

Fig. 8·2 Magnetic induction

8.3 MAGNETS

Methods of magnetizing

(*a*) *The touch method*

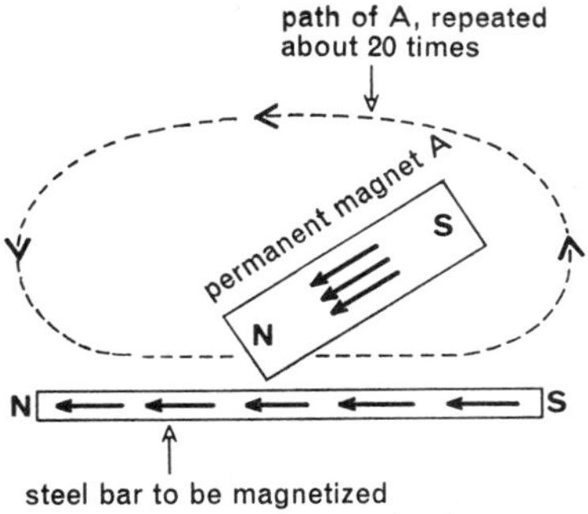

Fig. 8·3 Magnetizing by stroking

Note the resultant polarity. The permanent magnet loses hardly any of its magnetism while lining up the domains of the specimen. The method can be made more efficient by using two permanent magnets – *double touch.*

(*b*) *Solenoid method*

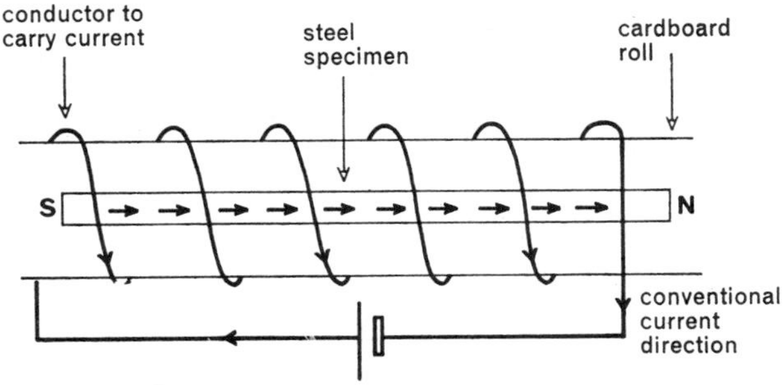

Fig. 8·4 Magnetizing by solenoid

The electric current creates a strong magnetic field which lines up the domains of the specimen more effectively than any other method (see *The magnetic effect of a current,* page 270).

(*c*) Gentle tapping of a bar while it is parallel to a magnetic field agitates the domains so that they fall into line. Mumetal becomes magnetized in the Earth's field without even being tapped.

Methods of demagnetizing

(*a*) Draw a permanent magnet out along the axis of a solenoid which is carrying *alternating current:* the specimen is magnetized less and less strongly in opposite senses 100 times a second.
(*b*) Heat the specimen above a temperature called the *Curie point.*
(*c*) Hammer the specimen while it is not aligned in any field.

These last two methods agitate the molecules and domains into random orientation.

Storage of magnets

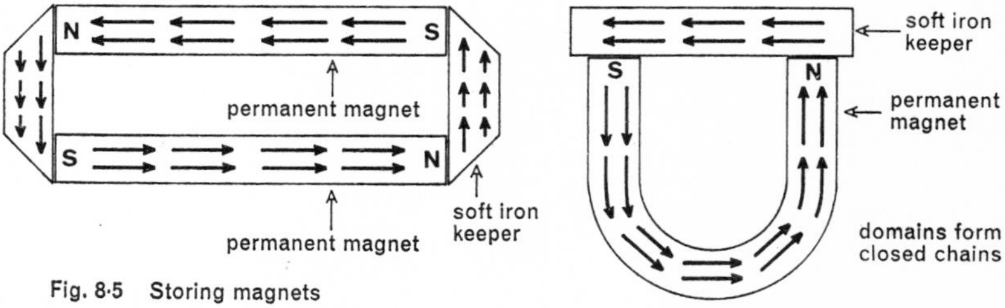

Fig. 8·5 Storing magnets

Avoid knocking. Use a **keeper** to reduce the natural tendency of domains to orientate into random alignment, as a result of their mutual repulsion.

Magnet materials

(*a*) **Soft iron** becomes a strong magnet when placed in a magnetic field, but just as easily loses its magnetism when the field is removed. It is therefore used for the core of the **electromagnet** (see page 273).
(*b*) Some alloys, such as **steel** or alcomax, are much more difficult to magnetize, but have the property of retaining their magnetism much better once they have become magnets. They are therefore used for making *permanent magnets.*
(*c*) **Ferrites,** which are mixtures of iron and other oxides, have the magnetic properties of steel and the mechanical properties of *ceramic* materials like china. These also are used for making permanent magnets.

8.4 MAGNETIC FIELDS

A **magnetic field** is any region in which

(*a*) a small pivoted magnet detects a magnetic effect, or
(*b*) a moving electric charge experiences a force.

A magnetic field will be found near a permanent magnet, or a current-carrying conductor.

A **magnetic line of force** (magnetic field line) is a line whose direction and sense at any point tell us the initial path which would be taken by an imaginary free N-pole placed at the point. The tangent to a line of force is the direction along which the axis of a small plotting compass will set itself.

Lines of force can be shown by

(*a*) plotting compasses, or iron filings, which act as small compasses when allowed to turn on being agitated (since they are already induced magnets),
(*b*) a long magnet floating in water so that its N-pole is at the surface, and its S-pole vertically beneath some distance away. The effect of the S-pole is negligible.

Properties of lines of force

(*a*) A complete line of force is always drawn from the N-pole of a magnet to an equal S-pole.
(*b*) They are drawn as though they repelled one another, and so never cross.
(*c*) They are drawn as though they were trying to contract like stretched elastic.
(*d*) Where they are
  (*i*) parallel, the field is uniform,
  (*ii*) closest, the field is strongest,
  (*iii*) diverging, the field is becoming weaker,
  (*iv*) converging, the field is getting stronger.
(*e*) The arrow on a line of force shows the sense of movement of an imaginary free N-pole placed at the point.

A **neutral point** is a point within a magnetic field at which the resultant magnetic force on an imaginary free N-pole is zero. It follows that no lines of force can pass through a neutral point.

Examples of magnetic fields

The diagrams in Fig. 8.6 are drawn by combining the forces that would be experienced by an imaginary free N-pole placed at a particular point in the field. It must be emphasized that lines of force are not real: they are, however, a very valuable help for visualizing the strength and direction of a magnetic field.

The Earth's magnetic field

Fig. 8.6*g* shows the main features of the Earth's magnetic field, which is thought to be caused by electric currents within the Earth itself. The

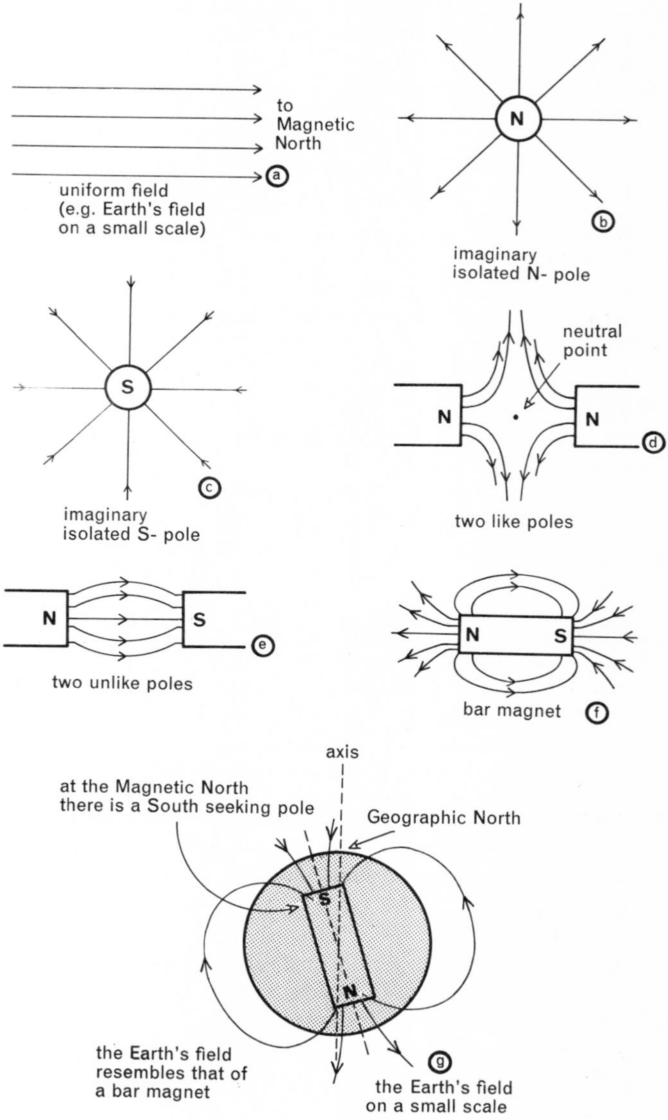

Fig. 8·6 Examples of magnetic field lines

following diagram shows those factors which are of importance at any given point A on the Earth's surface:

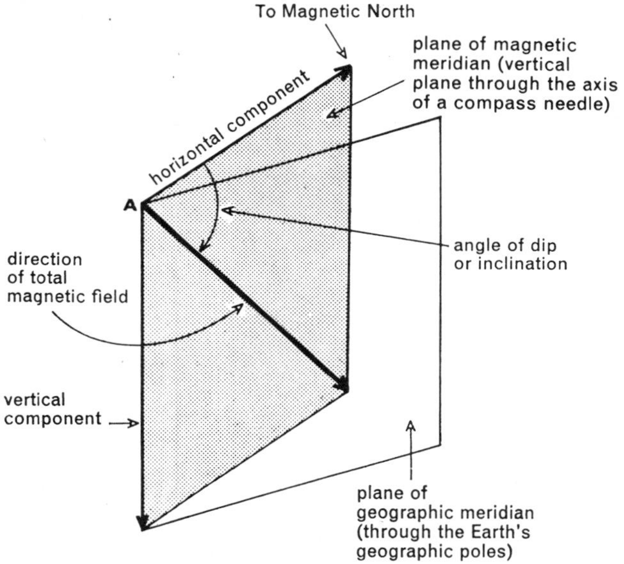

Fig. 8·7 Description of the magnetic field of the Earth at a given place

The **magnetic variation** (or declination) is the angle between the geographical and magnetic meridians. Its value must be known before a compass can be used effectively with a map: it varies both from place to place and from year to year.

Examine Fig. 8.6*g* to see how you would expect the **angle of dip** to vary over the Earth's surface.

8.5 THE ORIGIN OF PERMANENT MAGNETISM

Section 10 discusses the facts that a *moving charge*

(*a*) sets up a magnetic field (p. 270),
(*b*) experiences a force when in a magnetic field (p. 275).

A *still* electric charge on the other hand, is not influenced by a magnetic field. This supports the idea that the cause of permanent magnetism is to be found in small circulatory electric currents within a domain. This is why the ideas and phenomena of electricity and magnetism are so closely bound up together.

Electrostatics

8.6 EXPERIMENTAL FACTS

(*a*) If we rub two ebonite rods with fur, and two glass rods with silk, and then hang one of each so that it can swing freely in a stirrup, we find:
  (*i*) glass repels glass, and ebonite repels ebonite,
  (*ii*) ebonite attracts glass,
  (*iii*) no body can be found such that it repels an identical body, and both glass and ebonite.

  In all such experiments, Newton's Law III is obeyed.

(*b*) Some bodies, particularly metallic ones, do not repel or attract one another if they are held in the hand to be rubbed.

Some conclusions

(*a*) There are two, and only two, types of electrostatic charge.

(*b*) By convention, charged materials which repel **ebonite** are said to have a **negative charge:** those that repel glass are said to have a positive charge.

  Note: (*i*) that the terms positive and negative are chosen because the two types of charge can cancel each other's effect,
  (*ii*) that it is this arbitrary choice that determines that the charge associated with the **electron is negative.**

  In practice, we use polythene instead of ebonite (both acquire negative charges), and cellulose acetate instead of glass.

(*c*) Like charges (+ and +) or (− and −) repel.
  Unlike charges (+ and −) attract.
  This is the (qualitative) **law of force** between charges.

(*d*) The second experiment indicates that materials can be:
  (*i*) good conductors, such as metals,
  (*ii*) intermediate conductors, such as impure water and the human body,
  (*iii*) poor conductors (insulators), such as polythene, porcelain and air.

  There is no sharp boundary between the classes. The terms are explained in the next paragraph.

8.7 EXPLANATION

(See Fig. 2.1.) An atom can be conveniently visualized as made up of:

(1) a small nucleus containing almost all the mass of the atom: the nucleus is positively charged because it contains protons,
(2) an encircling cloud of electrons, which may be imagined as though they were in orbit round the nucleus.

The atom as a whole will normally be electrically neutral, because the number of protons will usually equal the number of electrons, and their charges are equal in magnitude.

Using these ideas, we can make the following deductions:

(*a*) When a body is charged by rubbing, it gains or loses one or more conduction electrons (outermost orbital electrons). If a body gains electrons, it acquires a negative charge: if it loses electrons, it acquires a positive charge, because it will then have an excess of protons. Protons are not removed from the nucleus in these experiments. The magnitudes of the charges produced by rubbing are necessarily the same, since one body can only gain electrons if the other has lost them.

(*b*) A body will be
  (*i*) a **conductor** if it has free electrons (or other charged particles) that can move easily within the boundaries of the body,
  (*ii*) an **insulator** if the electrons are not free to move, and if there are no other charged particles available.

(*c*) *Charging by rubbing*
  (*i*) An insulator prevents a charge moving from the area in which it was generated: it can therefore be charged by rubbing, but not significantly by contact.
  (*ii*) A conductor can either disperse a local excess of electrons, or supply electrons from elsewhere to make up a deficit. Its charge therefore spreads out over the whole conductor, and it can be shown that this excess charge resides entirely on the surface. It can be charged by contact, and by rubbing if it is insulated (but not if it is held in the hand).

8.8 ELECTROSTATIC INDUCTION

This process is similar to magnetic induction (see page 214).

In Fig. 8.8*a* the two spheres A and B are in contact. In Fig. 8.8*c* B has been pulled away from A. B now has a deficiency, and A an excess of electrons. The charges on A and B are equal in size and opposite in sign, as are the charges produced on the rubbing agent and the rubbed body when, for example, wool rubs polythene.

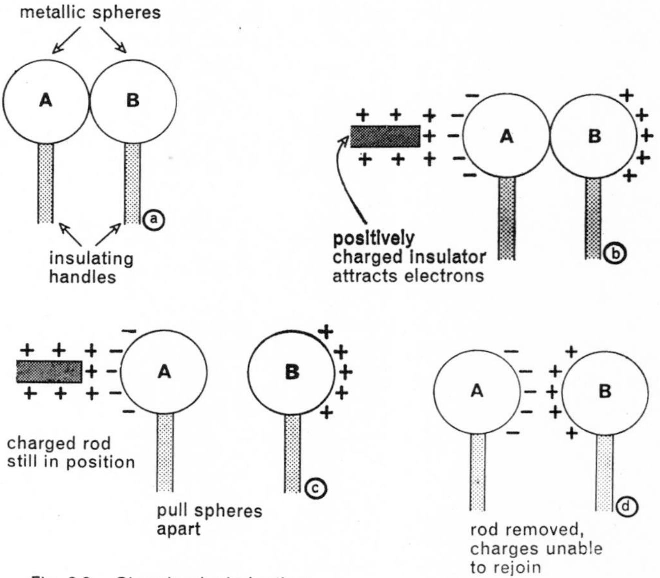

Fig. 8·8 Charging by induction

8.9 THE GOLD LEAF ELECTROSCOPE

This is a device for detecting and measuring charge, by using the difference of potential produced between the leaves and the case of the instrument.

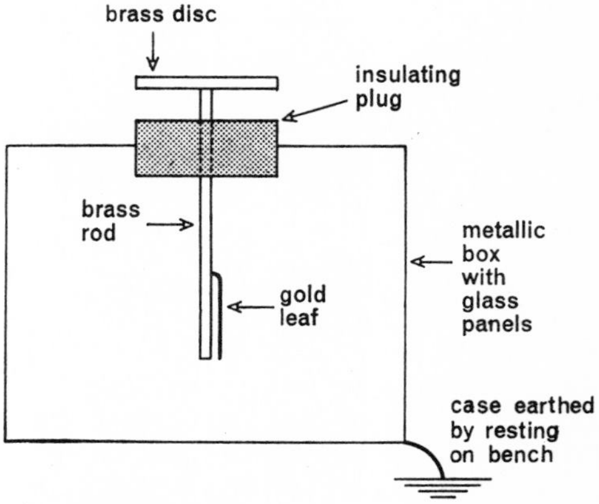

Fig. 8·9 Electroscope

The case is usually in contact with (e.g.) a bench top, and so is in effect 'earthed'. The wooden bench is a sufficiently good conductor to supply electrons from the Earth, or to take away excess electrons from the case if necessary.

The leaf divergence indicates a *difference of electrical potential* between the leaf and the case, not the charge on the leaf.

Charging the electroscope

(*a*) The electroscope can be charged by *direct contact,* particularly with a conductor. The leaf then acquires a charge of the same sign as the body that charged it.

(*b*) It can usually be charged more conveniently by *induction.* The figure makes the method clear. Note that the leaf acquires a charge opposite in sign to that on the charging body.

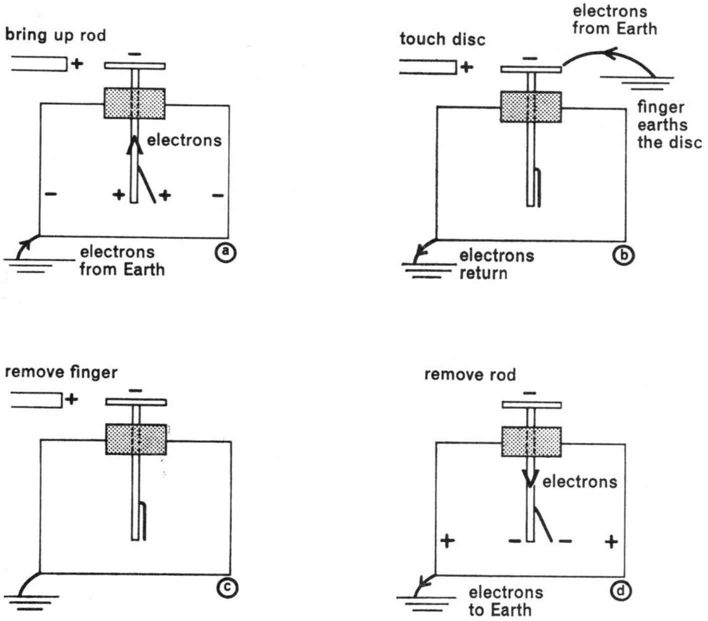

Fig. 8·10 An electroscope being charged by induction. (The actual sizes of charges are not shown)

Uses of the electroscope

(*a*) To *detect* a charged body: the leaf rises when the body approaches the cap.

(*b*) To *find the sign* of the charge on a body:

Unknown charge	*Reaction of electroscope*	
	if leaf is already +ve, then angle	if leaf is already −ve, then angle
positive	increases	decreases
negative	decreases	increases
neutral conductor	decreases	decreases

Note that *increased* angle is the sure way of finding the sign. Draw diagrams to confirm that you can explain all these results in terms of the behaviour of electrons.

(*c*) To discover whether a substance is a *conductor or an insulator*, touch the charged plate with a rod of the substance, and note the rate at which the leaf collapses. With excellent insulators the effect on the leaf cannot be detected.

Air is a good insulator under normal conditions, but if it becomes ionized the leaf may collapse quickly (see pp. 240 and 269).

8.10 POTENTIAL DIFFERENCE AND ELECTRIC FIELD

In Fig. 8.11*a*, a body has been separated from the Earth's surface: since the weight of the body has done negative work, the system (Earth and body) has acquired *gravitational potential energy* (see p. 81). The potential energy of the system with the body in position A is less than that in position B.

In Fig. 8.11*b*, we are separating positive and negative charges, and the electric forces do negative work: thus the system is said to have gained **electric potential energy.** If they are free to move, the two charges 'flow' towards one another: this movement of electric charge is an electric current, although it is not continuous in this case.

The idea of field

A **gravitational field** is a region in which any mass experiences a force, even though it has no direct contact with other bodies, and there are no electric or magnetic effects.

Similarly an **electric field** is a region in which a stationary electric charge experiences a force.

In Fig. 8.11*b*, the positive charge sets up an electric field which causes the negative charge to experience a force of attraction towards it:

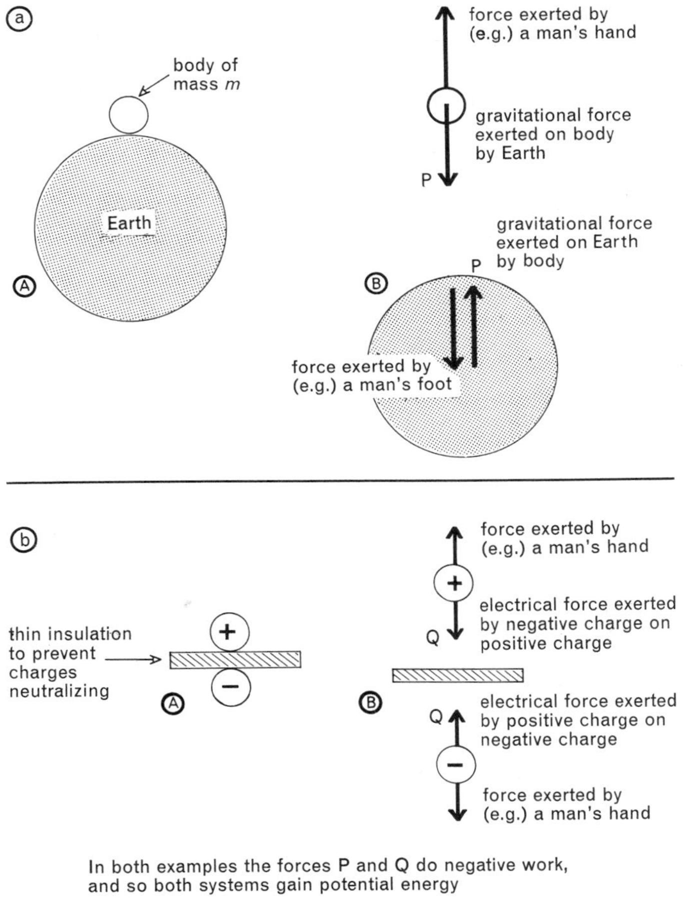

Fig. 8·11

similarly the negative charge sets up a field which causes the positive charge to be attracted, so that Newton's Law III is obeyed. For an example of a uniform electric field see *Millikan's experiment* (page 231).

It should be realized that the idea of a field supplements the idea of a force. A knowledge of field enables us to calculate what force would act on a given mass or charge, if it were placed at a particular point in a field.

8.11 THE ELECTRIC CURRENT

A current in a metallic conductor consists of the movement of electrons (see p. 249). In order that electrons may be in a position to move, work must be done to separate positive from negative charge, so that they may be gathered into one region. (The region from which the electrons have come will have a positive charge.)

This may be done using:

(*a*) *Mechanical energy*
  (*i*) by rubbing to produce an electrostatic charge,
  (*ii*) by direct pulling apart, as in induction methods such as the electrophorus and Van de Graaff machine,
  (*iii*) by rotation, as in the dynamo (see p. 279).

(*b*) *Heat* – a current may flow in a thermocouple (see p. 115) when heat is supplied to one junction so that it is maintained at a temperature different from the other.

(*c*) *Light* – electrons can be made to jump out of metals (the photo-electric effect) when light of high enough frequency is made to fall on them.

(*d*) *Chemical energy* – chemical changes in a cell liberate energy in such a way that electrons are forced to accumulate at the negative terminal, while the positive terminal has a deficiency of electrons (see p. 264).

When two such regions, between which there will exist a potential difference, are joined by a conductor, the electric field causes a charge to flow, and it is this that constitutes a current.

8.12 THE RELATION BETWEEN CURRENT AND STATIC ELECTRICITY

These experiments suggest that the same electric charges (in fact electrons) are responsible for most of the effects of both current and static electricity:

(*a*) A high tension battery (one having an e.m.f. of the order of 250 volts) can cause the leaf of an electroscope to deflect (Fig. 8.12).

(*b*) A Van de Graaff machine is a device to generate very high differences of potential between a sphere and its surroundings. It does this by depositing small quantities of charge (generated by an electrostatic method) which are carried by a conveyor belt, on a single spherical conductor. The moving charge on the conveyor belt is a small electric current; like other currents, it gives rise to a (small) magnetic field.

(*c*) A galvanometer detects and measures electric currents. A conductor that has been charged by an electrostatic method (e.g. a Van de

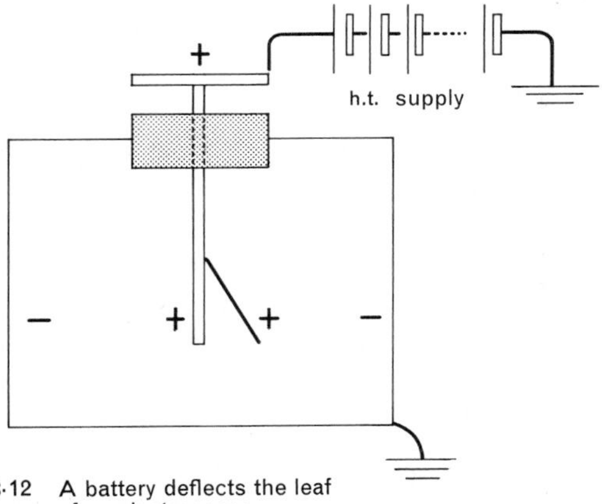

Fig. 8·12 A battery deflects the leaf of an electroscope

Graaff machine) can be made to pass its charge through a galvanometer. The galvanometer will give a deflection while the conductor discharges.

9 Atomic physics

9.1 HISTORICAL INTRODUCTION

Physics is most easily understood when ideas and facts are presented in a logical order with respect to the development of the subject. It is nevertheless important to bear in mind the order in which the facts were discovered. This series of dates should be consulted frequently.

1883 Edison investigated *thermionic emission.*
1895 Röntgen discovered *X-rays.*
1896 Becquerel discovered *radioactivity.*
1897 Thomson measured *e/m* for *cathode rays.*
1903 Rutherford and Soddy presented a theory for the *disintegration* of atoms of *radioactive substances.*
1905 Einstein published the theory of relativity.
1906 Millikan measured the *electronic charge.*
1911 Rutherford published the results of the scattering experiments which suggested that the atom had a *nucleus.*
1913 Bohr's theory of the atom was published.
1919 Rutherford first achieved *artificial transmutation.*
1932 Chadwick discovered the *neutron.*
1932 Cockcroft and Walton produced a high energy accelerator for protons, which enabled them to achieve *artificial transmutation* of the light elements.
1933 The Joliot-Curies produced an *artificially radioactive isotope.*
1938 Hahn and Strassman discovered *nuclear fission.*
1942 Fermi constructed the first nuclear reactor.
1945 The first *atomic bomb* was dropped.
1952 The first *hydrogen bomb* was exploded.

Items which are in italics are mentioned again in this book.

The electron

9.2 CATHODE RAYS

Experiments performed from 1870 onwards showed that when metals were heated in a vacuum, so-called **cathode rays** were produced, the idea of a ray being suggested by the first observation below. Other observations, and the deductions made, were:

Observation	*Deduction*
(*a*) They cast a shadow of an obstacle (such as a Maltese cross) on the wall of the tube (Fig. 9.1).	(*a*) They travel in nearly straight paths, despite the transverse force acting on them (their weight), and so are moving *very fast*.
(*b*) They can, indirectly, provide enough energy to set a small paddle wheel into rotation.	(*b*) They probably consist of fast moving *particles*, whose kinetic energy is being transferred to the paddle wheel.
(*c*) They can pass through aluminium foil.	(*c*) If they are particles, they must be *very small*.
(*d*) They are deflected by a magnetic field in the opposite sense to that in which the usual (+) current is deflected (see Fig. 9.3).	(*d*) According to the motor rule they are *negatively charged*.
(*e*) They are deflected in an electric field towards a positive plate (see Fig. 9.3).	(*e*) This confirms that their charge is negative.
(*f*) They can be collected in a metal cylinder which acquires a negative charge. This is proved by testing the charge using an electroscope (Fig. 9.2). (This experiment was first performed by *Perrin*.)	(*f*) This associates them with the negative charge produced in electrostatics experiments (see p. 220). (Perrin was careful to bend the rays into the metal cylinder using a magnet, in order to be sure that the effect was not being caused by any electromagnetic radiation emitted by the hot cathode.)
(*g*) They affect a photographic plate.	(*g*) This confirms that they have energy.

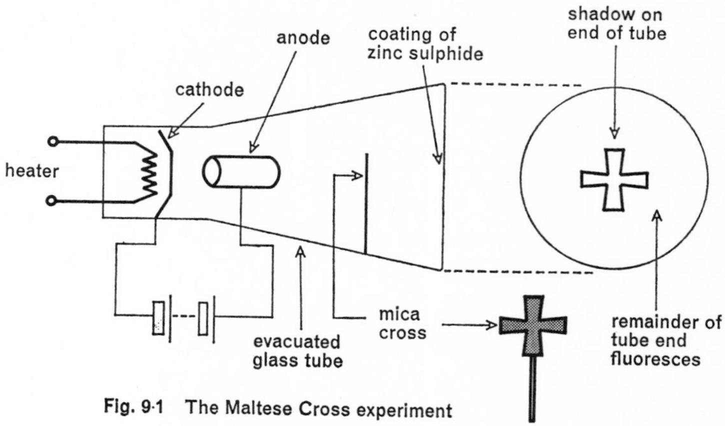

Fig. 9·1 The Maltese Cross experiment

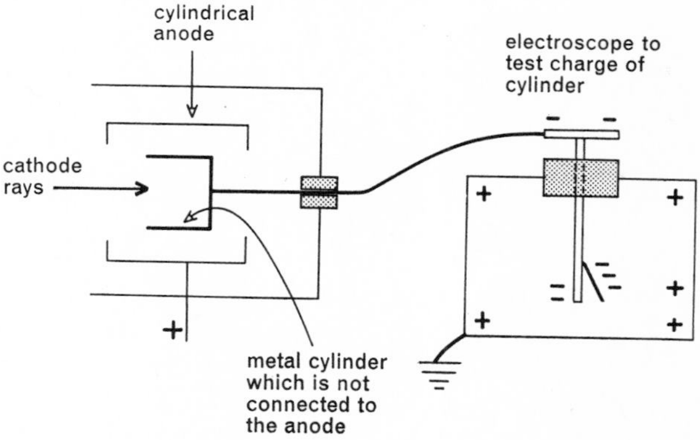

Fig. 9·2 The principle of Perrin's experiment

These observations suggest that cathode rays are streams of very small, very fast-moving, negatively charged **particles.** The **specific charge** (the ratio (charge/mass)) of these particles was measured by Thomson (1897), and the charge of the particles was indirectly measured by Millikan (1906).

9.3 THOMSON'S DETERMINATION OF THE SPECIFIC CHARGE OF THE CATHODE RAY PARTICLES

The apparatus shown in Fig. 9.3 is used, but with *uniform* electric and magnetic fields. By directing the fields to be at right angles, Thomson

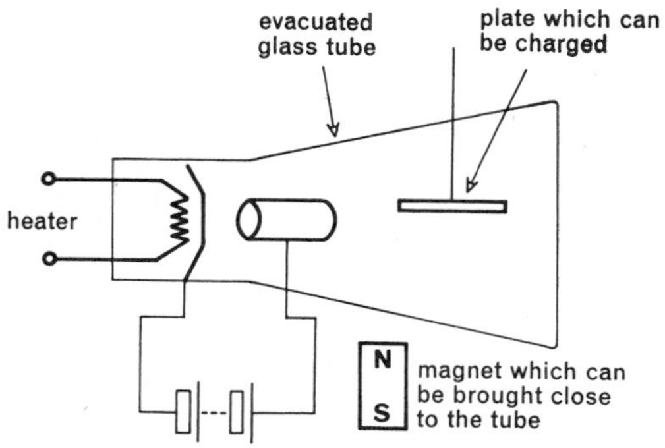

Fig. 9·3 If uniform fields are required
(i) magnetic: use a pair of coils arranged on either side of the tube
(ii) electric: add another plate parallel to the one shown and oppositely charged

arranged for their effects to be equal and opposite, so that the resultant deflection of the beam was zero. From his measurements he was able

(*a*) to calculate the speed of the particles,
(*b*) to calculate their specific charge,
(*c*) to show that this last ratio was the *same for all cathode materials.*

He concluded that the particles found in cathode rays are *common to all types of matter.*

9.4 MILLIKAN'S DETERMINATION OF THE CHARGE CARRIED BY OIL DROPS

The principle of the determination

Fig. 9.4*a* shows an experiment which enables the force on a charged object placed in a vertical electric field to be measured. The object, a small pith ball, coated with gold leaf, has three forces acting on it:

(*a*) the pull of the Earth,
(*b*) the pull of the thread,
(*c*) the electric force.

By measuring the distance the rider must be moved to restore equilibrium when the electric field is removed, the size of the electric force can be calculated, and can be shown to vary with the charge on the pith ball.

The Millikan experiment

Fig. 9.4*b* shows Millikan's actual arrangement. Oil drops were sprayed

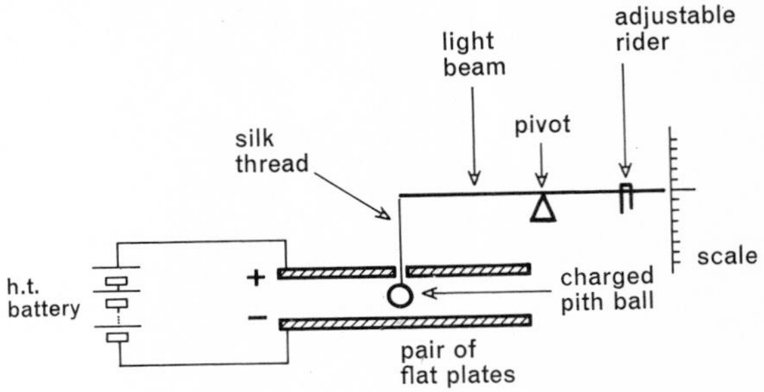

(a) The force on a charged sphere

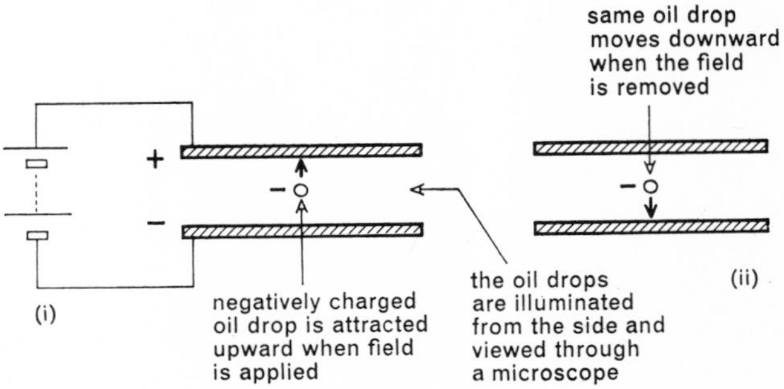

(b) The idea behind Millikan's experiment

Fig. 9·4

into the region between the plates, between which an electric field could be applied. The breaking up of the oil into very small drops was enough to charge some of them. By measuring

(*a*) the speed at which drops

  (*i*) rise if the field is applied,
  (*ii*) fall if the field is removed,

(*b*) the potential difference between the plates, and
(*c*) the distance of the top plate from the bottom,

Millikan was able to calculate the charge on the oil drop considered. He found that the charge on any drop was *a whole number times the smallest charge* that he measured. A typical set of results might have been:

minus 14·4, 11·2, 3·2, 11·2, 6·4, 1·6, 8·0, 1·6, etc., $\times 10^{-19}$ coulomb.

We assume that the smallest charge, $-1{\cdot}6\times10^{-19}$ coulomb, is **the fundamental unit of charge.** No fraction of this charge has ever been measured.

9.5 THE ELECTRON

From the previous two sections we have:

(*a*) a fundamental unit of charge, $-1{\cdot}6\times10^{-19}$ coulomb,
(*b*) a particle which *probably* has a fixed charge (since the specific charge is the same for all these particles).

The simplest conclusion is that *the particle carries the fundamental charge,* and nothing has yet been found to contradict this assumption.

We give the name **electron** to this particle, which

(*a*) is common to all matter,
(*b*) carries a charge of $e = -1{\cdot}6\times10^{-19}$ coulomb.

9.6 THOMSON'S CANAL RAYS

Thomson modified the apparatus shown in Fig. 9.5 so that he could find the specific charge for the *ions of gas,* which are positively charged. By using hydrogen in the tube, he found that the value for the hydrogen

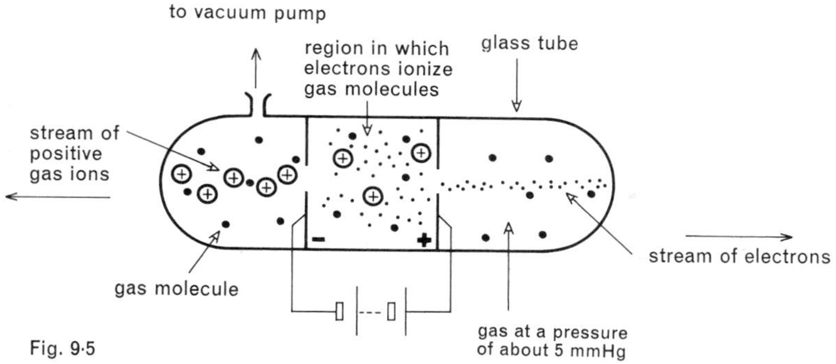

Fig. 9·5

ion was 1840 times smaller than that previously obtained for the electron, and was the same as that previously obtained from electrolysis experiments (see p. 268). He concluded that if their charges are numerically equal (of the same size but of opposite sign), then the mass of the hydrogen ion is 1840 times the mass of the electron. He was also able to calculate the masses of other positive ions, and this led to the discovery of **isotopes** (see p. 247).

9.7 X-RAYS

X-rays are produced when electrons strike matter: e.g. when the electrons of 'cathode rays' hit the end of a tube such as that in Fig. 9.3. They are electromagnetic waves (since in this situation electric charge is being rapidly decelerated) of very small wavelength. They have all the usual properties of electromagnetic waves (see p. 174). Note particularly that:

(*a*) They pass readily through matter containing atoms of small mass, but are absorbed far more by atoms of large mass. This is the basis of **radiography,** the study of bones by X-ray photography.
(*b*) They can use their considerable energy to separate electrons from the rest of a gas molecule, i.e. *they ionize gases,* and thus enable the gases to conduct electricity (see p. 269).

The atom

9.8 THE NUCLEUS

Atoms are electrically neutral, even though they contain electrons. What else does the atom contain? What is its structure?

Evidence for the existence of a hard core or nucleus inside the atom comes from *scattering experiments* carried out for Rutherford by Geiger and Marsden (Fig. 9.6).

Results

(*a*) A large proportion of α-particles (see p. 242) passes straight through the gold foil. This suggests that the atom is very nearly empty.
(*b*) Some α-particles are *repelled back,* and this gives the clue for the existence of the nucleus.
(*c*) Detailed measurements on the number of α-particles scattered in particular directions
  (*i*) confirm that the nucleus exists,
  (*ii*) enable its charge to be measured,
  (*iii*) enable its size to be measured.

The diameter of the nucleus is about 10^{-14} m, while the diameter of an atom is about 10^{-10} m (see p. 26). The charge of the nucleus is found to be a whole number multiple of the charge on an electron, but of opposite sign.

9.9 THE MATERIALS OF THE ATOM

The nucleus of the hydrogen atom is found to consist of a single positively charged particle, which we call a **proton.** It is sometimes

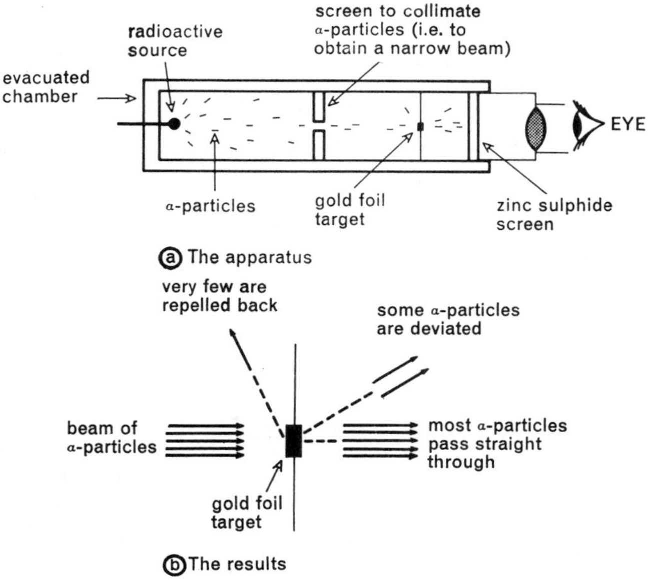

Fig. 9·6 Geiger and Marsden's experiment

convenient to express masses relative to that of the proton, which is

$$1{\cdot}7 \times 10^{-27}\,\text{kg}.$$

Other nuclei carry charges which are multiples of the electronic charge but have masses which are different multiples of the mass of the proton. It has been discovered that the nucleus consists of **neutrons,** which are electrically neutral, as well as protons.

Particle	*Charge relative to charge of proton*	*Mass relative to mass of proton*	*Discovery*
electron	-1	$\frac{1}{1840}$	Thomson, 1897
proton	$+1$	1·0	Early electrolysis experiments Named by Rutherford, 1920
neutron	0	1·0	Chadwick, 1932

The neutron and the proton are called **nucleons.**

9.10 THE ATOM

The emptiness of the atom suggests that we can visualize the electrons as being some distance from a nucleus made up of protons and neutrons, as shown in Fig. 2.1. The study of how the protons and neutrons are fitted into the nucleus, and the nature of the forces between them, leads to the topic of *nuclear physics*.

The **atomic number** of an element is the number of protons in the nucleus.

When an atom is electrically neutral, the atomic number is equal to the number of orbital electrons. The behaviour of the orbital electrons determines the *chemical* nature of an element – this means that it is the atomic number which fixes the position of an element in the periodic table.

The **mass number** of an atom is the number of nucleons in the nucleus.

The mass of the electrons can be neglected compared to the mass of the nucleus. The conventional way of representing atomic and mass number in symbols is given on page 245.

9.11 THE ORBITAL ELECTRONS

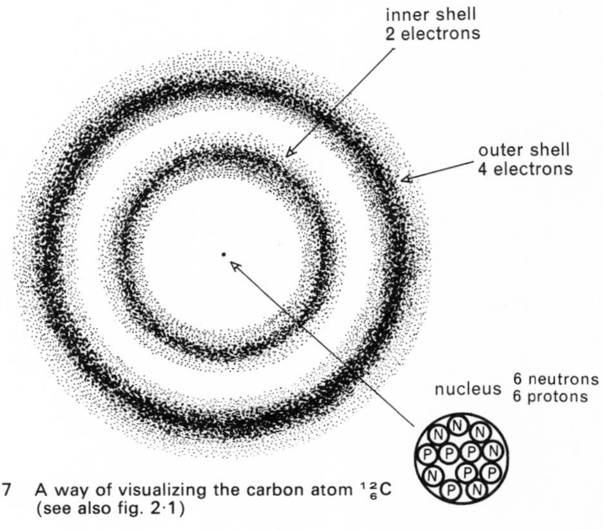

Fig. 9·7 A way of visualizing the carbon atom $^{12}_{6}C$ (see also fig. 2·1)

When elements are arranged in a pattern according to their **chemical** properties, we obtain a pattern called the **periodic table.** This arrangement enables us to guess how the orbital electrons may be arranged.

Example

Fig. 9.7 shows a way of representing a carbon atom. The electrons in this case fall into two outer **shells** or groups, the inner having two electrons, and the outer the remaining four. The arrangement of electrons into shells can be predicted on theoretical grounds, and the fact that our construction of the periodic table, on practical grounds, agrees with the theoretical arrangement, is good evidence in support of the theory.

Thermionic emission

9.12 ELECTRONS IN METALS AND THE THERMIONIC EFFECT

Within any volume of metal some of the outer electrons of an atom may have the property of being able to wander away from their parent nuclei. Although they leave positive ions, the metal as a whole remains electrically neutral. These electrons are called **conduction electrons,** since they are available to conduct either heat or an electric current (see p. 40).

If such an electron tries to escape from the surface, it will experience an attractive force back into the metal, because of the positive ion that it leaves behind. In order to escape it must therefore be given sufficient energy, and this can be achieved by heating the metal: when the temperature is high enough, electrons will start to *evaporate* from the metal surface.

Thermionic emission is the emission of electrons (called **thermions** in this situation) from a metal as a result of its being heated. If that metal is then used in a circuit, it will be called the *cathode* (see p. 263).

9.13 THE DIODE

(See Fig. 9.8.) An electric heater is placed near to the cathode to heat it. The electrons emitted from the cathode are attracted to the *anode,* since there is a large electric field between the anode and the cathode. The milliammeter registers a current. This is evidence for the movement of charge, and we suppose that the origin of this is the emission of electrons from the surface of the metal. (The thermionic diode is discussed further on page 249.)

Measurement of the current (rate of charge flow) through the cathode

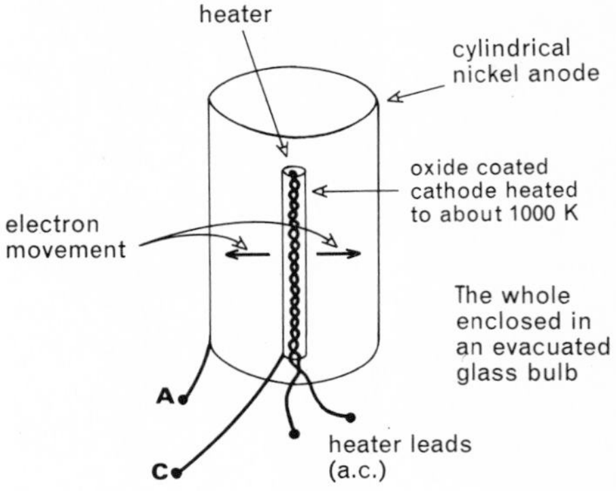

(a) Construction of the thermionic diode

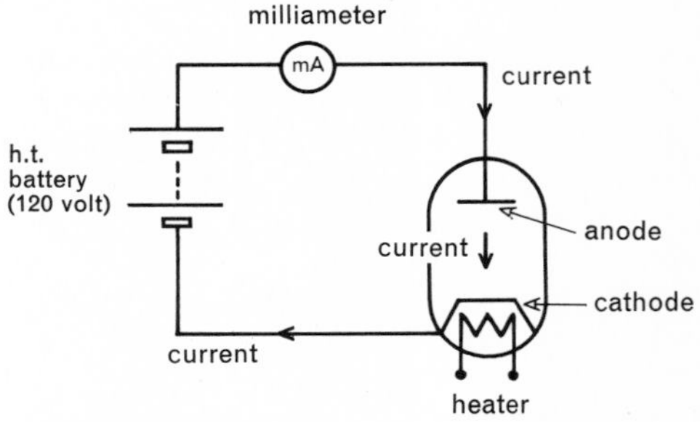

(b) Circuit diagram

Fig. 9·8

with a milliammeter enables us to calculate the number of electrons that leave the cathode in each second. Thus if N electrons, each of charge e, leave the cathode in time t, then

$$I = \frac{Q}{t} = \frac{Ne}{t},$$

from which N/t can be found.

The conventional sense of current flow is from the anode to the cathode.

9.14 THE CATHODE RAY TUBE

The cathode ray tube is a device for producing a beam of electrons by using the thermionic effect. We can calculate the speed v to which the

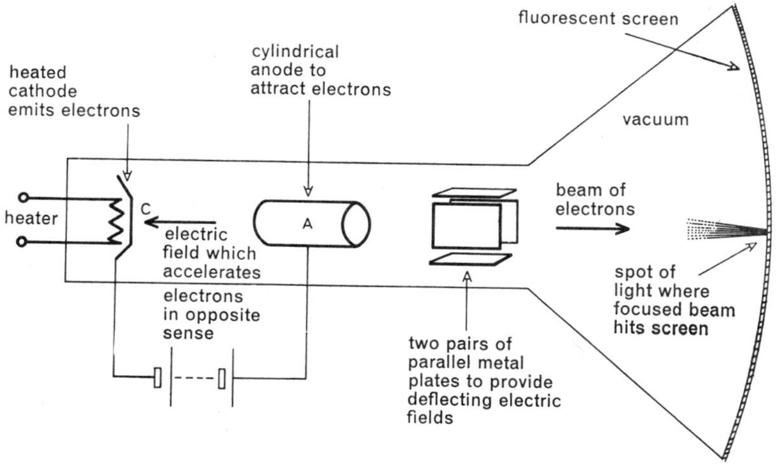

Fig. 9·9 Simplified form of cathode ray tube

electrons have been accelerated by the electric field in the space between the cathode and the anode:

Since $$W = QV$$ (see p. 251),

$$\begin{pmatrix}\text{the work done on an}\\ \text{electron which moves}\\ \text{from C to A}\end{pmatrix} = \begin{pmatrix}\text{charge of an}\\ \text{electron}\end{pmatrix} \times \begin{pmatrix}\text{potential difference}\\ \text{between C and A}\end{pmatrix}$$

But work done on an electron = gain of k.e. of electron,

so $$\tfrac{1}{2}m_e v^2 = eV.$$

The cathode ray tube is used in an oscilloscope and a television set. It can conveniently be used to demonstrate some of the properties of cathode rays.

Radioactivity

9.15 RADIOACTIVITY

Radioactivity is the spontaneous disintegration of the unstable nucleus of an atom. Elements, particularly those with atomic number greater than 82, are liable to disintegrate by emitting any of the following:

(*a*) **α-rays**
(*b*) **β-rays** } which are discussed in Section 9.16,
(*c*) **γ-rays**
(*d*) other particles, and X-rays.

Note: (*i*) The radiation is emitted at a rate that depends on the number of undisintegrated atoms that are present, and which varies from element to element. We cannot predict when a particular atom will disintegrate but only the average rate of **decay** if there are enough of them. That the process is **random** can be seen on a spinthariscope screen (see p. 244).

(*ii*) The rate of disintegration is not affected by any external conditions such as temperature and chemical combination: this suggests that the *nucleus is responsible*.

(*iii*) By emitting α-rays and β-rays of high kinetic energy, a radioactive substance can be used to supply energy steadily over a period of time.

Experiment

To show that some radioactive substances produce radiations which have enough energy to ionize large numbers of air molecules, use a gold leaf electroscope, and e.g. a radium source, as shown in Fig. 9.10. The rate at which the leaf drops in the absence of the source should first be established. The sign of the original charge on the electroscope *does not matter,* showing that it is not the nature of the radiation from the source which discharges the electroscope, but rather the production of ion pairs in the air close to the cap.

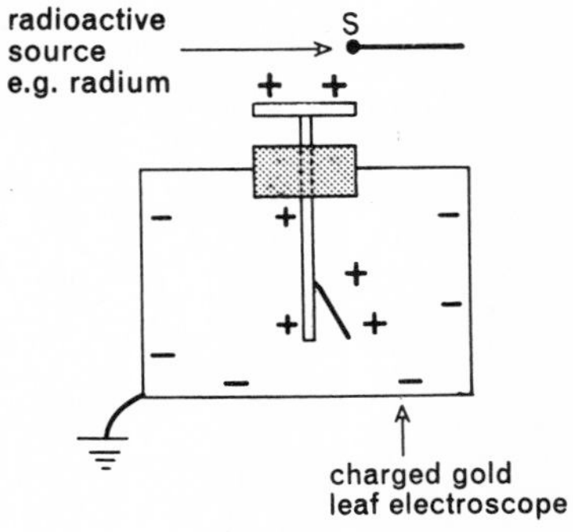

Fig. 9·10

(*a*) If S is held close to the cap the electroscope discharges.
(*b*) If (*i*) S is held away from the cap or (*ii*) a piece of paper 0·1 mm thick is placed between S and the cap in (*a*), the electroscope remains charged.

9.16 DISTINCTION BETWEEN THE RADIATIONS

(a) Penetration

Radiation	*Penetration*	*Deduction*
α	(*i*) is the same for any particular disintegration (*ii*) is typically about 10^{-2} mm in aluminium (*iii*) varies from 30 to 80 mm in air, for different disintegrations	α-rays are emitted with the same energy for any particular disintegration
β	(*i*) is variable for any particular nucleus (*ii*) typical maximum penetration varies from 10^{-2} mm up to about 3 mm in aluminium	variable energy
γ	variable from foils to several mm of lead	variable energy

(b) Apply electric field

(*i*) *α-rays* are deflected as positive charge would be deflected,
(*ii*) *β-rays* are deflected as negative charge would be deflected,
(*iii*) *γ-rays* are undeflected.

(c) Apply magnetic field

Fig. 9.11 shows that the experiment confirms the sign of charges suggested by (*b*) (see the motor effect on p. 280). In addition,

(*i*) *α-rays* – show a small deflection, which suggests that they are *particles* of relatively large mass,
– show little dispersion, which confirms that their speeds are the same for a particular disintegration;

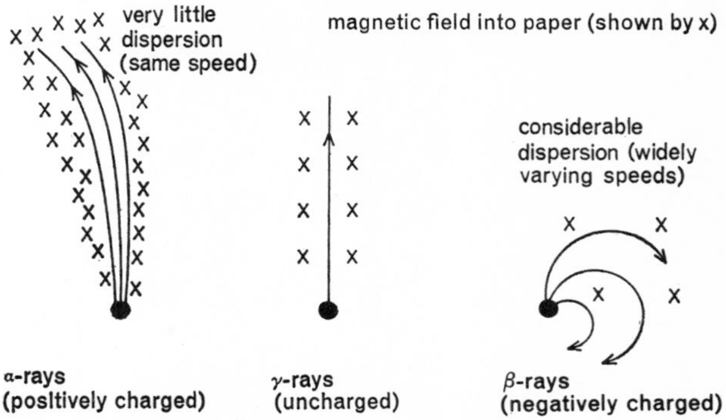

Fig. 9·11 Schematic deflection of radioactive radiations

(*ii*) *β-rays* – show a large deflection, which suggests that they are *particles* of relatively small mass,
– show considerable dispersion, which confirms that they are emitted with variable speeds.

Their nature

(*i*) It is now known that *α-particles* consist of two protons and two neutrons joined together, i.e. they are helium nuclei. They have a charge of plus two. They are useful for the bombardment of nuclei.

(*ii*) *β-particles* are electrons: they travel quickly, but their small mass explains their easy deflection.

(*iii*) *γ-radiation* does not consist of particles, but of electromagnetic waves of short wavelength (typically about 10^{-11} m, see p. 179). It has no charge, and so we can detect no deflection in a magnetic field.

9.17 APPARATUS FOR DETECTING THE RADIATION

Chambers

If a charged particle moves through a region in which there is vapour about to condense, or liquid about to boil, then it will encourage the formation of droplets and vapour bubbles respectively. Either of these will leave a *trail* to show the path of the particle: the trail may be photographed if the chamber is brightly lit from the side.

Note that the droplets and vapour bubbles do *not* form on the *particle* being detected, but on the *ions it forms* during its passage through the vapour or the liquid. The energy of the charged particle being detected is gradually used up in forming these ions.

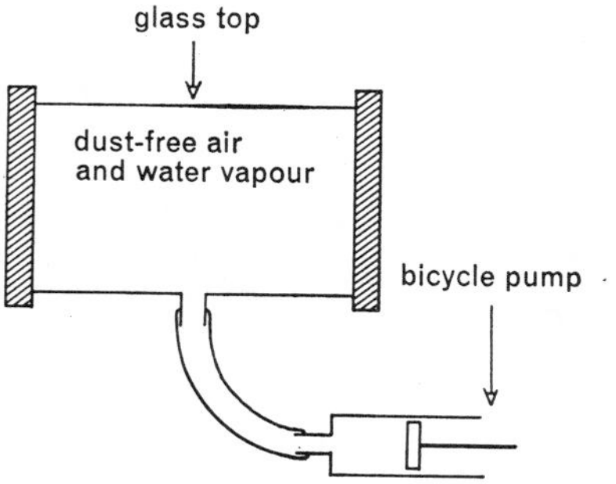

Fig. 9·12 The Wilson cloud chamber

(1) *The Wilson cloud chamber.* A sudden expansion of the right amount will cool the water vapour so as to produce condensation on the ions of either positive or negative charge.

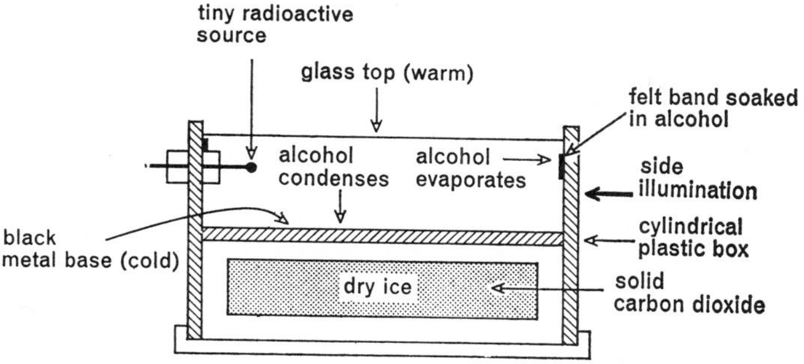

Fig. 9·13 The diffusion chamber

(2) *The diffusion chamber.* There is a region just above the floor where alcohol will condense only on charged particles, e.g. on the ions formed by the passage of the products of radioactive decay processes.

(3) In the *bubble chamber,* charged particles leave a trail of ions in liquid hydrogen which is then observed as a trail of bubbles.

The spinthariscope

A particle striking the screen in Fig. 9.14 gives out a flash of light lasting about 10^{-4} s. The material of the screen can be suited to the radiation to be detected. Zinc sulphide is suitable for α-particles, and barium platinocyanide for β-particles and γ-radiation. We view the flash through a magnifying glass, so that individual processes can be counted

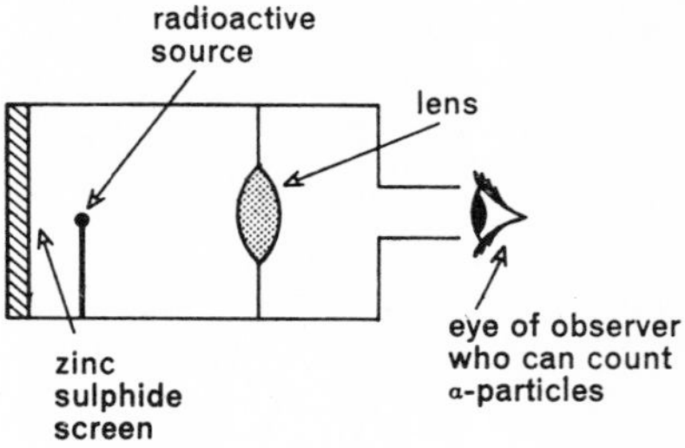

Fig. 9·14 A spinthariscope

over a period of time, although to do this the eye must be given time to adapt to the dark (about ten minutes).

The Geiger-Muller counter

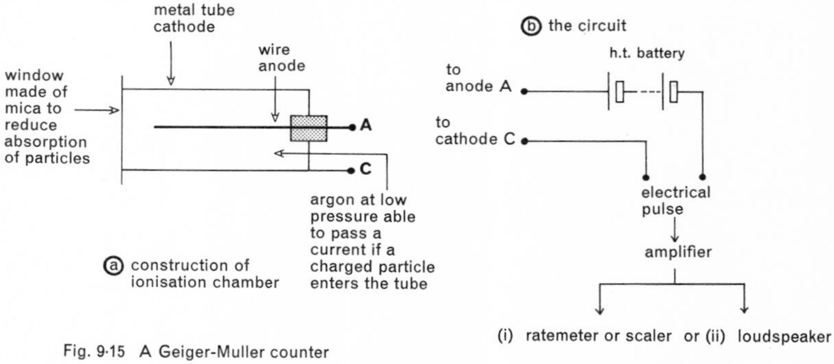

Fig. 9·15 A Geiger-Muller counter

Radiation which enters the tube ionizes gas molecules by collision, and so an electrical pulse passes through the circuit. This pulse is amplified, and is either

(*i*) fed into a loudspeaker so that a signal is heard, or
(*ii*) used to activate an automatic counter, which is called a **scaler** or **ratemeter.**

Photographic emulsion method

A charged particle will show its path on a photographic plate by a line of silver grains when the plate is developed. This is as though the film had been exposed to light energy along the track.

9.18 HALF-LIFE PERIOD

Suppose we have a large number of atoms of a radioactive material in a spinthariscope, as shown in Fig. 9.14. (Remember that 10^{-4} kg of material may consist of as many as 10^{21} molecules.) We can measure the rate of disintegration by counting flashes on the screen. Plot *number of flashes in each time interval* against *time:*

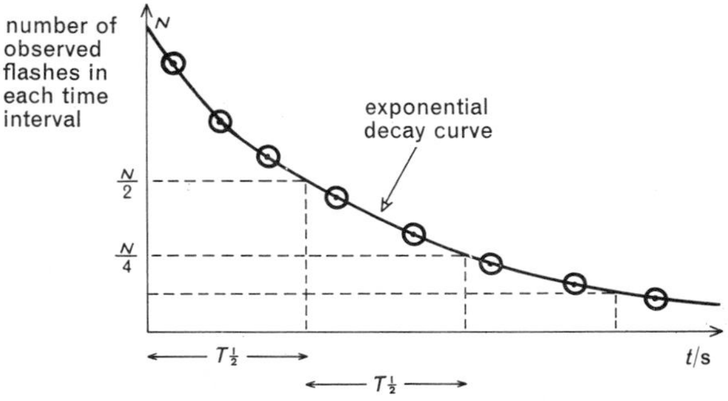

Fig. 9·16 Radioactive decay curve

The relative positions of the source and screen must be the same throughout the experiment. The time taken for the rate of flashing to be halved is called the **half-life period** ($T_{\frac{1}{2}}$). It is the time taken for half the atoms which were originally present to decay. If we were to repeat the experiment at a later time, but using the same source, we would again measure the same half-life period, even though we would be starting with fewer undisintegrated atoms. The decay is said to occur **exponentially.**

The half-life $T_{\frac{1}{2}}$ is a measure of the *activity* of the source. Depending on the nature of the radioactive source, the value of $T_{\frac{1}{2}}$ varies from, e.g. about 10^9 years for uranium I, to 10^{-6} s for some products of radium decay. In the laboratory a radioactive decay curve can conveniently be plotted using protactinium $^{234}_{91}Pa$, for which $T_{\frac{1}{2}} = 70$ s.

A rough idea of the value of $T_{\frac{1}{2}}$ can be established using a diffusion chamber. The nature of the tracks formed by α- and β-particles from a radioactive source is given in Fig. 9.17, together with the tracks formed by a beam of γ-radiation for comparison.

9.19 RADIOACTIVE TRANSFORMATIONS

Representation by symbols

By convention, $^{235}_{92}U$ is the symbol that denotes an atom of the element uranium, whose atomic number is 92, and whose mass number is 235.

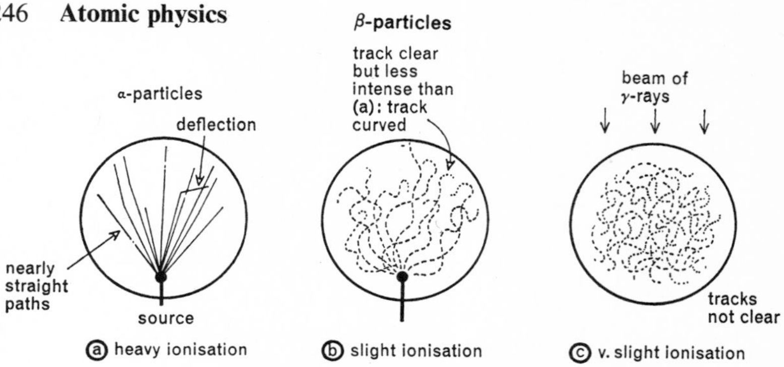

Fig. 9·17 Radiation tracks as seen in the diffusion chamber

Thus

particle	*symbol*	*particle*	*symbol*
α-particle electron	$^{4}_{2}\alpha$ $^{0}_{-1}e$	proton neutron	$^{1}_{1}p$ $^{1}_{0}n$

The rules for decay

(*a*) Suppose an *α-particle* is emitted: the nucleus loses

(*i*) two positive charges, so the atomic number is decreased by two,
(*ii*) four nucleons, so the mass number is decreased by four.

(*b*) Suppose a *β-particle* is emitted: the nucleus loses

(*i*) one negative charge. Since this is equivalent to gaining one positive charge, the atomic number is *increased* by one. (Note that the electron is lost *from the nucleus*),
(*ii*) the mass of one electron, which is negligible.

(*c*) Suppose that a *γ-ray* is emitted. There is a loss of energy, but not of charge.

The emission of a γ-ray frequently accompanies the emission of an α-particle or a β-particle. When this occurs, rule (*a*) or (*b*) will apply.

Examples

(*a*) *Natural*

$$\underset{\text{radium}}{^{226}_{88}\text{Ra}} \longrightarrow \underset{\text{radon}}{^{222}_{86}\text{Rn}} + \underset{\text{α-particle ejected}}{^{4}_{2}\alpha}$$

This is an example of **α-decay.**

(*b*) *Artificial*

Bombardment of a stable nucleus with a suitable missile (such as a proton, neutron or α-particle) may create a new nucleus, which is itself unstable, and which therefore starts to decay:

$^{2}_{1}H$	+	$^{23}_{11}Na$	$\longrightarrow$	$^{24}_{11}Na$	+	$^{1}_{1}p$
heavy hydrogen nucleus absorbed		sodium		radioactive sodium		proton ejected

The sodium-24 nucleus which is produced is radioactive, and decays relatively quickly:

$^{24}_{11}Na$	$\rightarrow$	$^{24}_{12}Mg$	+	$^{0}_{-1}e$
sodium		magnesium		electron

This is an example of **β-decay.**

Note that in these examples the number of nucleons and the total charge is *conserved* in any one equation, and this can be checked by adding the mass numbers or atomic numbers on each side of the equation.

9.20 MISCELLANEOUS TOPICS

Artificial transmutations

An enormous amount of research has been undertaken to determine the products when materials are bombarded with missiles such as neutrons, protons and α-particles. You should not attempt to learn any results, but in each equation you read, apply the rules of decay.

(*i*) *Rutherford* achieved the first artificial transmutation by firing α-particles at nitrogen: this produced an isotope of oxygen.

$^{14}_{7}N$	+	$^{4}_{2}\alpha$	$\longrightarrow$	$^{17}_{8}O$	+	$^{1}_{1}p$
nitrogen		absorbed α-particle		oxygen		ejected proton

(*ii*) *Cockroft* and *Walton* were the first people to accelerate the missiles to a high energy before bombardment. They fired protons at lithium, and α-particles were produced.

$^{7}_{3}Li$	+	$^{1}_{1}p$	$\longrightarrow$	$2\,^{4}_{2}\alpha$
lithium		artificially accelerated protons absorbed		α-particles ejected

Isotopes

If we add neutrons to, or take them away from, the nucleus of an element, then we change its mass number, but not its atomic number or chemical nature. The new atom and the old are said to be **isotopes** – they have the same atomic number, but different mass numbers. ${}^{12}_{6}C$ and ${}^{14}_{6}C$ are examples. Atoms which have the same mass number but different atomic numbers are called **isobars** (same weight). ${}^{24}_{12}Mg$ and ${}^{24}_{11}Na$ are examples.

Isotopes are most easily made within a nuclear reactor, where there is a good supply of neutrons to bring about the required change. If the isotope is radioactive, then it is called a **radioisotope.**

Uses

(*i*) In medicine; in the treatment of cancer with ${}^{60}_{27}Co$ (cobalt-60), the emitted γ-rays destroy the cancerous tissue.

(*ii*) As a *tracer element.* A radioisotope can be mixed with ordinary atoms of the same atomic number, and will experience the same chemical treatment. A Geiger counter can then be used to find the subsequent location of the isotope atoms.

(*iii*) The thickness of a material can be measured from the decrease in the intensity of the radiation that has passed through it.

Fission and fusion

Fission is the breaking up of a massive nucleus into two nearly equal parts, as opposed to the fragments that natural radioactivity on Earth produces. Any net reduction of mass is accounted for by an output of energy. This is the basis of the *atom bomb.*

Fusion occurs when two light atoms merge so as to form an atom with a greater atomic mass than either. This process is accompanied by an enormous output of energy, for the same reason. It is the mechanism by which the Sun converts mass into radiant energy, and is the basis of the *hydrogen bomb.*

Radiation hazards

(*a*) A source should never be present *inside the body,* since at all times its radiation will damage the living cells. For example ${}^{90}_{38}Sr$ (strontium-90) is absorbed into the bones, where its radiation damages the bone marrow.

(*b*) An *external source* is less dangerous because it will only cause damage while it is close to the body. Even while it is there,

(*i*) the α-radiation cannot penetrate the skin,

(*ii*) the other radiations can be screened: e.g. β-radiation by a sheet of Perspex, and γ-radiation by (typically) 50 to 100 mm of lead or a few metres of concrete.

10 Current electricity

Electric circuits

10.1 MOVING CHARGE

An **electric current** is a flow of electrically charged particles, usually ions or electrons.

The direction of the current is the direction of movement of the charge. The sense of the current is taken to be that of the positive charge, or, if only negative charge is moving, then in the reverse sense to its movement.

In (*a*) of Fig. 10.1 the charge will continue to flow while the belt is

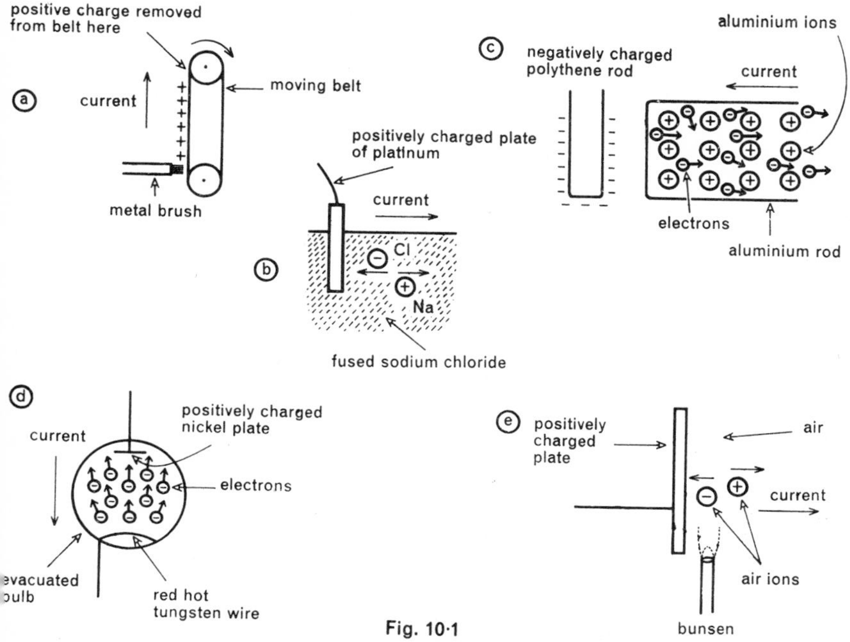

Fig. 10·1

kept moving, but in each of (*b*), (*c*), (*d*) and (*e*) the movement of charge will quickly produce an accumulation of charge. This charge sets up an electric field which will oppose the further movement of charge.

Possible **sources** of continuous current are:

(*a*) chemical cells,
(*b*) electromagnetic induction devices,
(*c*) thermoelectric devices,
(*d*) photoelectric cells,
(*e*) friction devices.

Each of these types of source uses energy in order to maintain a current.

A flow of charge can produce:

(*a*) a chemical effect (which also leads to a physiological effect),
(*b*) a heating effect,
(*c*) a magnetic effect (which also leads to a mechanical effect).

Each of these types of effect involves a transfer of energy. Thus electricity is a convenient way of transferring energy from one place to another. The charge is *not* used up.

10.2 DEFINITIONS

Current: a current is a flow of electrically charged particles.

> One **ampere** (A) is that current which, when flowing in each of two infinitely long straight parallel wires, placed one metre apart in a vacuum, produces a force between them of 2×10^{-7} newton per metre of wire.

This definition is based on the magnetic effect of a current (see p. 275).

Charge: current and charge are related by the definition:

$$(\textbf{charge}\text{ passing a point}) = (\text{current}) \cdot \begin{pmatrix}\text{time for which current}\\ \text{flows at the point}\end{pmatrix}$$

$$Q\,[\text{coulombs}] = I\,[\text{A}] \,.\, t\,[\text{s}].$$

$$\boxed{Q = It}$$

or

$$I = \frac{Q}{t}.$$

> One **coulomb** (C) is thus the charge (quantity of electricity) which passes any point when one ampere flows for one second.

Charge can be positive or negative (see p. 220).

Numerically 1 coulomb is approximately equivalent to the charge carried by $6{\cdot}25 \times 10^{18}$ electrons.

Potential difference: (see also p. 224)

The **potential difference** between two points $=$ $\dfrac{\text{work done}}{\text{charge transferred between the two points}}$

$$V\,[\text{volts}] = \frac{W\,[\text{J}]}{Q\,[\text{C}]}.$$

$$\boxed{V = \frac{W}{Q}}$$

Note that one volt means one joule/coulomb.

One **volt** (V) is thus the potential difference between two points when one joule of work is done in transferring one coulomb of charge from one point to the other.

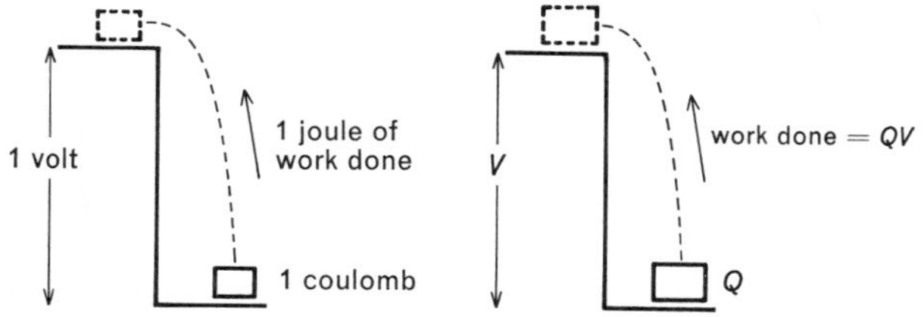

Fig. 10·2

Work is done on the charge by the *electric field* set up by the source. The source uses energy in order to maintain this electric field, and the energy thus gained by the charge is useful in producing one of the effects outlined on page 250.

10.3 THE POWER EQUATION

The equation

$$V = \frac{W}{Q}$$

defines potential difference; hence

$$W = QV.$$

Dividing both sides of this equation by a time interval t in which work W is done in transferring a charge Q, we obtain

$$\frac{W}{t} = \frac{Q}{t} . V,$$

i.e. $$\boxed{P = IV}$$

P being measured in J/s or watts (see p. 83):

$$P\left[\frac{\text{J}}{\text{s}}\right] = I\left[\frac{\text{C}}{\text{s}}\right] . V\left[\frac{\text{J}}{\text{C}}\right].$$

Thus if a current of 2·0 A flows from one point to another, the potential difference between the two points being 1·2 V, then electrical energy is converted into some other form at the rate of P, where

$$\begin{aligned} P &= 2{\cdot}0\,\text{A} \times 1{\cdot}2\,\text{V} \\ &= 2{\cdot}4\,\text{W}. \end{aligned}$$

This form might be:

(*a*) heat, e.g. in an electric fire,
(*b*) light, e.g. in a fluorescent lamp,
(*c*) chemical energy, e.g. in an electrolytic cell,
(*d*) mechanical energy, e.g. as kinetic energy in an electric motor, or when electrons are accelerated in a vacuum (see p. 239);

and in each case the *Principle of the Conservation of Energy* applies.

10.4 CURRENT – POTENTIAL DIFFERENCE RELATIONSHIPS

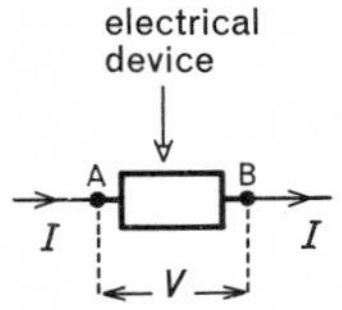

Fig. 10·3

If the potential difference V between the terminals A and B of different electrical devices is measured when a measured current I is passing through the devices, graphs such as those shown in Fig. 10·4 are obtained.

Note that the junction diode, vacuum diode and metal rectifier all possess a *one-way* property, which is widely used for rectifying alternating current (see p. 285). Hence they are called **valves.**

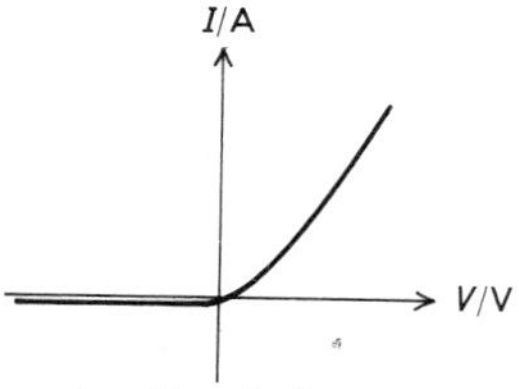

a junction diode
(p–n semi-conductor)
or a metal rectifier

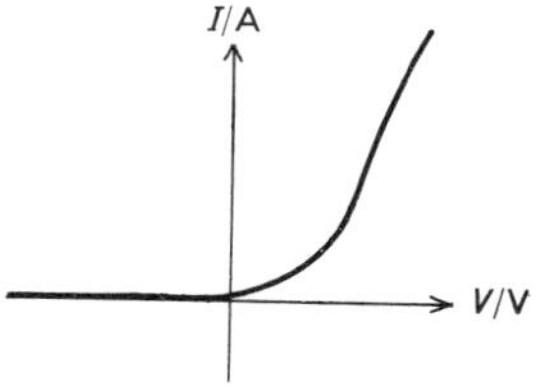

a vacuum diode

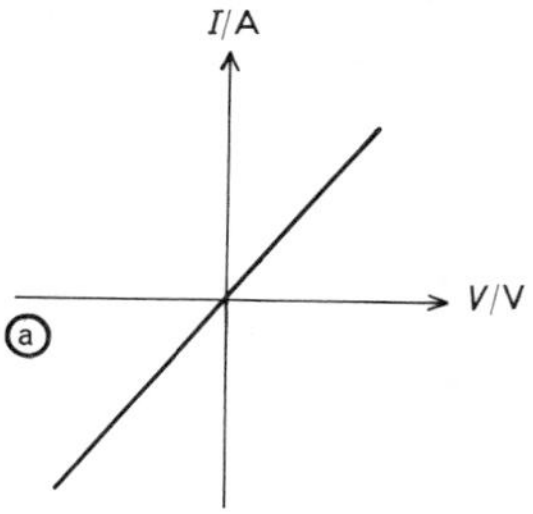

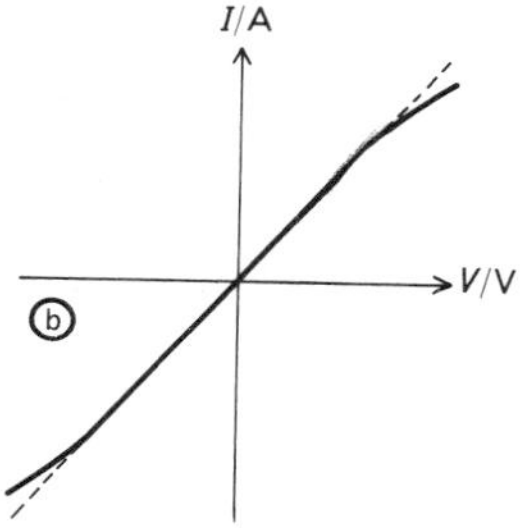

a pure metal or certain alloys when the physical conditions (a) are constant (b) alter for a good conductor

To be sure you appreciate the graphs, establish in particular examples, scales I and V; e.g. for a wire of the pure metal copper the current scale will be 0–1 while for a wire of the pure metal germanium it will be from $0–10^{-6}$

Fig. 10·4

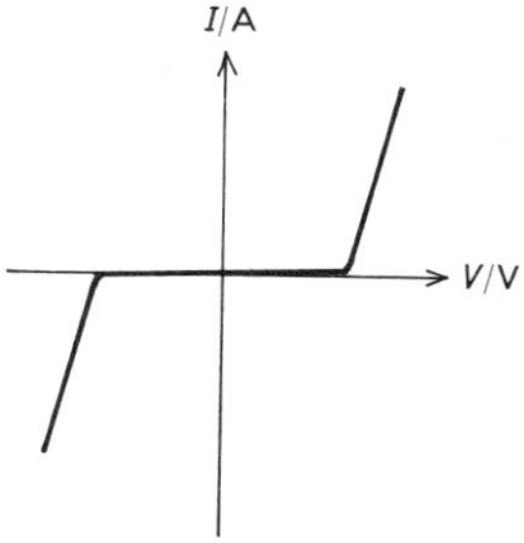

certain electrolytes

Resistance

In all the examples shown in Fig. 10.4 the ratio V/I is called the **resistance** of the device for the particular current flowing:

$$\frac{\text{potential difference between the ends of a device}}{\text{current flowing through the device}}$$

$$= \textbf{resistance} \text{ of the device}$$

$$\frac{V\,[\mathrm{V}]}{I\,[\mathrm{A}]} = R\,[\text{ohms}].$$

$$\boxed{\frac{V}{I} = R}$$

One **ohm** (Ω) is thus the resistance of an electrical device when a potential difference of one volt between the ends of the device causes a current of one ampere to flow through it.

Ohm's Law

For devices of pure metal or some alloys the value of R, the resistance of the device, is found to be constant under constant physical conditions (see Fig. 10.4).

Ohm's Law states that

$$\boxed{R = \text{constant}}$$

This means that the potential difference between the ends of the device is proportional to the current flowing through it. In this book we shall usually meet devices for which this law holds; we shall call them **resistors.**

Experiment

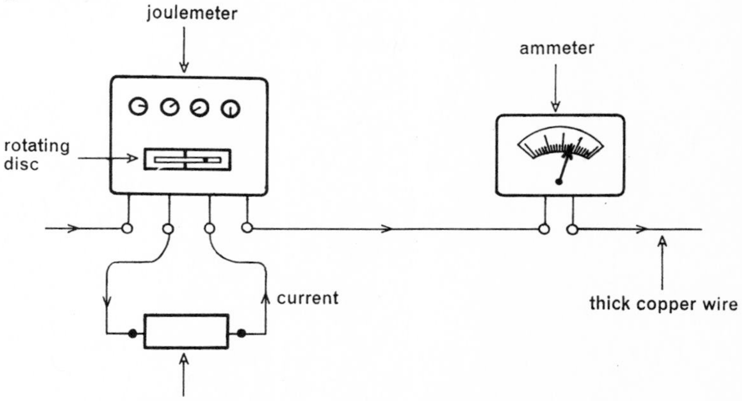

Fig. 10·5

To show that Ohm's Law holds for a pure metal or an alloy, pass a current through a length of the substance and measure:

(*a*) the current, I, using an ammeter,
(*b*) the energy dissipated per second, P, using a joulemeter and a clock.

If V is the potential difference between the ends of the device under test, then

$$P = IV \qquad \text{(the power equation)}$$

and

$$\frac{V}{I} = R$$

Hence $$P = I^2R.$$
If the graph of P against I^2 is a straight line, then $R =$ constant and the device obeys Ohm's Law. The value of $R = P/I^2$ can be calculated.

10.5 ELECTRICAL ENERGY AND POWER

The electrical properties of electric fires, kettles, light bulbs, etc., are described by two quantities:

(1) The potential difference which *should* be applied between the terminals of the device.
(2) The power which is consumed when this potential difference is applied; this, by the Principle of the Conservation of Energy, is equal to the power dissipated.

For example, for a light bulb the quantities might be: (1) 240 V, (2) 100 W. As $P = IV$ the current through the device can be calculated. Then $V/I = R$, and the resistance of the device when it is carrying this current can also be calculated. The *energy* converted in time t is

$$Pt = IVt = I^2Rt.$$

In the middle of the nineteenth century Joule performed experimental tests to show that the internal energy produced, Q, was proportional to I^2Rt, using simple calorimetric techniques. At the time that he did this the concept of internal energy was not fully appreciated and the relationship became known as **Joule's Law of heating.**

Electrical energy is bought from the Electricity Board in 'units'.

$$1 \text{ unit} = 3{\cdot}6 \times 10^6 \text{ J}.$$

One buys energy and the rate at which it is consumed does not matter. 1 'unit' costs about 1 p in Britain.

Not all the energy converted in electrical devices is used in the desired way, but heating devices are very efficient.

(*a*) An ordinary tungsten filament lamp will convert only 10 per cent of the electrical energy it consumes into light energy; the remaining 90 per cent is converted into invisible rays – mostly infra-red. A fluorescent light does better; about 40 per cent is converted to light energy (see p. 180).
(*b*) In electric motors the useful energy is the mechanical work done by the motor, but some of the electrical energy is dissipated as internal energy in the coils of the motor (see p. 279).

A **fuse** is a piece of metal which melts if too high a current passes through it. It can thus protect electrical devices by being the first part of a circuit to overheat. The melting of a fuse thus indicates a fault by breaking the circuit.

Transmission of electrical energy

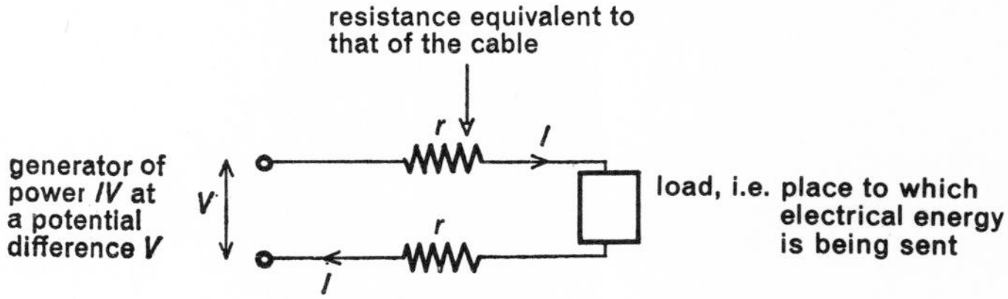

Fig. 10·6

$$\begin{aligned}\text{Power generated} &= IV,\\ \text{power dissipated in wires} &= I^2r+I^2r,\\ &= 2I^2r,\\ \text{power available at load} &= IV-2I^2r,\end{aligned}$$

r should be as small as possible, but this is limited by the cost, and thus, to reduce the loss $2I^2r$, I is made as small as possible. To do this the potential difference V at the power station should be as big as possible for a given IV. Alternating current is used so that *transformers* can produce this potential difference V, which can be at least as high as 264 000 V.

10.6 RESISTORS

Resistors are represented in circuit diagrams as shown in Fig. 10.7.

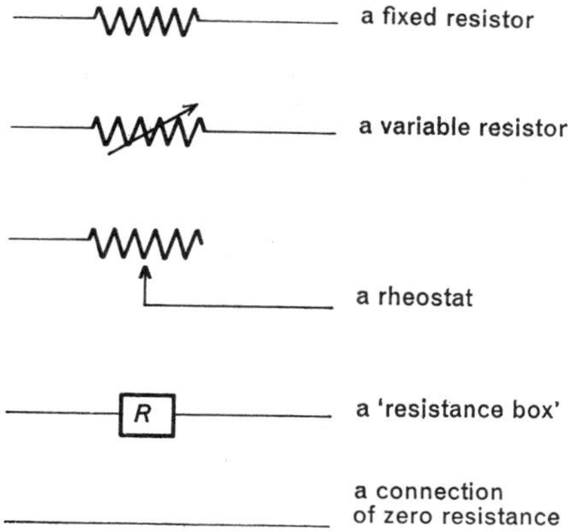

Fig. 10.7

Resistors may be combined in series or in parallel.

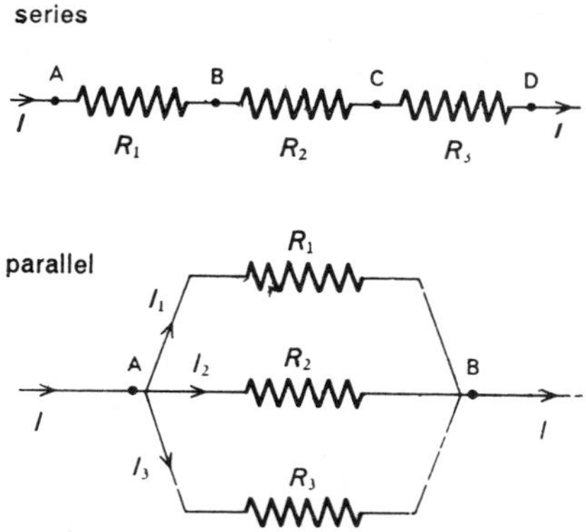

Fig. 10·8

Series

(*a*) The same charge and thus the same current flows through each resistor. Let the current be I.

(*b*) If the potential difference between A and B is V_1, that between B and C is V_2 and that between C and D is V_3, then the potential difference between A and D is

$$V = V_1 + V_2 + V_3.$$

(*c*) As $V/I = R$, i.e. $V = IR$, the total effective resistance between A and D is R, where

$$IR = IR_1 + IR_2 + IR_3.$$

Thus

$$R = R_1 + R_2 + R_3.$$

Parallel

(*a*) The charge flowing into A cannot disappear, and thus (see Fig. 10.8)

$$I = I_1 + I_2 + I_3.$$

(*b*) The work done in transferring one coulomb of charge from A to B is not dependent on the path taken, i.e. the potential difference between the ends of each resistor is the same. Let it be V.

(*c*) As $V/I = R$, i.e. $I = V/R$, the total effective resistance between A and B is R, where

$$\frac{V}{R} = \frac{V}{R_1} + \frac{V}{R_2} + \frac{V}{R_3}.$$

Thus
$$\frac{1}{R} = \frac{1}{R_1} + \frac{1}{R_2} + \frac{1}{R_3}.$$

Note that R will be less than the smallest of R_1, R_2 and R_3. Both of the above proofs have referred to three resistors, but similar proofs can be followed for any number of resistors.

10.7 RESISTIVITY

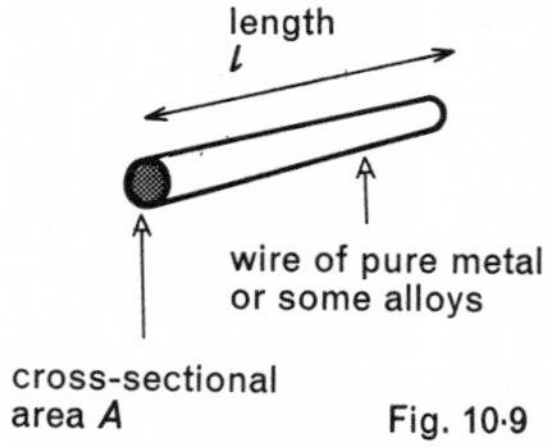

Fig. 10·9

For a given metal substance (pure or alloyed) maintained at a constant temperature the resistance R is found to be proportional to l and $1/A$, i.e.

$$R \propto \frac{l}{A} \quad \text{or} \quad R = \text{constant}.\frac{l}{A}.$$

The constant is called the **resistivity of the substance** and has the unit Ω m.

$$R\,[\Omega] = \rho\,[\Omega\,\text{m}].\frac{l\,[\text{m}]}{A\,[\text{m}^2]}.$$

$$\boxed{R = \rho\frac{l}{A}}$$

$$\rho = \frac{RA}{l}.$$

This equation *defines* ρ.

When using it, be careful of

(*i*) units,
(*ii*) confusion between radius and diameter when the substance is in the form of a wire of circular cross-section.

Resistivity and temperature

The resistivity of pure metals and alloys varies with temperature.

(*a*) For copper, tungsten and most metals which are good conductors and are used in electrical circuits, the resistivity doubles if the temperature rises from 300 K to 500 K, and the increase continues as the temperature rises further. Thus at the working temperature of an electric light filament bulb the resistivity (and thus the resistance) of the filament will be several times its value at room temperature.
(*b*) For germanium and some other materials which are *semiconductors*, the resistivity is lowered if the temperature rises and the variation of ρ can be very great, an increase as small as from 280 K to 300 K, halving the resistivity. Such metals can be used as sensitive thermometers. (See p. 42.)

Material	ρ/Ω *m at 20°C*	
copper	$1{\cdot}5\times10^{-8}$	a good (metal) conductor
germanium	0·5	a semiconductor
quartz	2×10^{12}	an insulator

A molecular view of resistivity and resistance

On p. 40 the nature of metallic conduction was described and the presence of *ions within a metal* substance identified with the resistance of the metal. Consider now a specimen of metal of length l and cross-section area A. For a specimen of length $2l$ and area A the electric field affecting the electrons will be halved if the potential difference is maintained, while for a specimen of length l and area $2A$ the electric field will be able to affect twice the previous number of electrons across a given section. In this way we can see that this theory of the nature of metallic conduction also supports the experimental relationship $R \propto l/A$.

10.8 ELECTROMOTIVE FORCE AND INTERNAL RESISTANCE

A **source** which can convert energy into electrical energy, i.e. which can produce and maintain an electric field, is said to have an **e.m.f.** (e.m.f. stands for **electromotive force,** and in this book the abbreviation is used throughout).

$$\textbf{e.m.f. of a source} = \frac{\text{energy converted within a source}}{\text{charge which thus flows round a circuit}}$$

$$E\,[\mathrm{V}] = \frac{\text{energy converted [J]}}{Q\,[\mathrm{C}]}$$

$$\boxed{E = \frac{\textit{energy converted}}{Q}}$$

Note: (*a*) The circuit round which the charge flows will include the source.
(*b*) The unit (J/C, or V) is the same as that for the potential difference between two points.

The e.m.f. of a source is equal to the potential difference between the terminals of the source when no charge is moving through it, i.e. when it is on **open circuit.**

Note: This statement is *not* a definition of e.m.f.

In Fig. 10.10 the arrow indicates the sense in which positive charge will go: the *electrons* go the other way.

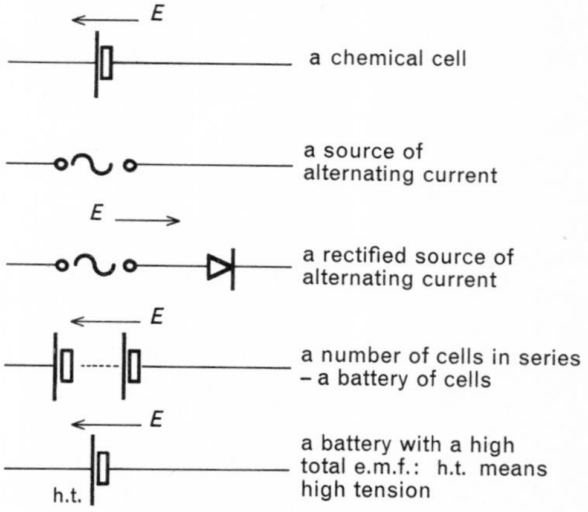

Fig. 10·10

Internal resistance

All sources dissipate energy within themselves and are described as having **internal resistance.** When a source is supplying a current I the product Ir is called the *lost volts,* and represents the potential difference which must be applied between two points to send the current I through a resistance of r. The internal resistance of the cell is thus r.

10.9 THE SIMPLE CIRCUIT

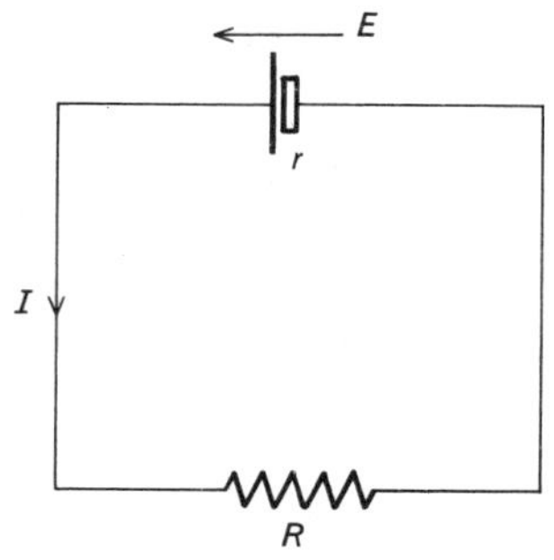

Fig. 10·11 A 'simple circuit'

In each second, for the simple circuit shown in Fig. 10.11, the chemical energy converted to electrical energy within the cell is IE while the electrical energy dissipated as heat energy is I^2R in R and I^2r in the cell (see p. 255). I being the current in the circuit.

By the Principle of the Conservation of Energy for the circuit:

$$EI = I^2R + I^2r.$$

$$\boxed{E = I(R+r)}$$

This is called the **circuit equation** and should be remembered in words: for a simple circuit

$$(\textit{the total e.m.f. in a circuit}) = (\textit{the current flowing}) \cdot \begin{pmatrix} \textit{the total resist-} \\ \textit{ance of the circuit} \end{pmatrix}.$$

For more than one cell (see Fig. 10.12):

(a) in **series:**

$$\text{total e.m.f.} = E_1 + E_2 - E_3,$$
$$\text{total resistance} = r_1 + r_2 + r_3;$$

(*b*) in **parallel** (if the cells are identical):

$$\text{total e.m.f.} = E,$$

$$\text{and the total resistance} = \frac{r}{3}.$$

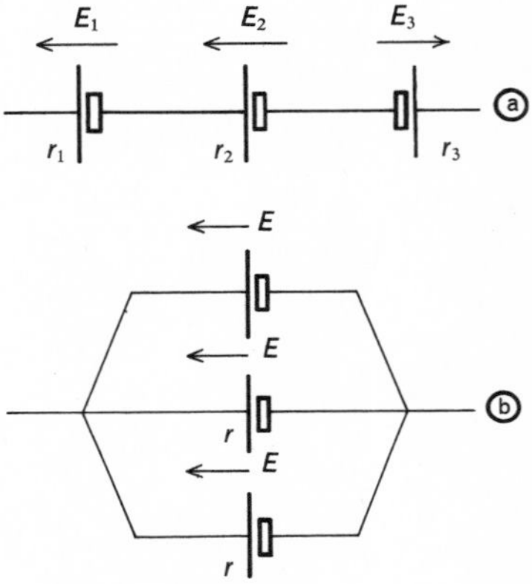

Fig. 10·12

Circuit problems

When attempting any quantitative problem involving electrical circuits or parts thereof, always

(*a*) draw a circuit diagram,
(*b*) check the units of the given quantities, e.g. kilovolts, milliamperes, megohms,
(*c*) consider the laws applying to cells in series or parallel and to resistors in series or parallel (see above and p. 257);

and when using

(*d*) the circuit equation $E = I(R+r)$, reduce the problem to one about the basic simple circuit shown in Fig. 10.11,
(*e*) $V/I = R$, where R is assumed to be constant, either say so or indicate that you are using Ohm's Law,
(*f*) the power equation $P = IV$, or the energy relationship $W = IVt$, state which electrical device you are considering,
(*g*) the Principle of the Conservation of Energy, make it clear that you are so doing.

Electrical energy and chemical energy

10.10 DEFINITIONS

A device in which chemical energy is converted to electrical energy is called a **chemical cell.**

A **primary cell** is one in which the energy conversion cannot be reversed.

A **secondary cell** (accumulator) is one in which this energy conversion can be reversed; the cell is said to be rechargeable.

A **battery** is a number of connected cells, usually arranged in series.

The **positive pole** or terminal of a cell is the one from which positive charge is thought of as flowing into the external circuit when the cell is producing current. The other terminal is called the **negative pole.**

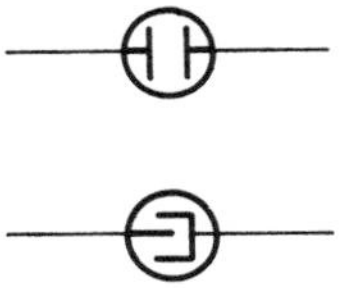

Fig. 10·13 Two circuit symbols for a voltameter

A device in which electrical energy is converted into chemical energy is called a **voltameter.**

Electrolysis is the name given to the process which takes place in a voltameter.

An **electrolyte** is a liquid which conducts electricity and in so doing undergoes a chemical change.

The bodies at whose surfaces the current enters and leaves the electrolyte are called **electrodes.** The electrode connected to the positive pole of the cell is called the **anode** and the other one the **cathode.** The current flows from the anode to the cathode *within* the voltameter, and so:

positive ions are drawn to the *cathode,*
negative ions are drawn to the *anode.*

An **ion** is any charged particle, usually an atom or a group of atoms which has lost or gained one or more electrons.

10.11 THE IONIC THEORY

An electrolyte contains ions whether it is conducting electricity or not. An ion carries a charge which is usually numerically equal to one or two times the electronic charge. The total charge of an electrolyte is zero.

For liquids:

strong electrolytes are those which contain a large proportion of ions, since they are completely or almost completely dissociated; they are *good conductors* of electricity. For example, silver nitrate exists as Ag^+ and NO_3^- ions.

weak electrolytes contain a very small proportion of ions; they are *poor conductors* of electricity. A water molecule dissociates thus:

$$H_2O \rightleftharpoons H^+ + OH^-$$

(OH^- is a hydroxyl ion.) If the ions are removed from a weak electrolyte more ions become available as a result of further dissociation. If positive ions move to the right and/or negative ions move to the left in an electrolyte, there is said to be a current to the right. The *size* of the current depends upon the number of ions passing a point in one second and the charge on each ion.

10.12 PRIMARY CELLS

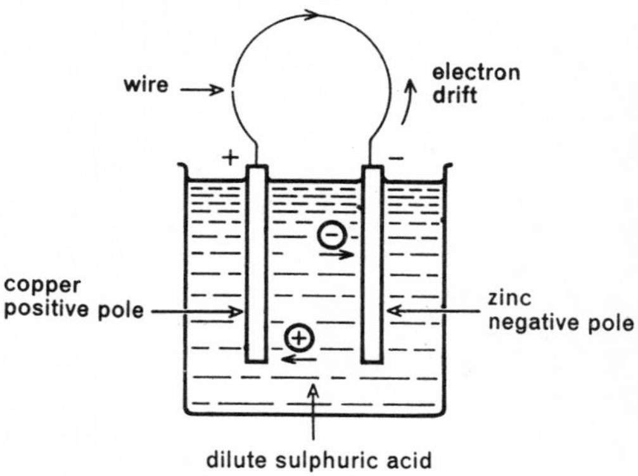

Fig. 10·14 A simple cell
Note that the current travels from the − ve pole to the + ve pole within the cell

The simple cell

The source of the electrical energy is a chemical reaction between a zinc plate and a solution of sulphuric acid. The e.m.f. of the cell is about 1·1 V when it is operating properly.

The dry Leclanché cell

The source of the electrical energy is a chemical reaction between a zinc plate and a paste of ammonium chloride. The zinc is the negative pole, the positive pole being a carbon rod. In the usual **dry cell** the case is the zinc plate. The e.m.f. is about 1·5 V when it is operating properly. It is commonly used in torches, portable radios, etc., in which the battery is a number of cells in series.

Other primary cells

(*i*) The Weston *standard* cell,
(*ii*) The **fuel cell.** The electrical energy comes from a controlled reaction between oxygen and hydrogen.

10.13 SECONDARY CELLS

There are two commonly used secondary cells:

(*a*) lead-acid,
(*b*) cadmium-iron (formerly nickel-iron, NiFe).

Each *while discharging* acts like a primary cell, converting chemical energy to electrical energy, the e.m.f.s being respectively about 2·0 V and 1·2 V. For a lead-acid cell the state of discharge can be tested by measuring the density of the acid.

By passing a current through these secondary cells against the electric field they set up, i.e. in the opposite sense to their e.m.f., each can be **recharged.** The initial chemical constitution of each cell is restored by converting electrical energy into chemical energy.

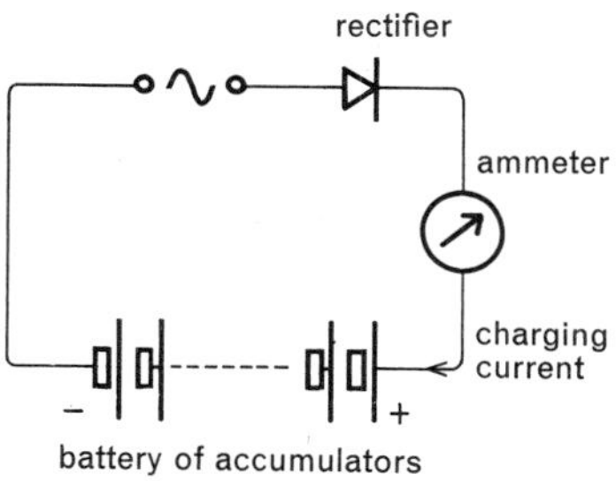

Fig. 10·15 Charging secondary cells

Note that when being charged the current travels from the + ve pole to the − ve pole within the cell

10.14 CAPACITY OF CELLS

Suppose a typical cell has an e.m.f. of E, e.g. 2·0 V or 2·0 J/C. The **total electrical energy** which the cell can supply depends upon the total charge which can pass through the cell before all its chemical energy is used up. As

$$Q = It,$$

this total charge is measured in coulombs or ampere seconds, and sometimes in ampere hours.

For example, a cell with a capacity of 80 ampere hours could supply 1 ampere for 80 hours, 0·25 ampere for 320 hours, and so on. The total charge it could cause to pass through the cell would be

$$80 \times 60 \times 60 \text{ C} = 2{\cdot}88 \times 10^5 \text{ C}.$$

Note that this is equivalent to the charge carried by

$$2{\cdot}88 \times 10^5 \times 6{\cdot}25 \times 10^{18} \text{ electrons,}$$

i.e. about 10^{24} electrons pass any point in the external circuit.

The capacity of a cell depends upon its physical size. The e.m.f. of a cell does *not* depend on its physical size, but only on the nature of the chemical reaction from which it derives its energy. To obtain a source of e.m.f. 6 V we do not make a large dry cell but use a battery of four dry cells in series.

From the definition of e.m.f. we see that a cell of e.m.f. E which has a capacity of Q will supply energy W where

$$W = QE.$$

A given cell is thus a store for a quantity of energy.

10.15 ELECTROLYSIS

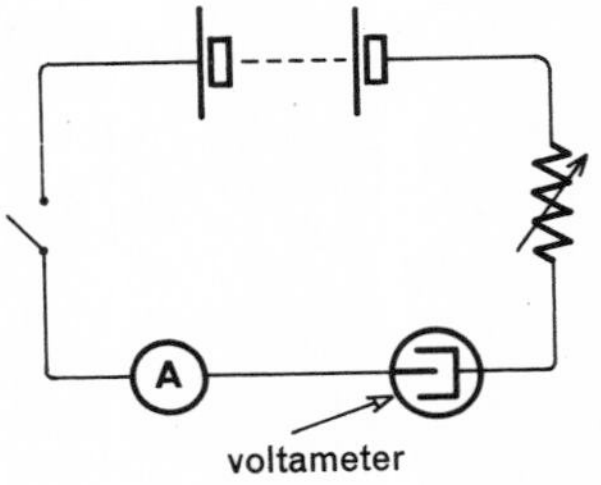

Fig. 10·16

Fig. 10.16 shows a typical circuit where a liquid electrolyte conducts an electric current. In order to study the chemical processes which accompany this conduction consider the particular voltameters shown in Fig. 10.17.

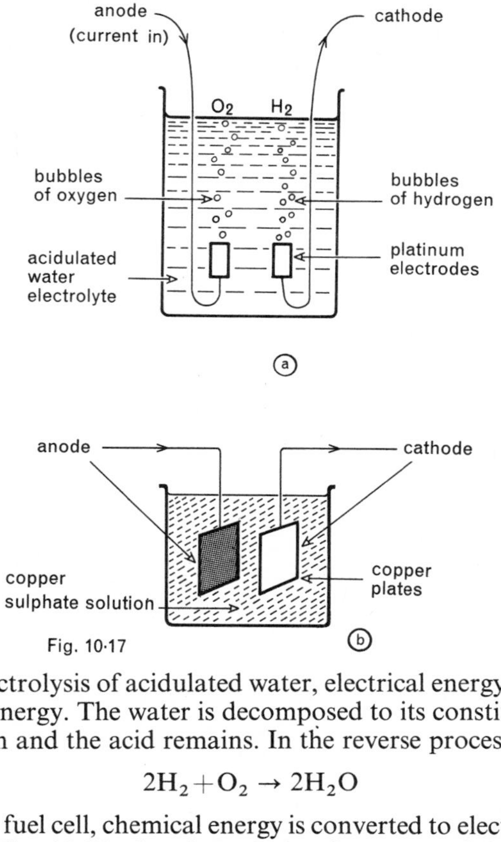

Fig. 10·17

In (*a*), the electrolysis of acidulated water, electrical energy is converted to chemical energy. The water is decomposed to its constituent oxygen and hydrogen and the acid remains. In the reverse process

$$2H_2 + O_2 \rightarrow 2H_2O$$

as used in the fuel cell, chemical energy is converted to electrical energy.

In (*b*) of Fig. 10.17, the electrolysis of copper sulphate solution, copper is transferred from the anode to the cathode. When the anode is made of crudely refined copper, pure (electrolytic) copper is formed on the cathode; this process is the main commercial source of copper for use in electrical circuitry.

Other useful applications of electrolysis include

(*a*) the manufacture of aluminium,
(*b*) electroplating,

(*c*) the extraction of sodium and potassium,
(*d*) the production of printed circuits.

10.16 FARADAY'S LAW OF ELECTROLYSIS

The mass of an element liberated during electrolysis is proportional to the charge (quantity of electricity) passing.

$$m \propto Q,$$
$$m = \text{constant}\,.\,Q.$$

The constant is called z, the **electrochemical equivalent** of the element (e.c.e.), and has the unit kg/C.

$$m\ [\text{kg}] = z\left[\frac{\text{kg}}{\text{C}}\right].\,Q\ [\text{C}],$$

$$m = zQ,$$

$$\boxed{m = zIt}$$

The equation *defines* z.

Numerically, z is equal to the mass of an element liberated in a voltameter when a charge of one coulomb passes through it.

Experiment

To verify this law, use the circuit and apparatus shown in Figs. 10.16 and 10.17, with a graduated cylinder to catch the gas in the first experiment. Run the experiment several times with a different *steady* current each time. Measure the current and the time for which it flows. To establish the law plot a graph of m against Q (see p. 23). If the graph is a straight line through the origin the law is verified.

The **ionic theory** accounts for the law as follows:

For every two H^+ ions, two electrons flow out of the cathode and one H_2 molecule escapes. The total number of molecules produced is thus proportional to the total charge passing; i.e.

$$\text{mass liberated} \propto \text{charge passing},$$

and similarly for other ions.

As $z = \dfrac{m}{Q}$, then the specific charge for an ion, $\dfrac{Q}{m}$, is equal to $\dfrac{1}{z}$. For copper the specific charge is $3{\cdot}0\times10^6$ C/kg and the largest measured specific charge found for liquid ions is that for hydrogen $9{\cdot}6\times10^7$ C/kg. It was only when Thomson measured the specific charge for the particles of cathode rays (electrons) (see p. 230) that a larger value was found.

10.17 THE FARADAY CONSTANT

The **mole** (mol) is the amount of substance which contains as many particles as there are atoms in 0·012 kg of carbon-12.

0·012 kg of carbon-12 contains $6{\cdot}02 \times 10^{23}$ atoms and we say that that number of atoms is $6{\cdot}02 \times 10^{23}$/mol. This quantity is called the **Avogadro constant** and denoted by N_A.

If $6{\cdot}02 \times 10^{23}$ ions are liberated during electrolysis then 1 mol of ions is liberated. The charge passing through the voltameter during this process depends on the charge carried by each ion; for 1 mol of *any* ion which carries plus or minus *one* elementary charge, e, $9{\cdot}65 \times 10^4$ coulombs are required. *This* charge per mole is called the **Faraday constant,** F.

$$F = 9{\cdot}65 \times 10^4 \text{ C/mol}.$$

Clearly, $F = N_A e$ and so

$$e = \frac{F}{N_A} = \frac{9{\cdot}65 \times 10^4 \text{ C/mol}}{6{\cdot}02 \times 10^{23}\text{/mol}} = 1{\cdot}6 \times 10^{-19} \text{ C}.$$

10.18 CONDUCTION IN GASES

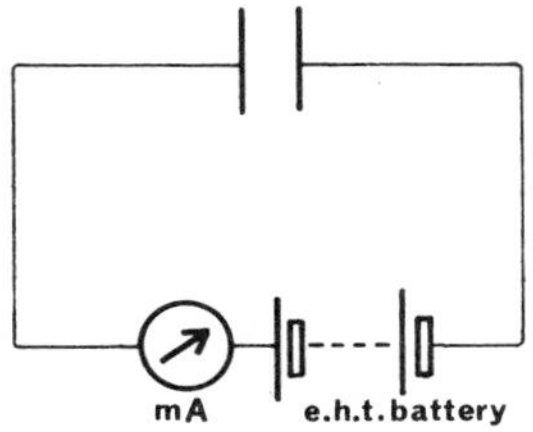

Fig. 10·18

If a large battery is connected to two separated metal plates as shown in Fig. 10.18, no current is registered on the sensitive ammeter. If the air in the gap can be ionized, i.e. if some of the particles of the air can be made to lose an electron, then a current can flow. Methods of ionizing the air include

(*a*) local heating with a white hot filament,
(*b*) irradiation by X-rays,
(*c*) bombardment by charged particles, e.g. from radioactive materials.

If the electric field in the gap is steadily increased there will come a stage when the few ions already present (as a result of particularly violent random collisions or from cosmic ray bombardment) accelerate sufficiently to ionize other air particles by collision and a chain reaction occurs. Sparking is seen in the gap: this spark is atmospheric lightning on a small scale. If the plates are enclosed in a glass envelope, and the pressure of the air reduced, a continuous glow discharge can be achieved, the resistance of the air gap dropping dramatically. The accelerated ions convert some of their kinetic energy to light when they collide with other particles; the colour of this light is characteristic of the particles involved, e.g. the yellow of sodium street lamps, and the red of neon signs.

The magnetic effect of current

10.19 MAGNETIC FIELD PATTERNS

Moving electric charge produces a magnetic field. A current flowing in a metal wire consists of a *drift* of electrons in the wire. This drift is superimposed upon their random movement and produces a magnetic field which can be detected outside the wire. The **lines of force** of the magnetic field form **closed loops** in a vacuum, in air or in any one medium. *In a vacuum* the magnetic field patterns may also be called magnetic flux patterns.

In order to establish the magnetic field patterns shown in Figs. 10.19–21 *experimentally,* large currents must be used to produce fields near the wires which are big enough for us to ignore the Earth's field, or the apparatus must be carefully shielded from the Earth's field.

The lines are plotted using small compasses or iron filings (see p. 217). The arrangement for a flat coil is shown in Fig. 10.22.

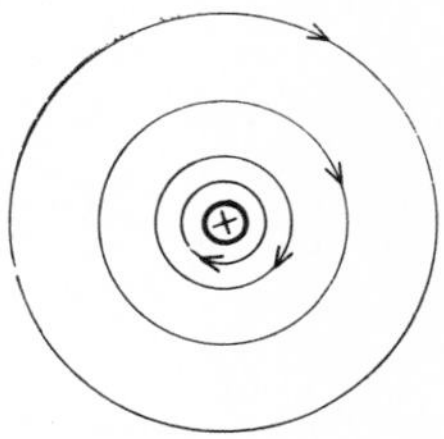

⊗ represents current going into paper

⊙ would be used to represent current coming out of paper

→ represents direction and sense of magnetic line of force

Fig. 10·19 Magnetic field pattern produced by a long straight wire

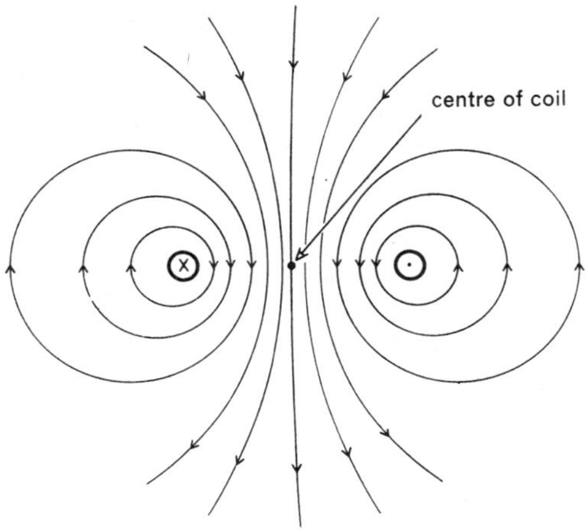

Fig. 10·20

Magnetic field pattern produced by a flat circular coil

All the lines do form closed loops, though space does not permit this to be shown. It is useful to remember that they behave like self-repellent elastic in a state of tension (see p. 217)

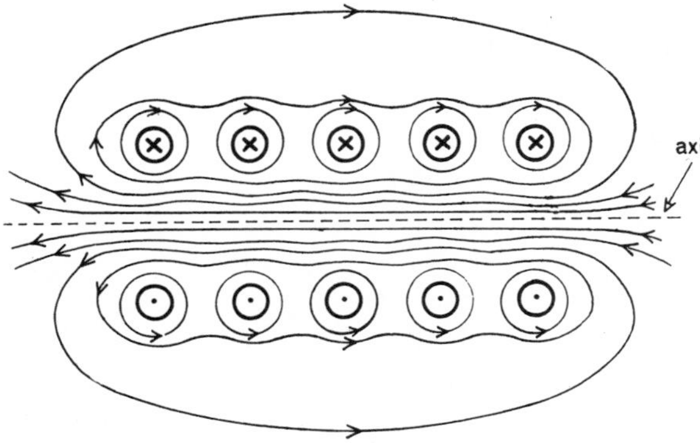

Fig. 10·21 Magnetic field pattern produced by an extended coil, a solenoid

As in fig. 10·20 all the lines do form closed loops

10.20 THE SENSE OF THE MAGNETIC FIELD

The right hand grip rule

Hold the wire in the right hand with the *thumb* in the direction of the current and pointing in the sense of the current. The *fingers* now coil around the wire in the sense of the magnetic lines of force. (Or, **Maxwell's rule:** if a right-handed corkscrew is held in the direction of the wire and screwed so as to move the screw in the sense of the current, the sense of rotation of the corkscrew is that of the magnetic lines of force.)

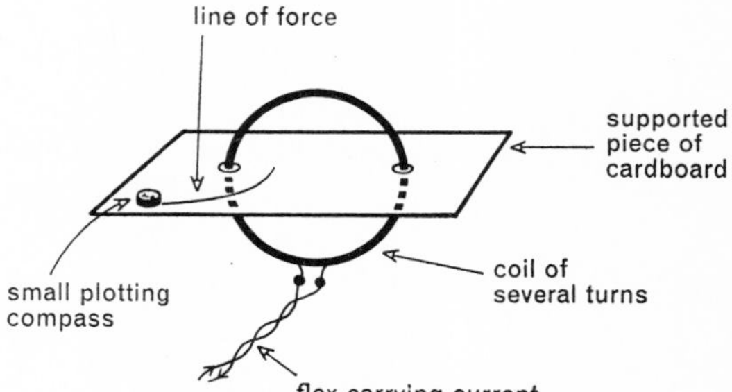

Fig. 10·22

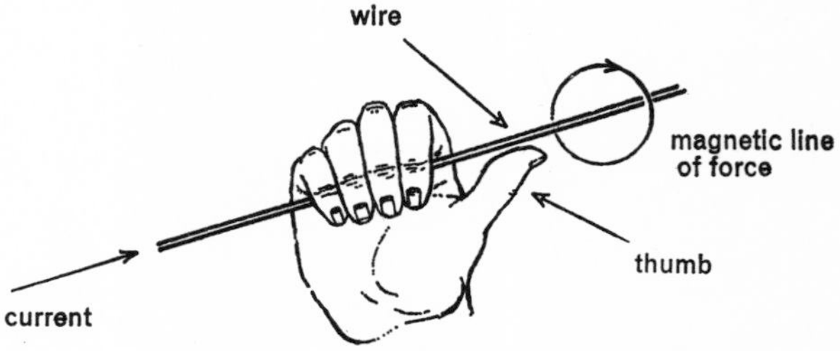

Fig. 10·23 How to apply the right hand grip rule

For *coils* and *solenoids* consider a small length of wire and decide the sense of the lines of force *through* the coil or solenoid, produced by this length of wire. All the lines of force will follow in this sense. For example:

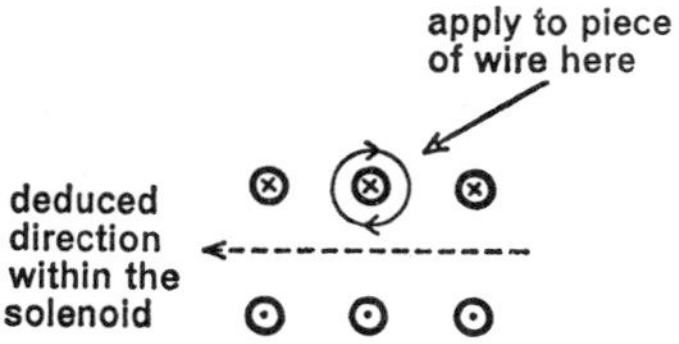

Fig. 10·24

The end of the coil or solenoid from which the lines of force emerge is called the *North-seeking,* or simply N, end. The other end is called the *South-seeking,* or S, end.

The external field pattern of the solenoid closely resembles that of a bar magnet (see p. 218). That their magnetic behaviour is similar can be

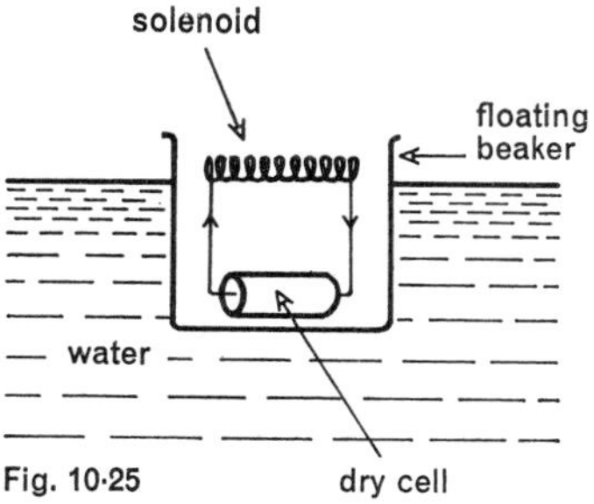

Fig. 10·25

further demonstrated by floating a solenoid. It will set magnetic North–South, repel and attract bar magnets or other solenoids as expected from the laws given on p. 212.

10.21 ELECTROMAGNETS

The effect of the field of the electromagnet in the gap between the poles can be increased by:

(*a*) increasing the current,
(*b*) increasing the number of turns of the coil round the soft iron,

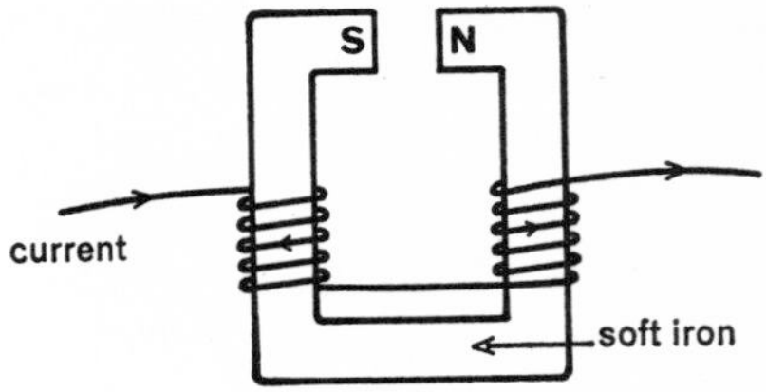

Fig. 10·26 An electromagnet

(*c*) placing the poles closer together,
(*d*) using a softer magnetic material (see p. 216).

Soft iron or other soft magnetic materials are also desirable because the magnetic effect largely disappears when the current is switched off.

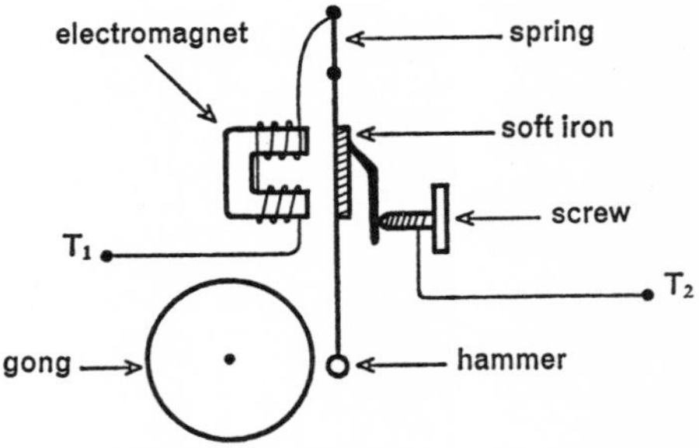

Fig. 10·27 A trembler bell

Uses

(*a*) *Electric bells.* In the trembler bell the electromagnet and screw form a make-and-break device when a cell is connected across T_1T_2. The bell achieves the conversion of electrical energy to sound energy.
(*b*) *The relay.* This is a device whereby a current in one circuit can be switched on by a change of current in a neighbouring circuit.
(*c*) *Magnets* used for lifting.
(*d*) *Magnetic separators.*
(*e*) *Telephone earpiece.* Oscillations of an electric current entering an

earpiece are turned into mechanical oscillations of a diaphragm and thus produce sound waves in the air near the diaphragm.

(*f*) *Electric motors* (see p. 279).

(*g*) *Electrical generating devices* (see p. 284).

10.22 THE MOTOR EFFECT ON A STRAIGHT WIRE

If a straight wire carrying a current is placed perpendicular to a uniform magnetic field, the resulting magnetic field pattern is as shown in Fig. 10.28. The *wire* experiences a downward *force,* and the magnet experiences an equal but upward force. This force is directly proportional to the current.

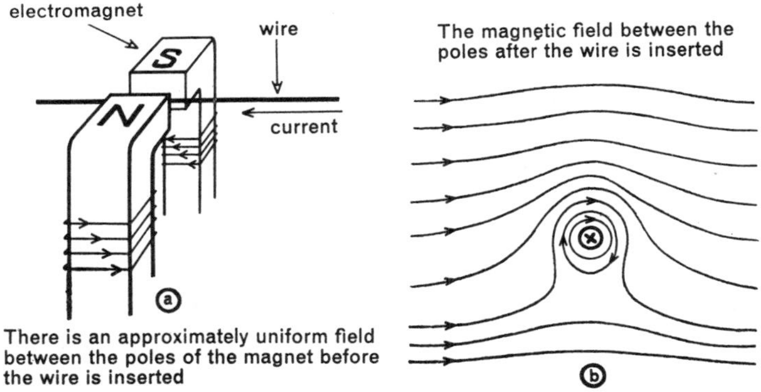

Fig. 10·28

The current balance

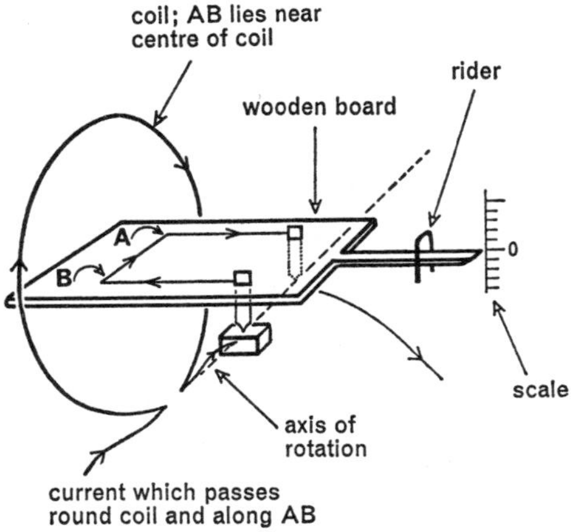

Fig. 10.29

When the current is switched on, the wire AB (see Fig. 10.29) experiences an upward force. If the board is in equilibrium with the pointer at 0 before switching on, it is possible to restore this equilibrium position by moving the rider. By applying the principle of moments the force on AB can be found, and hence the current.

Fleming's left hand motor rule

For a **left** hand, if:

(*a*) the **F**orefinger represents the **F**ield
and (*b*) the se**C**ond finger represents the **C**urrent,
then (*c*) the thumb represents the force on the wire carrying the current in the field

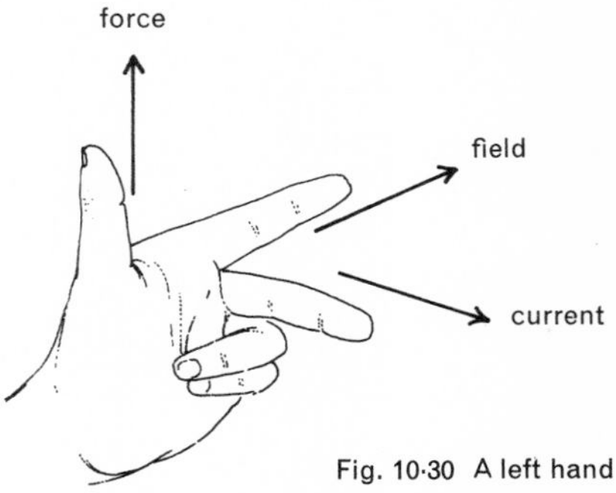

Fig. 10·30 A left hand

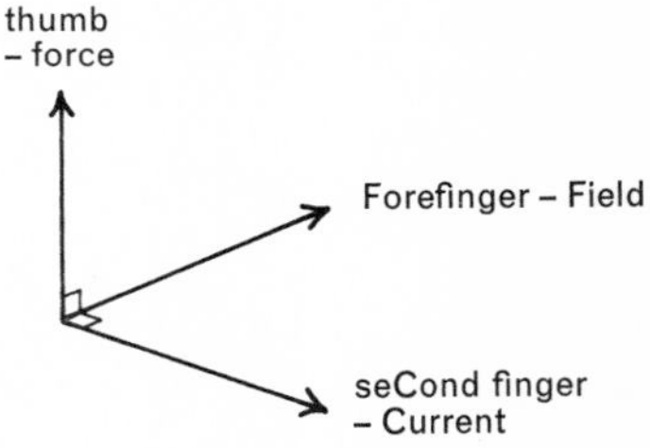

Each digit represents its quantity in direction and sense. Note that for (*a*) it is only the resolved part of the field perpendicular to the current which determines the size of the force; e.g. if the current is parallel to the field the force is zero.

10.23 THE MOTOR EFFECT ON A RECTANGULAR COIL

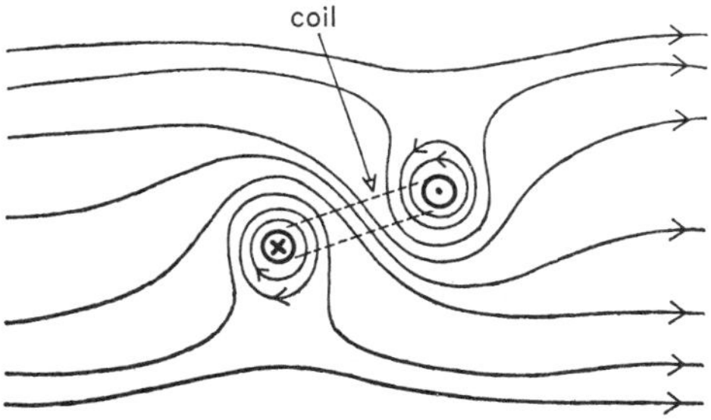

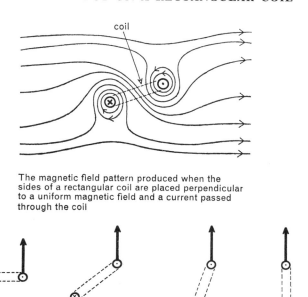

The magnetic field pattern produced when the sides of a rectangular coil are placed perpendicular to a uniform magnetic field and a current passed through the coil

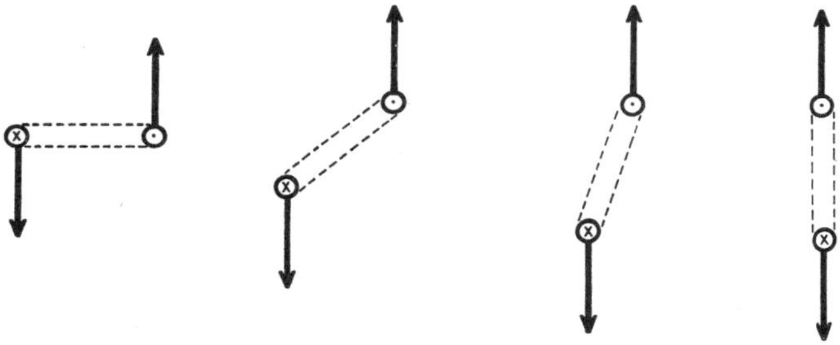

maximum couple — Fig. 10·31 — zero couple

Each vertical side of the coil experiences a force. As the forces are equal in magnitude and direction for a rectangular coil, but opposite in sense, they form a **couple** (see p. 75). *The coil is twisted,* the couple tending to rotate it being greatest when the coil lies along the field and zero when it lies across it. The other two sides of the coil may have forces on them, but these forces do not twist the coil at all.

The moving coil galvanometer

Fig. 10.32*a* shows a rectangular coil mounted on jewel bearings and having control springs which exert a restoring torque when the coil is twisted.

Fig. 10.32*b* shows (from above) the coil mounted between the poles of a permanent magnet and surrounding a soft iron core to which it is *not* attached; i.e. the core does not rotate with the coil.

When a current flows in the coil it rotates to a position of equilibrium,

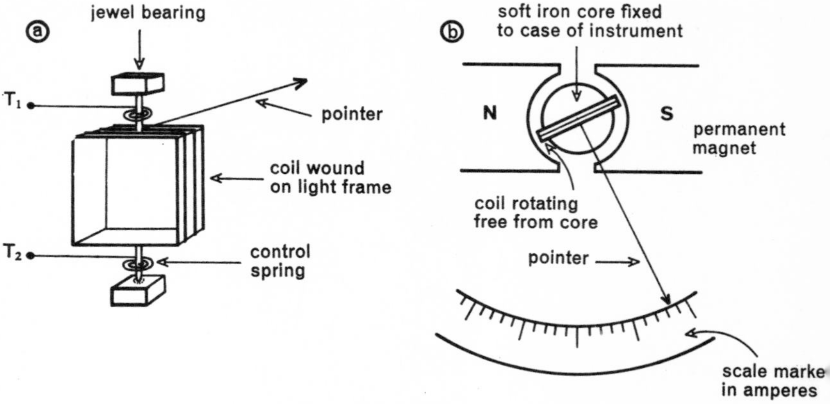

Fig. 10·32

there being a *different* position for each value of the current. The scale is graduated with reference to a current balance.

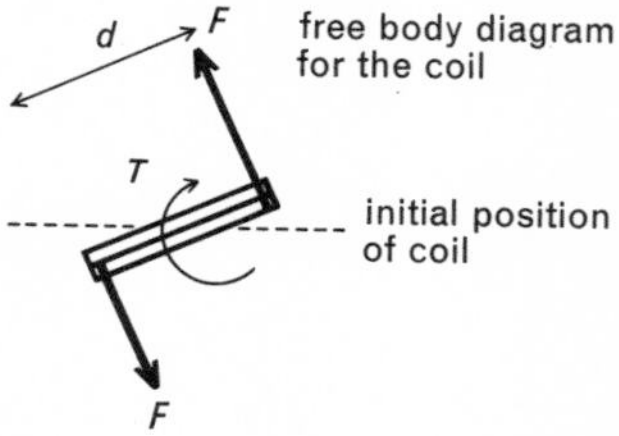

Fig. 10·33

F, *F* are the magnetic forces on the sides of the coil.
T is the torque produced by the suspension

In Fig. 10.33, *F* and *F* are determined by the current. For equilibrium $T = Fd$, and so the coil twists until the torque T produced by the suspension increases to Fd.

The purpose of the soft iron core is to produce a field which is *radial*. This has the effect of producing a constant torque Fd for a given value of the current. The scale of the instrument is then uniform.

To increase the sensitivity of the galvanometer we need:

(*a*) more turns for the coil,
(*b*) a stronger magnet,
(*c*) weaker control springs or even a fibre suspension,
(*d*) a long, light pointer or a beam of light reflected from a mirror which is attached to the coil.

The moving coil galvanometer will *not* measure alternating current.

10.24 THE DIRECT CURRENT MOTOR

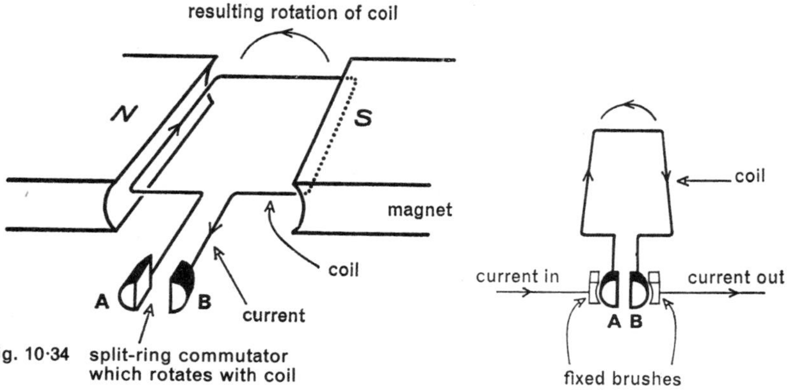

Fig. 10·34

A direct current motor is a device which converts *electrical energy into mechanical energy* plus some internal energy which is dissipated as heat.

$$\textbf{Efficiency of motor} = \frac{\text{useful mechanical energy got out}}{\text{electrical energy put in}}.$$

Principle

A coil carrying a current experiences a torque if placed along a uniform magnetic field (see Fig. 10.34). This torque rotates the coil, but when it reaches the vertical the torque is zero. Since, however, the coil has *inertia* it will overshoot the vertical and if, at the same moment, the current in the coil is reversed, the coil will continue to rotate. The device which reverses the current every time the coil reaches the vertical is called a **commutator.**

Practical details

(*a*) The coil is wound on a soft iron core which rotates with the coil; the coil and core together are called the **armature.** This

  (*i*) increases the inertia of the coil, and
  (*ii*) produces a strong radial field and thus a fairly constant torque.

(*b*) The magnet is an electromagnet, the coil being either in series or in parallel with the **windings** of the electromagnet.

(*c*) When the coil rotates an induced e.m.f. is created, the coil and the magnet acting as an alternating current generator (see p. 283). This effect is called a *back* e.m.f., *E*. *E* increases as the speed of rotation of the motor increases and rises to a large fraction of the potential difference used to drive the motor.

(*d*) Several coils are usually used so that the motor need not rely on the inertia of the armature when one coil is vertical. This results in a steadier driving torque.

(*e*) There are eddy currents in the soft iron core (see p. 288).

10.25 THE MOTOR EFFECT AND ELECTRONS

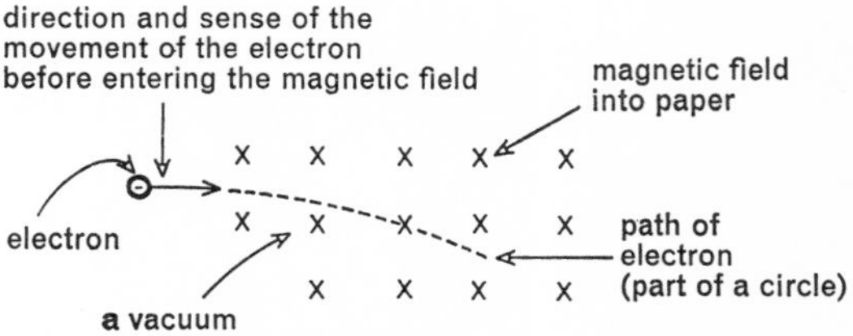

Fig. 10·35

Fleming's left hand motor rule applies to *all* moving charge, but the *sense* of the current for a flow of electrons is the *reverse* sense to that of the electron flow (see also p. 249).

Electromagnetic induction

10.26 INDUCED CURRENTS

Electromagnetic induction involves the conversion of *mechanical or magnetic energy to electrical energy*. Some of the energy will be converted to internal energy.

An *e.m.f.* is induced in a conductor when

(1) **relative motion** causes the conductor to cut across magnetic lines of force, or

(2) the **growth** or **decay** of a magnetic field causes magnetic lines of force to cut across the conductor.

If the conductor forms part of a circuit an **induced current** will flow. If the conductor is not part of a complete circuit the current will not be maintained.

Opposite are some examples of how a current can be induced in a circuit.

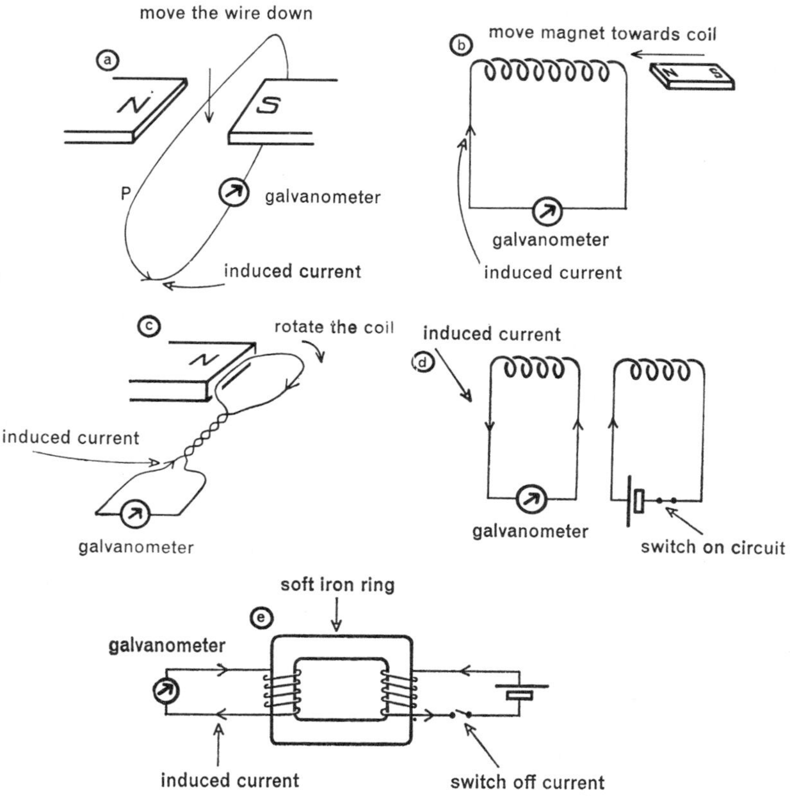

Fig. 10·36 Some examples of how a current can be induced in a circuit

Fleming's right hand dynamo rule

For a **right** hand, if:

(*a*) the **F**orefinger represents the **F**ield
and (*b*) the thu**M**b represents the **M**otion of the conductor relative to the field,
then (*c*) the second finger represents the induced e.m.f., and thus the induced current, if any.

Each digit represents its quantity in direction and sense. Note that for (*a*) it is only the resolved part of the field perpendicular to the motion which determines the size of the induced e.m.f.; e.g. if the relative motion is parallel to the field, the induced e.m.f. is zero.

As it is not always convenient to apply this rule, we usually apply Lenz's Law to more difficult situations (see below).

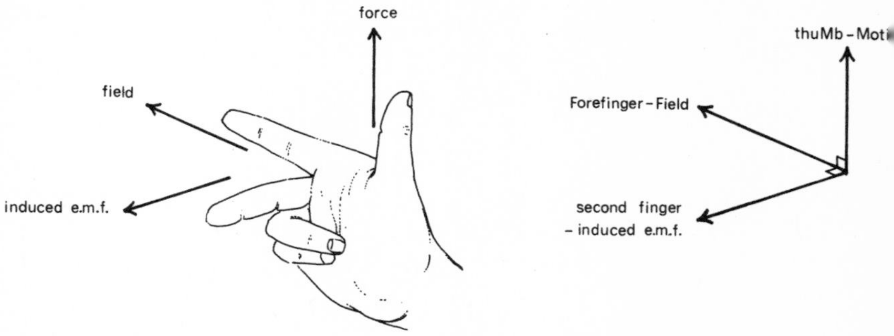

Fig. 10·37 A right hand

Cause. The cause of the e.m.f. *in a conductor* is the motor effect on the free electrons within the conductor. If Fleming's left hand motor rule is applied to the electrons, then it is seen that the force on them will be from B to A, i.e. there will be an e.m.f. directed from A to B. (Note that the current, caused by the *bodily* movement of the electrons in the wire, is upward when the conductor moves downward.)

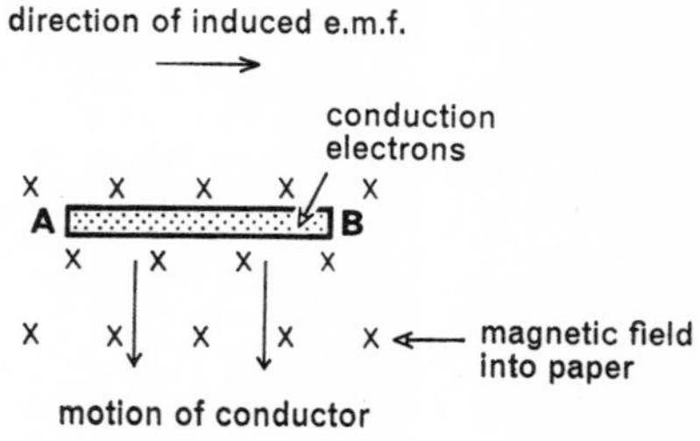

Fig. 10·38

10.27 THE LAWS OF ELECTROMAGNETIC INDUCTION

Lenz's Law

> The sense of an induced e.m.f. is such as to produce a current which opposes the action which causes it.

This is a special case of the Principle of the Conservation of Energy, for if Lenz's Law were not true it would be possible to design a machine which could be made to drive itself.

Faraday's Law

The *size* of the induced e.m.f. produced by the methods suggested in Fig. 10.36 is proportional to:

(*i*) the resolved part of the magnetic field perpendicular to the relative motion,
(*ii*) the speed at which the relative motion of the conductor and the magnetic field occurs.

We can summarize (*i*) and (*ii*) thus:

The induced **e.m.f.** is proportional to the rate at which the conductor cuts magnetic lines of force.

The induced *current* depends not only on the e.m.f. but also on resistance.

Verification

Lenz's Law: see Fig. 10.36*b* on p. 281. The sense of the induced current is such as to make the magnetic field of the solenoid emerge from the right, i.e. the right hand end behaves like a N-seeking pole, thus opposing the movement of the magnet. If the motion of the magnet is reversed then so is the sense of the induced current.

Faraday's Law: see Fig. 10.36*a* on p. 281. The closer the poles or the faster the movement of the wire, the greater is the induced current. As the circuit remains unaltered this means that the induced e.m.f. is greater. If a part of PQ is held parallel to the field and moved downward, no induced current is produced.

10.28 SIMPLE CURRENT GENERATORS

A **generator** or **dynamo** converts mechanical energy to electrical energy.

$$\textbf{Efficiency of generator} = \frac{\text{electrical energy got out}}{\text{mechanical energy put in}}.$$

Principle

An e.m.f. is induced in a coil if it is rotated in a uniform magnetic field. The coil must be *driven* (see Fig. 10.39). The sense of this e.m.f. is found by Fleming's right hand dynamo rule, and will be from A to B in the external circuit when the coil moves through the position shown. Half a revolution later the e.m.f. will be from B to A and so on.

Alternating current generators. In the generator shown the leads to A and B are connected to **slip rings,** and so do not tangle. The slip rings rotate *with* the coil about a common axis. The e.m.f. between A and B

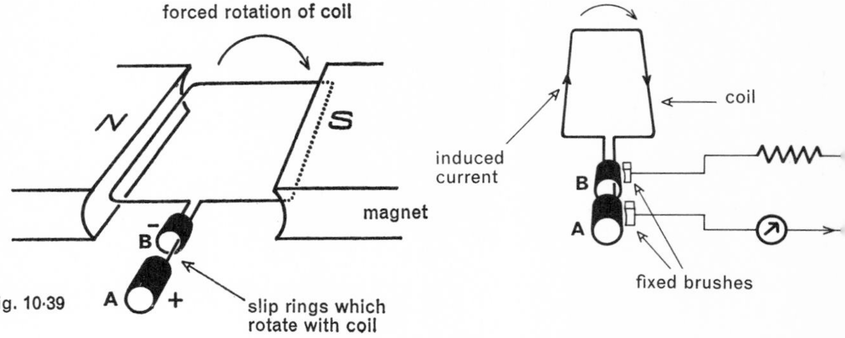

Fig. 10·39

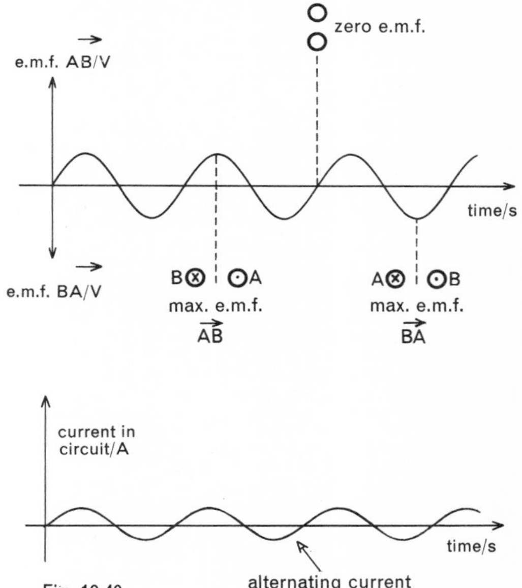

Fig. 10·40

and the resulting current in the external circuit are shown in Fig. 10.40. The current is said to be sinusoidal and is called **alternating current (a.c.).** The magnitude and sense of the e.m.f. can be deduced at every instant, using the laws of electromagnetic induction.

Direct current generators. If the slip rings and brushes above are replaced by a **split-ring commutator** and brushes as described on page 279, the current in the external circuit will always be in the same sense. It is also possible to obtain a one-sense current (pulsating **direct current,**

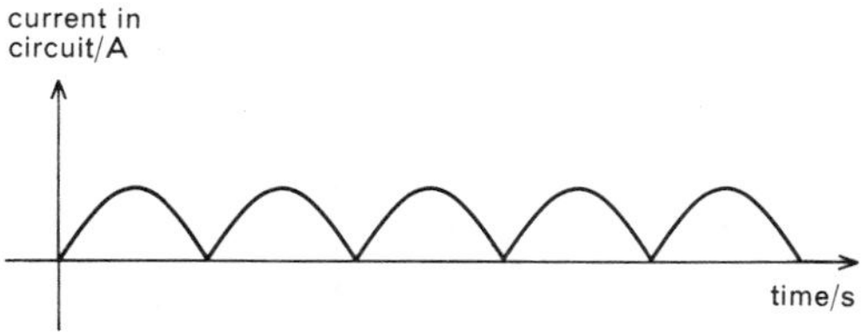

Fig. 10·41 The result of using a split-ring commutator

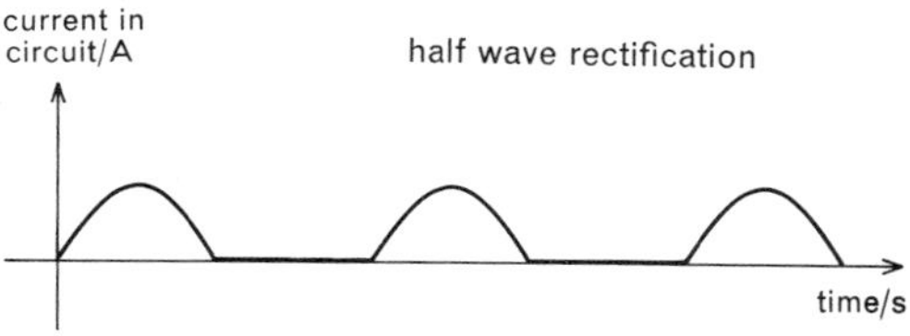

Fig. 10·42 The result of using an electrical valve

d.c.) by **rectifying** the alternating current using electrical **valves,** such as metal rectifiers, vacuum diodes or junction diodes.

Practical details

(*a*) The e.m.f. can be increased by increasing

(*i*) the number of turns of the coil,
(*ii*) the strength of the magnetic field (usually set up by an electromagnet),
(*iii*) the speed of rotation of the coil, although this would alter the frequency of the alternating current.

(*b*) Possible sources of the mechanical energy for driving the coil are shown in Fig. 10.43.

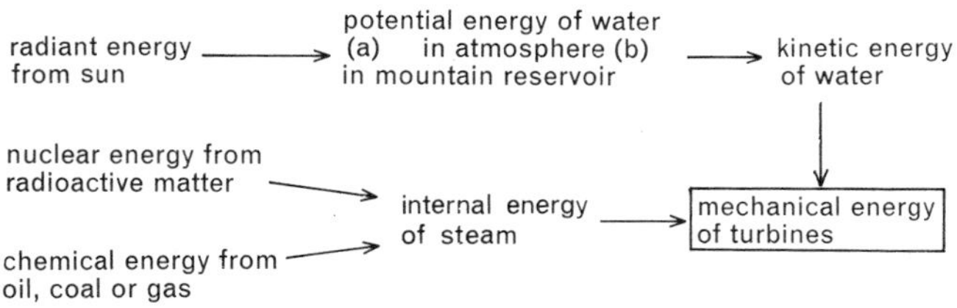

Fig. 10·43

10.29 ALTERNATING CURRENT

The frequency of the **mains a.c.** is 50 Hz. This means that the current becomes zero 100 times during each second. This frequency can be measured by viewing a filament lamp through a stroboscope (see p. 166). The *average* value of the current is zero, and there would be no reading on a moving coil galvanometer placed in series with the lamp.

Electrons and a.c.

The conduction electrons in a wire carrying d.c. have a drift speed of the order of 10^{-4} m/s (see p. 41). When a conductor is carrying a.c. there is no steady drift of electrons, but they **pulse** back and forward at the frequency of the a.c. with an amplitude of the order of 10^{-6} m for the usual 50 Hz supply.

Measurement of a.c.

The effective size of an alternating current is equal to that direct current which will produce the same heating effect. This is found to equal the square root of the average value of the current squared, and is called the **root mean square current** or **r.m.s. current.** Thus

$$I_{\text{effective}} = I_{\text{d.c.}} \text{ which has the same heating effect}$$
$$= I_{\text{r.m.s.}} = \sqrt{(\text{average value of } I^2)}.$$

Possible ways of measuring the r.m.s. current include

(*a*) the hot wire ammeter,
(*b*) the current balance (see p. 275), which does record a value as the sense of the current changes in *both* the coil and the wire AB,
(*c*) the moving iron ammeter (see p. 293),
(*d*) the moving coil galvanometer and a bridge arrangement of rectifiers.

10.30 THE ALTERNATING CURRENT TRANSFORMER

Using r.m.s. values for the e.m.f.s it can be shown that

$$\frac{\text{e.m.f. across primary}}{\text{e.m.f. across secondary}} = \frac{\text{number of turns on primary}}{\text{number of turns on secondary}},$$

$$\frac{E_p}{E_s} = \frac{N_p}{N_s}.$$

Thus, for example, an *alternating* e.m.f. of 240 volts r.m.s. can be transformed

(*a*) to 4000 V r.m.s. **(stepped up)** for a TV set, or

(*b*) to 3 V r.m.s. **(stepped down)** for a telephone bell, by using a transformer with suitable windings.

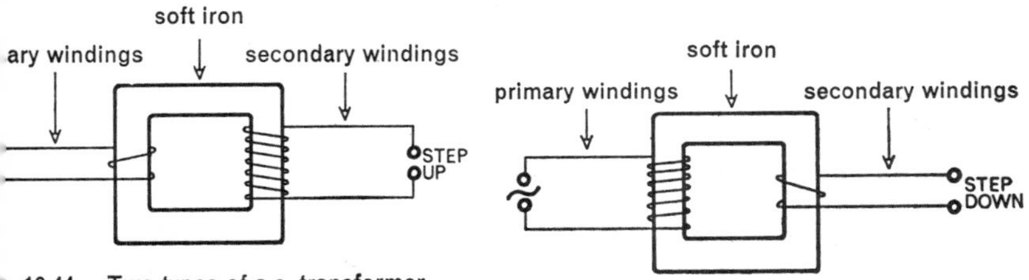

. 10·44 Two types of a.c. transformer

The transformer links the **primary** and **secondary** circuits by using the soft iron core as a path for the magnetic field set up by the primary windings. This field links the secondary windings, and when it changes, sets up an induced e.m.f. in them according to Faraday's Law of electromagnetic induction.

Perfect transformer

By the Principle of the Conservation of Energy

power into primary windings = power out of secondary windings,

$$E_p \, . \, I_p = E_s \, . \, I_s.$$

Thus if the e.m.f. is stepped up, the current is correspondingly stepped down.

Practical transformer

In practice

$$E_p \, . \, I_p > E_s \, . \, I_s.$$

The energy is lost

(*a*) as internal energy in the windings,
(*b*) because of induced currents in the soft iron core (see p. 288) which generate internal energy,
(*c*) when the magnetism of the soft iron is reversed, as this produces internal energy,
(*d*) because there is imperfect linking between the primary and secondary windings.

Uses. The transformer is used in the transmission of power through the Grid (see p. 256).

10.31 EDDY CURRENTS

The motion of pieces of conducting material relative to magnetic fields, or the rise and decay of magnetic fields in the region of conducting objects, produce induced e.m.f.s. Such induced e.m.f.s will produce induced currents in the body of the conductor which are called **eddy currents.**

Eddy currents can be *useful* in

(*a*) induction furnaces, where their heating effect is used to melt the conductor,
(*b*) eddy current brakes and eddy current damping, where the resulting motor effect on the conductor carrying the eddy current *opposes* the motion of the conductor; a moving coil galvanometer is damped in this way to facilitate a quick reading.

Eddy currents can be a *nuisance* in

(*a*) transformers, where the production of internal energy lowers the efficiency of the transformer and necessitates the use of cooling systems,
(*b*) the cores of alternating current generators and electric motors.

Both these difficulties can be partially avoided by the use of **laminated** (i.e. layered) materials, which reduce the size of the induced currents by increasing the resistance of the paths that they take.

Electrical measurements

10.32 ELECTRICAL MEASUREMENTS

The quantities to be measured are **current, potential difference, electromotive force** and **resistance.** Definitions of these quantities are given in Section 10.2. Methods of measurement dealt with or mentioned in previous sections include:

(*a*) current, using a current balance (see p. 275) or a moving coil galvanometer (see p. 278),
(*b*) potential difference, using an ammeter and a joulemeter (see p. 254).

10.33 THE MOVING COIL GALVANOMETER AS AN AMMETER OR A VOLTMETER

If a galvanometer is placed in a circuit its deflection is determined by the current passing through its coil. The size of this current can be used to deduce the size of a larger current or of a potential difference.

Consider, for example, a galvanometer which will show a full scale deflection when the current through its coil is 0·015 A. It will not register currents of *more* than this and may be damaged by them. Suppose the galvanometer obeys Ohm's Law and has a resistance of 5Ω.

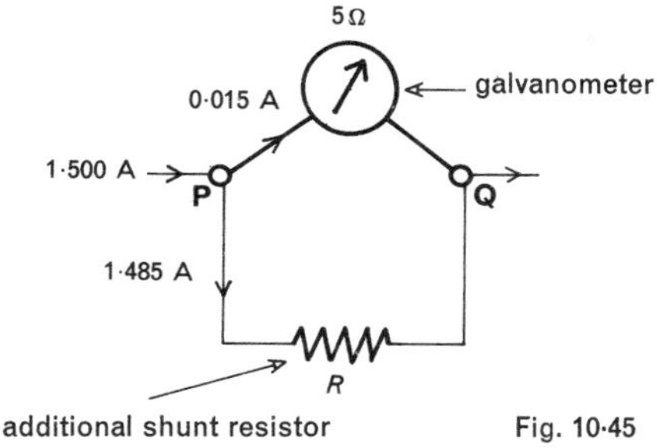

Fig. 10·45

(a) Larger currents

The galvanometer is *shunted* by a resistor through which a known proportion of the current passes.

In our example (Fig. 10.45) it is required to measure currents up to 1·500 A. For 1·500 A, 1·485 A must by-pass the meter, while the 0·015 A makes the meter register a full scale deflection. The potential difference between P and Q will be V for either path; thus, using $V/I = R$ for each resistor:

$$\frac{V}{0{\cdot}015\,\text{A}} = 5\Omega \quad \text{and} \quad \frac{V}{1{\cdot}485\,\text{A}} = R,$$

whence
$$R = \frac{5}{99}\,\Omega = 0{\cdot}0505\,\Omega.$$

(b) Potential differences

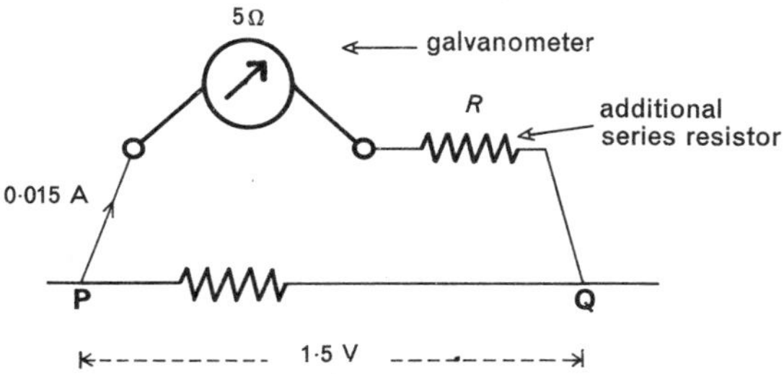

Fig. 10·46

The galvanometer is connected across the two points in a circuit between which the potential difference is required, and a resistor is placed in *series* with the galvanometer.

In our example (Fig. 10.46) it is required to measure potential differences up to 1·5 V. For 1·5 V between P and Q, 0·015 A must flow through the meter, and thus also through R. Using $V/I = R$ for the galvanometer plus R:

$$\frac{1{\cdot}5\,\text{V}}{0{\cdot}015\,\text{A}} = 5\,\Omega + R,$$

whence

$$R = 95\,\Omega.$$

In our example, if no series resistance is added, then the galvanometer will act as a voltmeter up to 0·075 V.

10.34 THE AMMETER–VOLTMETER METHOD FOR MEASURING RESISTANCE

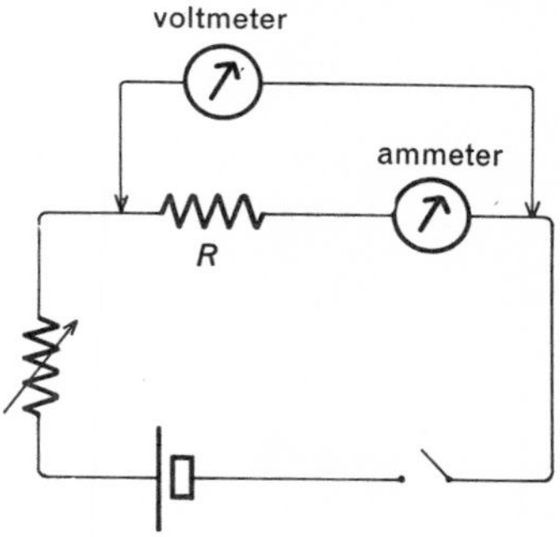

Fig. 10·47

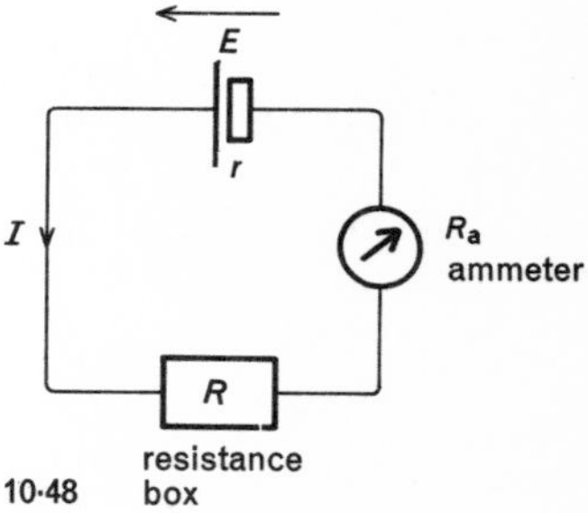

Fig. 10·48

In Fig. 10.47:
Measure I, the current through the resistor, and V, the potential difference across its ends; then its resistance, R, is given by $V/I = R$. If the voltmeter drains any current in order to work then the ammeter will *not* register the current which flows through the resistor. Galvanometers used as voltmeters in this experiment drain a little current, though the effect is often unimportant, but potentiometer devices do not.

Internal resistance

For the circuit shown in Fig. 10.48:

$$E = I\,(R + r + R_a) \qquad \text{(see p. 261).}$$

To find r, measure I for two known values of R and solve for $r + R_a$.

The resistance of the ammeter must be known or assumed to be negligible so that we can deduce r, the internal resistance of the cell.

10.35 THE POTENTIOMETER

A **potentiometer** is a device for **comparing two potential differences.**

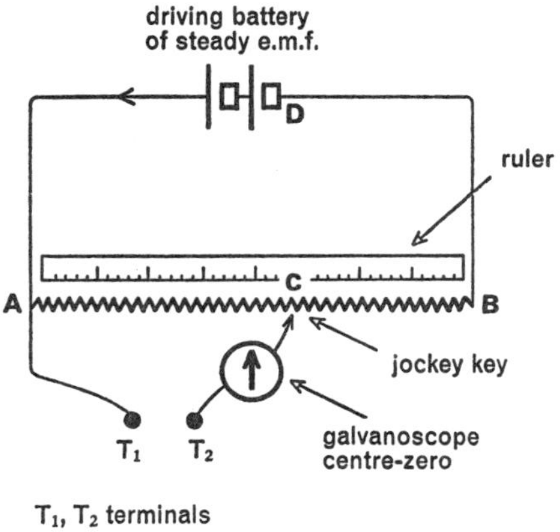

Fig. 10·49 A potentiometer

Construction

(*a*) AB is a straight wire which has *the same resistance for each mm of its length.* It rests on a ruler.
(*b*) A *steady* current is sent through AB by the driving battery at D.
(*c*) From A is a lead to T_1.
(*d*) At C is a sliding contact which is connected to T_2 through a sensitive centre-zero galvanoscope.

Theory

When T_1 and T_2 are connected to two points then the potential difference between the two points is equal to the potential difference V, between A and C *when no current flows in the galvanoscope.* As

$$V \propto \text{length AC} \qquad \text{(see (}a\text{) above)},$$
$$V = \text{(constant)}.\text{(length AC)},$$

and thus, for two potential differences, V_1 and V_2, connected in turn to T_1 and T_2 which balance for lengths AC_1 and AC_2,

$$\frac{V_1}{V_2} = \frac{AC_1}{AC_2}.$$

Practice

The balance, that is the situation when there is no current through the galvanoscope, is found by tapping the jockey key C at various places along AB. *No* balance can be obtained if

(*a*) the terminals T_1 and T_2 are the wrong way round, or
(*b*) the e.m.f. of the driving battery is too small.

Comparison of e.m.f.s

The potentiometer drains *no* current from the device across which it is connected when the balance point has been found. The potential difference between the terminals of a cell on open circuit can thus be measured. For each of two cells placed between T_1 and T_2, at balance

$$V_1 = E_1 \quad \text{and} \quad V_2 = E_2,$$

$$\frac{E_1}{E_2} = \frac{AC_1}{AC_2}.$$

10.36 THE METRE BRIDGE

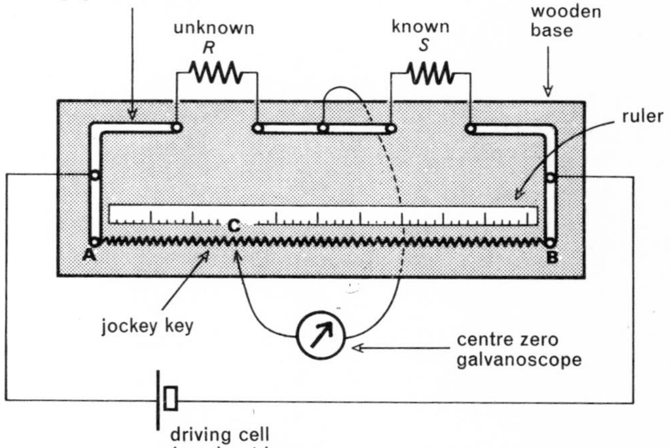

Fig. 10·50 A metre bridge

If C, the balance point, is found by tapping along the *uniform* resistance wire AB until a zero reading is obtained on the galvanoscope, then

$$\frac{R}{S} = \frac{\text{resistance of length AC}}{\text{resistance of length CB}} = \frac{AC}{CB}.$$

R can thus be found if S is known.

It is advisable for S and R to have about the same resistance for the most accurate measurements, and a second reading can be obtained by reversing them. This principle for *comparing two resistances* is often referred to as the **Wheatstone bridge principle.**

10.37 MISCELLANEOUS ELECTRICAL DEVICES

The moving iron ammeter

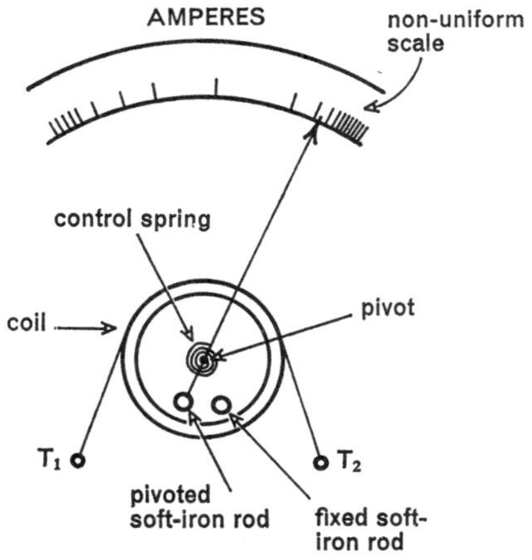

Fig. 10·51 The principle of the moving iron ammeter

When a current passes through the coil *both* iron rods become magnets (see p. 215) as shown in Fig. 10.51. The rods repel one another and the pivoted rod swings away until the control spring produces equilibrium. The scale is not uniform and the instrument must be used in the correct position.

The moving iron ammeter *will* also measure *alternating current* since each of the rods will always be magnetized in the same sense.

The induction coil

The action of the induction coil is a combination of

(1) the electric bell make-and-break technique (see p. 274).
(2) the alternating current transformer (see p. 286).

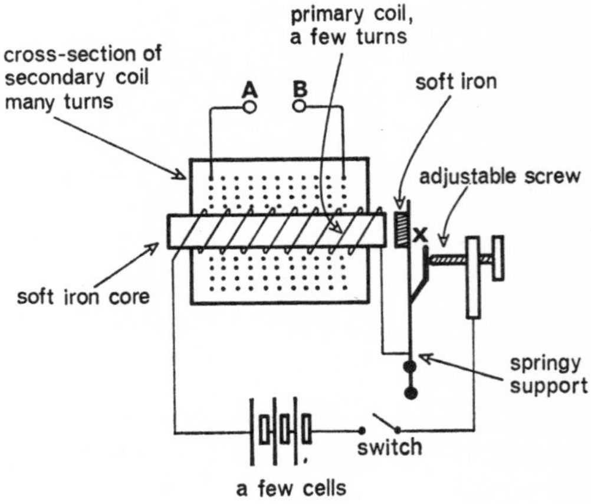

Fig. 10·52 An induction coil

The e.m.f. induced between A and B is

(*a*) governed in size by Faraday's Law of electromagnetic induction, and thus depends upon (*i*) relative number of turns of the two coils, and (*ii*) the rate at which the magnetic field in the soft iron core rises and falls when contact at X is made or broken;

(*b*) governed in sense by Lenz's Law of electromagnetic induction, and thus is in opposite senses for the make and the break.

As the e.m.f. induced when contact at X is broken is much greater than when contact is made, the e.m.f. between A and B will be largely in one sense.

Use

A modified form of induction coil is used to produce a potential difference of a few thousand volts between the electrodes of a sparking plug in the ignition system of cars. The energy of the spark is provided by a battery whose e.m.f. is usually 12 V.

Index